THE LOGICAL LEAP

THE LOGICAL LEAP

INDUCTION IN PHYSICS

David Harriman

With an Introduction by
Leonard Peikoff

NEW AMERICAN LIBRARY

NEW AMERICAN LIBRARY
Published by New American Library, a division of
Penguin Group (USA) Inc., 375 Hudson Street,
New York, New York 10014, USA
Penguin Group (Canada), 90 Eglinton Avenue East, Suite 700, Toronto, Ontario M4P 2Y3, Canada
(a division of Pearson Penguin Canada Inc.)
Penguin Books Ltd., 80 Strand, London WC2R 0RL, England
Penguin Ireland, 25 St. Stephen's Green, Dublin 2, Ireland (a division of Penguin Books Ltd.)
Penguin Group (Australia), 250 Camberwell Road, Camberwell, Victoria 3124, Australia
(a division of Pearson Australia Group Pty. Ltd.)
Penguin Books India Pvt. Ltd., 11 Community Centre, Panchsheel Park, New Delhi - 110 017, India
Penguin Group (NZ), 67 Apollo Drive, Rosedale, North Shore 0632, New Zealand
(a division of Pearson New Zealand Ltd.)
Penguin Books (South Africa) (Pty.) Ltd., 24 Sturdee Avenue, Rosebank, Johannesburg 2196, South Africa

Penguin Books Ltd., Registered Offices:
80 Strand, London WC2R 0RL, England

First published by New American Library,
a division of Penguin Group (USA) Inc.

First Printing, July 2010
10 9 8 7 6 5 4 3 2 1

Copyright © David Harriman, 2010
Introduction copyright © Leonard Peikoff, 2010
Illustrations by Coral Cruz Harriman and Tom VanDamme
All rights reserved

 REGISTERED TRADEMARK—MARCA REGISTRADA

Library of Congress Cataloging-in-Publication Data:

Harriman, David.
    The logical leap: induction in physics/David Harriman; with an introduction by Leonard Peikoff.
        p.   cm.
    Includes index.
    ISBN 978-0-451-23005-8
    1. Induction (Logic)   2. Reasoning.   3. Science—Philosophy.   I. Title.
    BC57.H36 2010
    161—dc22   2010009813

Set in Bulmer MT
Designed by Ginger Legato

Printed in the United States of America

PUBLISHER'S NOTE
While the author has made every effort to provide accurate telephone numbers and Internet addresses at the time of publication, neither the publisher nor the author assumes any responsibility for errors, or for changes that occur after publication. Further, publisher does not have any control over and does not assume any responsibility for author or third-party Web sites or their content.

The scanning, uploading, and distribution of this book via the Internet or via any other means without the permission of the publisher is illegal and punishable by law. Please purchase only authorized electronic editions, and do not participate in or encourage electronic piracy of copyrighted materials. Your support of the author's rights is appreciated.

To Alyssa

With the hope that this book helps you

achieve a life filled with exciting discoveries

CONTENTS

Introduction   ix
Preface   1

1. The Foundation   5

The Nature of Concepts   9

Generalizations as Hierarchical   14

Perceiving First-Level Causal Connections   21

Conceptualizing First-Level Causal Connections   25

The Structure of Inductive Reasoning   29

2. Experimental Method   36

Galileo's Kinematics   38

Newton's Optics   58

The Methods of Difference and Agreement   67

Induction as Inherent in Conceptualization   74

3. The Mathematical Universe   81

The Birth of Celestial Physics   84

Mathematics and Causality   103

The Power of Mathematics   109

Proof of Kepler's Theory   113

4. Newton's Integration   116

The Development of Dynamics   117

The Discovery of Universal Gravitation   131

Discovery Is Proof   143

5. The Atomic Theory   151

Chemical Elements and Atoms   153

The Kinetic Theory of Gases   164

The Unification of Chemistry   170

The Method of Proof   177

6. Causes of Error   189

Misapplying the Inductive Method   191

Abandoning the Inductive Method   211

7. The Role of Mathematics and Philosophy   224

Physics as Inherently Mathematical   225

The Science of Philosophy   232

An End—and a New Beginning   243

References   259
Index   269

INTRODUCTION

Physics is the most universal of the natural sciences. It teaches us the basic laws of the material world as a whole, and serves as a paradigm of rational thought.

The explosion of knowledge in physics during the seventeenth century had a profound influence on men's view of the world and of their own nature. Most people do not acquire such views by reading philosophy books, but rather by seeing and dealing with the products of man in action, for example, novels, schools, governments, and the achievements of scientific discovery.

In their battle to establish the heliocentric theory, the new scientists provided a philosophic lesson that changed the course of history. They broke the stranglehold of religious dogma, at least for a while, and demonstrated that man *can* know the world—if he uses the method of observation, measurement, and logic. They rebelled against the view that astronomers should seek to "save the appearances," i.e., to concoct a baseless scheme for predicting the data—and pursued instead the ambitious goal of understanding the universe. The revolution was completed when Isaac Newton presented a fully intelligible universe, open to the human mind and ruled throughout by causal law. No philosophic treatise could have done more than the *Principia* to teach man philosophy, and to undercut mysticism and skepticism. Modern man had come of age as a rational being.

The message spread throughout the West and led to the Enlightenment. Innovators began to remake the world in man's new image—secular, thinking, self-reliant, and eager to enjoy life. The results showed up in every field (not least in the movement from monarchy to the Declaration of Independence). It was not long until Newton's physics led to the Industrial Revolution, and another milestone of that: Man could discard the ancient dichotomy between theory and practice and finally grasp that reason is his basic means of survival.

The influence of physics on culture cuts both ways. When, thanks to Kant, the most advanced science departs from the proper method—for example, when physicists renounce causality in the subatomic realm and revert to the menial job of "saving appearances," or when they entirely detach theory from reality and wander around an eleven-dimensional geometry of spacetime—the cultural consequences are devastating. People hear about such views and conclude: If this is rationality, who needs it? There must be something better. Then we see *un*reason become ubiquitous, from the rise of fundamentalist religion and pseudoscience to the rise of multiculturalism and nihilism.

Philosophy of science, which should have fought this trend, has descended to a point so low that it would have been inconceivable a century or so ago. The field has been hijacked by the "sociology of knowledge" movement, which claims that scientific theories are "social constructs" based on peer pressure.

This book is an antidote to all such apostles of irrationality. David Harriman unveils the logic of physics, identifying the method by which scientists discover laws of nature. The book begins with a discussion of how we arrive at our first inductive generalizations, which are the foundation of scientific knowledge, and then answers the key questions: What is the nature of experimental method? How does the proper interpretation of an experiment depend on the scientist's context of knowledge? Why is mathematics the language of physics? How is the role of mathematics related to the nature of concepts? And, putting it all together: What are the objective criteria of proof for a scientific theory? All of these issues are studied in relation to the discoveries of Newtonian mechanics and/or to the atomic theory of matter; the methodological results are then formulated as general principles. By thus inducing principles of method from the history of science, his book is a tour de force, demonstrating that epistemology is itself an inductive science.

A theory of generalizations presupposes a theory of concepts. One must grasp how the constituent concepts of a generalization are related to reality before one can grasp how the generalization itself is related to reality. The theory developed here is based on Ayn Rand's theory of concepts, presented in *Introduction to Objectivist Epistemology*. Ayn Rand regarded the question of how we prove inductive generalizations as the only fundamental problem still unsolved in philosophy.

Although she did not provide the solution, she did provide the key to it. Mr. Harriman shows that valid concepts, in her definition of "concepts," not only make possible but also guide our search for true generalizations. A similar point holds at a higher level of abstraction: A *theory* of concepts not only makes possible but also guides our search for a theory of generalizations. Every major aspect of the Objectivist view of concepts—including the role of similarities and differences, of integration, of hierarchy, of context—has a counterpart in the theory of generalizations. Indeed, generalization, Mr. Harriman explains, "is nothing more (or less) than an essential form of the method of concept-formation."

This book represents the first major application of Ayn Rand's epistemology to a field other than philosophy. Within this field, it answers the question she regarded as most crucial. And it thereby dams (and damns) the torrent of skepticism unleashed by David Hume and company.

Since this book is a model of inductive thinking, it *shows* the reader, rather than *telling* him, what induction is in essential terms and on what it is based. Such an assignment requires Mr. Harriman to shuttle continually from narrow to broad abstractions and back—a feat he performs brilliantly. Nothing essential to an objective conclusion is omitted and no unnecessary detail is included. In the end, the nature of the proper inductive method is not only clear, but luminously so.

Science is a very recent development. The unbelievable wonders it can bestow on man have just now become believable. I say "just now" because if we compress human history into a day, man became a scientist only in the last twenty minutes.

Will he still be a scientist tomorrow? Perhaps—with the help of this book.

—Leonard Peikoff

PREFACE

This book is the result of collaboration between myself and Leonard Peikoff.

It began several years ago when Dr. Peikoff became interested in the problem of induction, i.e., the epistemological question of how we can know the truth of inductive generalizations. Realizing that he needed to know more about the scientific discovery process in order to tackle this question, he hired me as his private tutor. Over the next year, we covered the history of physical science from ancient Greece through the nineteenth century.

After Dr. Peikoff had digested this material and integrated it with his knowledge of philosophy, what emerged was a new theory of induction that he discussed in a lecture course titled "Induction in Physics and Philosophy." I was excited by his breakthrough discoveries in a field that had been left for dead by contemporary philosophers, and so I decided to write this book, which is a full presentation of his theory as it applies to physical science.

Good work in philosophy of science requires a range of knowledge and of interests that few individuals possess. In a book that provides practical guidance to research scientists, E. Bright Wilson expressed the difficulty in this way:

There is a great need for further work on the subject of scientific inference. To be fruitful, it should be carried out by critical, original minds who are not only versed in philosophy but also familiar with the way scientists actually work. . . . Unfortunately, the practical nonexistence of such people almost suggests that the qualities of mind required by a good philosopher and those needed by a working scientist are incompatible.[1]

Our solution to the problem has been the attempt, insofar as possible, to combine our two brains. The reader may judge for himself the success of this operation. Here I limit myself to a personal comment: I found the procedure not only painless but uniquely rewarding and enjoyable.

It should not be difficult to identify which parts of the book came from which brain. In essence, the original philosophic ideas belong to Dr. Peikoff, while I provided their illustration in the history of science. In particular, the philosophic foundation presented in Chapter 1 is taken nearly verbatim from Dr. Peikoff's lectures. Also, I have incorporated into Chapter 2 his discussion of concepts as "green lights to induction." Finally, many of the essential points in Chapter 7, including the explanation for the role of mathematics in physical science, are taken from his lectures.

In addition, every chapter of the book has benefited greatly from his line-by-line scrutiny. The balancing act that I have tried to achieve— moving back and forth between the science and the philosophy, covering the former in sufficient depth while keeping the focus on the latter—was a challenging job, and Dr. Peikoff has been a very generous editor and teacher. Of course, any errors in the science and its history are entirely my responsibility.

While Dr. Peikoff taught me how to write this book, the Ayn Rand Institute gave me the time to write it. For the past decade, ARI has provided the financial support that allowed me to pursue work in philosophy of science. There is truth in the old adage "time is money"; from a writer's perspective, however, it seems more apt to say that "money is time"—time to research, to think, to make false starts and correct them, and eventually to complete a book. ARI and its contributors have my everlasting gratitude for supplying this invaluable commodity that is a writer's treasure.

I have received help from others as well. Tom VanDamme, the founder with me of Falling Apple Science Institute, kept me going with his unwavering enthusiasm for this work. Keith Lockitch, by his own example, has reminded me that physicists, even today, can not only have a deep understanding of philosophy, but also fully appreciate its relevance to their field.

Last, but to me always first, I thank my wife, Coral, for possessing the rare type of mind that combines clarity and passion, and giving me the love I needed to cross the finish line.

—David Harriman

1.

The Foundation

More than three centuries have passed since the scientific revolution culminated in the outstanding achievement of Isaac Newton. During that time, human life has been transformed by science and the technology springing from it.

Yet we find ourselves in a peculiar and unstable position. As our knowledge of the physical world has advanced, our understanding of knowledge itself has lagged behind. I witnessed this gap between physics and epistemology during my college years at the University of California, Berkeley. In my physics lab course, I learned how to determine the atomic structure of crystals by means of x-ray diffraction and how to identify subatomic particles by analyzing bubble-chamber photographs. In my philosophy of science course, on the other hand, I was taught by a world-renowned professor (Paul Feyerabend) that there is no such thing as scientific method and that physicists have no better claim to knowledge than voodoo priests.[1] I knew little about epistemology at the time, but I could not help noticing that it was the physicists, not the voodoo priests, who had made possible the life-promoting technology we enjoy today.

The triumphs of science stand as a monument to the power of reason, and they stand as a clear refutation of the skepticism that is epidemic in contemporary philosophy of science. Why then does this situation persist in universities around the world? How did we arrive at this bizarre contradiction—with scientists developing technology that exploits our detailed knowledge of atomic structure, while philosophers bewail or revel in the alleged impotence of reason to grasp even relatively simple facts?

E. Bright Wilson, who was a professor of chemistry at Harvard, once stated the problem in this way:

> Practical scientists who rashly allow themselves to listen to philosophers are likely to go away in a discouraged frame of mind, convinced that there is no logical foundation for the things they do, that all their alleged scientific laws are without justification, and that they are living in a world of naïve illusion. Of course, once they get out into the sunlight again, they know that this is not so, that scientific principles do work, bridges stay up, eclipses occur on schedule, and atomic bombs go off.
>
> Nevertheless, it is very unsatisfactory that no generally acceptable theory of scientific inference has yet been put forward. . . . Mistakes are often made which would presumably not have been made if a consistent and satisfactory basic philosophy had been followed.[2]

The central issue here is the failure of philosophers to offer a solution to what has been called "the problem of induction." Induction is the process of inferring generalizations from particular instances. The complementary process of applying generalizations to new instances is deduction. The theory of deductive reasoning was developed by Aristotle more than two millennia ago. This crucial achievement was a start toward understanding and validating knowledge, but it was only a start. Deduction presupposes induction; one cannot apply what one does not know or cannot conceive. The primary process of gaining knowledge that goes beyond perceptual data is induction. Generalization—the inference from some members of a class to all—is the essence of human cognition.

When we reason from "Men in my experience are mortal" to "All men are mortal"; or from "These fires burn me when touched" to "Fire by its nature burns"; or from "This apple and the moon obey the law of gravity" to "Every physical object in the universe obeys the law," in all such cases we are passing from one realm to another: from the observed to the unobserved; from the past behavior of nature to its future behavior; from what we discover in a narrow corner of a vast cosmos to what is true everywhere in that cosmos. This passage is the epistemological dividing line between man and animals.

Animals are perceptual-level organisms. They learn from experience, but only by highly delimited perceptual association. They cannot imagine the unobserved, the future, or the world beyond such associations. They know, deal with, and react to concretes, and only concretes. But this is not a level on which man can live and prosper. To act successfully in the present, a human being must set long-range goals and a long-range course of action; to do so, he must know the future—perhaps months ahead, often years, sometimes decades.

A generalization is a proposition that ascribes a characteristic to every member of an unlimited class, however it is positioned in space or time. In formal terms, it states: All S is P. This kind of claim, on any subject, goes beyond all possible observation.

But man is neither omniscient nor infallible. His generalizations, therefore, are not automatically correct. Thus the questions: How can man know, across the whole scale of space and time, facts that he does not and can never perceive? When and why is the inference from "some" to "all" legitimate? What is the method of valid induction that can prove the generalization to which it leads? In short, how can man determine which generalizations are true (correspond to reality), and which ones are false (contradict reality)?

The answer is crucial. If a man accepts a true generalization, his mental contents (to that extent) are consistent with one another, and his action, other things being equal, will succeed. But if a man accepts a false generalization, it introduces in his mind a contradiction with his authentic knowledge and a clash with reality, leading unavoidably to frustration and failure in his actions. Therefore the "problem of induction" is not merely a puzzle for academics—it is the problem of human survival.

The problem is to identify the method of induction, not to seek its "justification." One cannot ask for a justification of induction, any more than for a justification of deduction. Inducing and deducing are man's means of justifying anything. Their validity as cognitive processes, therefore, is an unchallengeable given. Aristotle did not ask: Is deduction legitimate? but rather: How should it be performed so as to reach valid conclusions? Similarly, our question regarding induction is not: Is it legitimate? but rather: Given the validity of induction, how should one perform it so as to reach a knowledge of facts?

In considering this question, one must start with observation and focus on the steps of the proper method of reaching generalizations. One cannot start with generalizations already in existence, and then, ignoring their genesis, attempt to evaluate them. This last, however, has been the common practice among philosophers. They are indifferent, they say, to questions of genesis (which they dismiss as psychology rather than epistemology), and are concerned only with questions of validation. But this elevates the fallacy of dropping context into a formal policy. It is futile to ponder the validity of a generalization unless we know how we arrived at it—by what steps, in accordance with what method, and whether the method used is valid. Nothing else can enable us to know whether the product of that method does or does not correspond to reality.

One widely held but false view is that induction is based simply on enumeration. According to this superficial approach, the inducer's method is merely to collect instances of a generalization; the greater the number of instances, the greater the probability of the generalization (the proponents of this view deny that we can ever reach certainty).

The classic example of this approach, still discussed by philosophers, is the case of the swans. A philosopher observes a great many white swans; at some point he ventures (as highly probable) the claim "All swans are white," whereupon a black one appears and his generalization is dashed to the ground. Where do we go from here? he then moans.

Enumeration is not the method of induction, and it provides no basis to infer from "some" to "all," not even with a degree of probability. This is why all attempts to ground inductive reasoning on statistics have failed. A generalization reached merely from enumeration is necessarily arbitrary, and must therefore be dismissed without discussion from the field of rational consideration. As we shall see, there are valid inductions based on a single case; and there are generalizations with millions of instances, which are yet utterly illegitimate (e.g., "All men seek pleasure"). Why such a difference? Simple enumerators have no answer.

In order to understand how inductive generalizations are reached in the physical sciences, we will look closely at the reasoning of scientists such as Galileo, Kepler, Newton, Lavoisier, and Maxwell. We will follow them as they perform experiments, search for mathematical relationships, and prove their most abstract theories. The purpose is to identify, in detail, the steps and the essence of the method they have used so brilliantly.

A theory of induction presupposes answers to the fundamental questions of metaphysics and epistemology. For instance, I take for granted the law of causality (which states that the action of an entity follows from its nature) and the validity of sense perception. In large part, philosophers have foundered on the topic of induction because they have been confused on these prior issues. The philosophic foundation of the theory presented here can be found in Chapters 1 to 5 of Leonard Peikoff's book *Objectivism: The Philosophy of Ayn Rand*.

The Nature of Concepts

There is, however, one prior topic that deserves special attention.

Ayn Rand presented her revolutionary theory of concepts in a book titled *Introduction to Objectivist Epistemology*. In this section, I briefly indicate a few points that are particularly relevant to validating inductive generalizations.

Reason is our faculty of acquiring knowledge by means of concepts.

We form concepts by grasping similarities among existents, similarities that make a group of existents stand out against a background of different existents. Similarity, of course, does not mean identity; Rand recognized that the existents united by a valid concept can differ in every respect. But she also recognized the nature of those differences: They are *quantitative*, i.e., they are differences in the measurements of the characteristics. When we form a concept, our mental process consists in retaining the characteristics but omitting their differing measurements.

Consider the concept "pendulum," a simple device that has played a crucial role in the history of physics. A pendulum is a weight suspended from a fixed support so that it swings freely back and forth. In forming the concept, our minds retain this essential characteristic while omitting the measurements that differentiate one pendulum from another. Pendulums differ in length (the distance from the fixed support to the weight), in the size and shape and magnitude of the weight, and in material composition (which is identified by various measurements that distinguish one material from another). All these measurements are omitted in forming the concept.

Since the concept refers to actual pendulums, and to be is to be something specific (the law of identity), we do not deny the existence of measurements when we omit them. Rather we recognize that the relevant measurements must exist in some quantity, but may exist in any quantity. By not specifying the measurements we can integrate all pendulums into a single mental entity and treat them as interchangeable members of a class.

In concept-formation, the measurement-omission process is subconscious and automatic. We grasp that an attribute can vary within some range, and we retain the attribute without specifying its quantity. We do not need to know how to make the measurements in order to omit them when forming the concept. On the contrary, we must form the relevant concepts before we can progress to the advanced stage of learning how to make the numerical measurements.

"A concept," in Rand's formal definition, "is a mental integration of two or more units possessing the same distinguishing characteristic(s), with their particular measurements omitted."[3] Contrary to skeptics, a concept is not merely a name for an arbitrarily chosen group of particulars; rather, it is an *integration* of similar particulars into a single mental unit. The integration is not arbitrary; it is possible because the existents in question do in fact possess the same attributes; they differ from one another only in the measurement of these attributes. By dropping—not specifying—the measurements, therefore, the mind forms a new unit that includes and applies to all such existents, past, present, and future. Thereafter the mind retains and deals cognitively with this unlimited sum by means of a single (appropriately defined) word.

Ayn Rand's analysis of similarity enabled her to identify an intimate connection between concept-formation and mathematics. She wrote:

> The basic principle of concept-formation (which states that the omitted measurements must exist in *some* quantity, but may exist in *any* quantity) is the equivalent of the basic principle of algebra, which states that the algebraic symbols must be given *some* numerical value, but may be given *any* value. In this sense and respect, perceptual awareness is the arithmetic, but *conceptual awareness is the algebra of cognition.*
>
> The relationship of concepts to their constituent particulars is the same as the relationship of algebraic symbols to numbers. In the equation $2a = a + a$, any number may be substituted for the symbol "a" without affecting the truth of the equation. For instance, $2 \times 5 = 5 + 5$, or $2 \times 5{,}000{,}000 = 5{,}000{,}000 + 5{,}000{,}000$. In the same manner, by the same psycho-epistemological method, a concept is used as an algebraic symbol that stands for *any* of the arithmetical sequence of units it subsumes.
>
> Let those who attempt to invalidate concepts by declaring that they cannot find "manness" in men, try to invalidate algebra by declaring that they cannot find "a-ness" in 5 or in 5,000,000.[4]

Philosophers have often upheld mathematics as the model of human thought. Yet many have missed the point by characterizing mathematics as a purely deductive science. On the contrary, mathematics reveals in explicit form the process of conceptualization, which is man's method of extrapolating from observed data to the total of the universe.[5]

As children, we begin by forming concepts in cases where the similarity among the referents is grasped by direct perception, for example, concepts such as "table" or "dog." After forming such "first-level" concepts, we can grasp the similarity among tables, chairs, and beds and thereby arrive at the wider abstraction "furniture"; or we can grasp the similarity among dogs, cats, and fish and thereby arrive at the wider abstraction "animal." We do not see furniture or animals—we see only particular tables, dogs, and so on. The units of higher-level concepts are the lower-level concepts from which they are formed. Thus concepts are developed in a hierarchy, which starts from the first-level concepts of a toddler and extends to the widest abstractions of a theoretical physicist.

When properly formed, higher-level concepts are objective in the same sense as lower-level concepts: Both are based on fact, but for a higher-level concept the similarity among the referents cannot be grasped without the aid of prior concepts. Consider the advanced concept "electricity." The Greeks knew of four phenomena that we classify as electrical: the lightning seen from thunderclouds, the strike of a torpedo fish when it stuns its prey, the glow seen on the tips of spears during stormy weather ("St. Elmo's fire"), and the capacity of rubbed amber to attract bits of straw or paper. Perceptually, these phenomena are very different; the Greeks did not and could not grasp any similarity uniting them. A long chain of concepts and generalizations, culminating in the modern theory of electricity, is necessary in order to reveal the similarity.

At the early stages of cognitive development, the meaning of first-level concepts can be made clear simply by pointing to instances. A child can point to a table or a dog and say: "I mean this kind of thing." But for higher-level concepts, where the similarity is not perceptually given, this method does not work. We need some other way to hold in mind the meaning of our concepts, i.e., to identify the nature of the referents and differentiate them from other existents. This is the role of definitions.[6]

A concept refers to existents, including all of their characteristics (known and unknown). The definition states the distinguishing characteristic(s) that explains the greatest number of other known characteristics (the differentiae), and it states the wider class of existents from which the referents of the concept are being distinguished (the genus). By doing so, the definition tells us the essential nature of the existents, i.e., that which makes them the kind of existents they are. Thus definitions are brief, retainable statements that both identify the referents and condense our knowledge of them.

It is crucial to recognize that characteristics are identified as essential (and thus defining) within a specific context of knowledge. As our knowledge of the referents expands, the characteristic(s) that best explains and condenses that knowledge may change. For example, consider the concept "temperature." Initially temperature was defined as "the attribute of a material that is a measure of its hotness or coldness." Based on discoveries made during the nineteenth century (see Chapter 5), the definition became "the attribute of a material that is a measure of the average translational kinetic energy per molecule." This later definition explains a great deal more about temperature by relating it to Newtonian mechanics and the atomic theory of matter.

Thus definitions are empirical statements; the identification of an essential characteristic is based on the total of one's knowledge about the referents and about other existents from which they are being distinguished. As Rand put it, "A definition is the condensation of a vast body of observations—and stands or falls with the truth or falsehood of these observations."[7]

In today's confusion, it is necessary to emphasize that a concept cannot be equated with its definition. The concept "temperature" had the same meaning for Galileo as for Einstein, i.e., both men referred to the same physical property. The difference is only that Einstein knew much more about this property; he understood its relation to heat, to motion, and to the fundamental nature of matter. But that expansion of knowledge was possible only because the concept itself did not change. Because concepts are stable, we can communicate and advance our knowledge.

Rand offered a helpful metaphor that captures important aspects of her theory of concepts:

Since concepts represent a system of cognitive classification, a given concept serves (speaking metaphorically) as a file folder in which man's mind files his knowledge of the existents it subsumes. The content of such folders varies from individual to individual, according to the degree of his knowledge—it ranges from the primitive, generalized information in the mind of a child or an illiterate to the enormously detailed sum in the mind of a scientist—but it pertains to the same referents, to the same kind of existents, and is subsumed under the same concept. This filing system makes possible such activities as learning, education, research—the accumulation, transmission and expansion of knowledge.[8]

A definition is the label that identifies and condenses the folder's contents. The concept is the total of the contents, and it entails the commitment to file all further knowledge of the referents in the same folder.

Concepts are the tools of knowledge—the file folders—but are not by themselves claims to knowledge (although they do presuppose knowledge); that is why concepts are referred to as valid or invalid (rather than true or false). If we are to gain knowledge with these tools, they must be used to create a cognitive product, such as a generalization—which either does or does not correspond to reality, i.e., which, being a claim to knowledge, is described as true or false (rather than valid or invalid). Generalizations are the essential items that go into the conceptual file folders. But to qualify as knowledge of reality, generalizations, like any cognitive product, must be validated by reference to a rational method.

Thus the purpose of this book is to answer a dual question: Given the nature of concepts, how are generalizations about the physical world formed? And how, therefore, do they relate to reality?

Generalizations as Hierarchical

Science does not begin in a void; it emerges, after centuries, from prescience. Men must first acquire and assimilate an enormous context of knowledge, including the conceptual identification of the observed concretes around them and a wealth of early generalizations (along with the essentials of a pro-reason, secular philosophy). Only then can a few great innovators grasp the disciplined, sophisticated method of knowledge we call science.

Generalizations, like concepts themselves, are hierarchical. The generalizations discovered by scientists are advanced or higher-level ones; for example, "white light is a mixture of colors," or "planets travel in elliptical orbits," or "a changing electric current induces a magnetic field." These are not available to direct perception.

Such generalizations rest on a great number of preceding observations and lower-level generalizations, which go back ultimately to first-level generalizations. These latter are the empirical starting points, and thus the base, of all subsequent induction, whether performed by primitives or by our own children, by ancient thinkers or by modern scientists. There is an exact parallel here to first-level and higher-level concepts.

To understand the generalizations of physics down to their roots, therefore, we must first study the prescientific induction out of which scientific induction grows. As Leonard Peikoff has explained, the process of identifying the first-level roots of a higher-level generalization is "reduction":

> Reduction is the means of connecting an advanced knowledge to reality by traveling backward through the hierarchical structure involved, i.e., in the reverse order of that required to reach the knowledge. "Reduction" is the process of identifying in logical sequence the intermediate steps that relate a cognitive item to perceptual data. Since there are options in the detail of a learning process, one need not always retrace the steps one initially happened to take. What one must retrace is the essential logical structure.[9]

I will sketch two examples here.

In the next chapter, we will discuss Galileo's discovery of the generalization that horizontal motion is unaccelerated. When a body travels freely (i.e., leaving aside friction) in a horizontal direction, it moves with constant speed (in contrast to a body that is falling vertically, which undergoes a constant acceleration). How did Galileo discover this generalization? Among other things, he experimented by rolling metal balls with a known speed off the edge of a table, and demonstrating that the place where the ball hits the floor implies that the horizontal speed remains constant during the descent. He carefully designed such experiments so as to reduce the effects of friction. Clearly, this presupposes knowledge of the ever-present existence of friction and of its impeding effect on the motion of bodies. Without such knowledge, Galileo would never have thought to minimize friction, nor, therefore, would he have seen the horizontal motion continuing at an unchanged rate. You cannot ask: What happens when friction is removed? until you have first learned about friction.

So how would an individual discover the earlier generalization, that friction impedes motion? It is an integration of many still earlier generalizations reached by observing moving bodies in varying circumstances. For example, when a ball is rolled through tall grass it slows and comes to a stop relatively quickly (a generalization); across thick rugs, it slows less quickly and rolls farther (a generalization); across a smooth floor, the motion continues longer and the ball goes still farther (a generalization).

Consider each of these generalizations. What must an inducer know before he can discover anything about how different conditions affect the motion of a ball that has been pushed? Before he can know that pushing a ball under conditions X makes it roll in the particular way Y, he must first know the simpler fact that pushing a ball (in contrast to a block or a pillow) causes it to roll at all. Only then can he discover the influence of varying conditions on the rolling motion. Thus the scientific principle of Galileo goes back level by level to an irreducible first-level generalization: Pushing a ball causes it to roll. That is one "axiom"—or starting point—of induction.

Now consider, in outline, a more complex case. Let us reduce to the perceptual level the advanced generalization: "Light travels in straight lines." On what earlier generalizations does it depend?

Obviously, it presupposes the generalization that light travels at all, i.e., that light moves through space. But this fact is not available on the perceptual level; no one can see light moving, because its speed is too great. Scientists had to prove that there is a time lapse between light being in one place and then in another. If it takes a measurable amount of time for light to get from A to B, then light from a given source is not instantaneously at A and B and everywhere, as it seems to be perceptually; rather, the light must be moving. Because of the enormous speed of light, however, early scientists could detect this time interval only when light moved across astronomical distances. It was Olaus Roemer, a seventeenth-century Danish astronomer, who first measured the speed of light by studying the eclipses of the moons of Jupiter.

And what did this discovery presuppose? A host of earlier scientific generalizations, including those that led to the heliocentric theory (see Chapter 3), and also many generalizations as to how light behaves in relation to lenses and mirrors, which knowledge was needed to invent the telescope and thus bring the moons of Jupiter into view. So a long chain of earlier generalizations was required in order to discover that light travels.

Given the fact that light travels, how do we know that it does so in straight lines (when moving through the same material)? Here there are a number of different proofs, but let us say we reach this conclusion by observing the shadows of objects. We discover that we can explain the shape of a shadow only if light is moving from a source in straight lines to the object casting the shadow.

But in order to arrive at this conclusion about the shapes of shadows, we must first have discovered a much simpler connection between light and shadows, namely: light does cast shadows behind any opaque object it strikes (a generalization)—which itself is an integration of many still earlier generalizations, such as "candles cast shadows behind people" and "shadows appear on sunny days."

But all of this requires that men first have the concept of "shadow"— which depends on our ability to distinguish the dark areas behind lighted objects from the objects themselves. And how did we learn this distinction? From a wealth of earlier data, such as "The dark areas, in contrast to the objects they abut, have no tactile properties" (a generalization) and "The dark areas appear or vanish with changes in the light source, while the objects remain constant" (a generalization). From these (along with other such generalizations), we conclude that the dark areas are not objects, but rather an effect produced when an object blocks light (a generalization)—which gives us the concept "shadow."

But this presupposes the concept of one entity "blocking" another. How did we learn about this type of phenomenon? From having observed it in many forms in the world of physical objects long before we could understand such abstractions as "light" and "shadow." For example, we discover that "walls block balls, i.e., stop them from rolling" (a generalization). And how do we know that the wall is what stopped the ball, as against the ball merely stopping by itself at the wall? We push or hammer against a wall with our hands and actually feel its resistance, its refusal to yield. Here again we finally end with a first-level generalization, such as "Walls resist hammering hands."

In the above, I have deliberately come back to first-level generalizations of the kind a toddler reaches in his earliest explorations of what, much later, will be called "dynamics." But a great many other first-level generalizations, from a variety of areas, are also involved in the above examples. I have attempted to give merely a schematic indication of some steps in the reductions, enough to make the pattern of the process clear.

Only if its reduction to first-level generalizations is possible can a generalization be regarded as objectively true. As Dr. Peikoff has pointed out, "Man's only direct contact with reality is the data of sense. These, therefore, are the standard of objectivity, to which all other cognitive material must be brought back."[10] A generalization not reducible to sensory data is merely an arbitrary claim, the source of which is some emotion or authority. Such a claim is inadmissible into the field of knowledge or science.

First-level generalizations are to induction what sense perception is to knowledge in general; they are the "axioms of induction." The study of the process of induction, therefore, must start with the study of first-level generalizations. Only then can we turn to consider the higher-level generalizations built on them.

A "first-level generalization" is one derived directly from perceptual observation, without the need of any antecedent generalizations. As such, it is composed only of first-level concepts; any form of knowledge that requires the understanding of higher-level concepts cannot be gained directly from perceptual data.

Since the perceptual is the self-evident, first-level generalizations are self-evident; being the basis of inductive (and therefore of deductive) knowledge, they admit and require no proof. They are available, as certainties, to anyone with the requisite simple vocabulary who takes the trouble to look at reality.

And they are available by no other means. How do you know that pushing a ball makes it roll? There is no answer, not even by Newton or Einstein, except this: Look and see. One cannot "prove" such a generalization by deriving it from any abstract laws of motion. On the contrary, without a fund of such generalizations established at the outset, one could not discover or prove any laws of motion. The laws are valid only if their first-level antecedents are valid, not the other way around.

Since first-level generalizations are the basis of all higher-level inductions, they cannot be threatened or undermined by the latter. Like sense perception itself, they are impregnable to overthrow by any future discovery. This does not mean that the first-level generalizer is omniscient. On the contrary, it means that knowledge is contextual, and, therefore, that—on any level of generalization, from first to last—certainty does not require omniscience.

Since generalizations are always reached in and through a specific cognitive context, their proper statement necessarily includes that context. To quote from *Objectivism: The Philosophy of Ayn Rand*:

> Man is a being of limited knowledge—*and he must, therefore, identify the cognitive context of his conclusions.* In any situation where there is reason to suspect that a variety of factors is relevant to the truth, only some of which are presently known, he is obliged

to acknowledge this fact. The implicit or explicit preamble must be: "On the basis of the available evidence, i.e., within the context of the factors so far discovered, the following is the proper conclusion to draw." Thereafter, the individual must continue to observe and identify; should new information warrant it, he must qualify his conclusion accordingly.

If a man follows this policy, he will find that his knowledge at one stage *is not contradicted* by later discoveries. He will find that the discoveries expand his understanding; that he learns more about the conditions on which his conclusions depend; that he moves from relatively generalized, primitive observations to increasingly detailed, sophisticated formulations. He will also find that the process is free of epistemological trauma. The advanced conclusions augment and enhance his earlier knowledge; they do not clash with or annul it.[11]

A child learns, for example, that pushing a ball makes it roll. Later he discovers that this does not happen if the ball reaches a certain weight, or if it is glued to the floor, or if it is made of iron and sitting on top of a strong magnet. None of this overthrows the initial first-level generalization. On the contrary, the latter is necessary for anyone to be able to consider subsequent qualifications. One cannot reach or validate "Pushing moves a ball only under X conditions" until one has first grasped the elementary fact that "pushing moves a ball."

Similarly, Newton's laws are not contradicted by Einstein's discovery of relativity theory (see Chapter 4). On the contrary, Newton's science remains absolute within Newton's context, and that science alone is what makes possible the later expansion of this context, when men discover operative factors unknown in Newton's day.

The knowledge possessed by a rational inducer is always limited, but it is nevertheless real. Because it is limited, it is open to future qualifications. Because it is real, however, the qualifications have no negative significance; they are purely positive, an epistemological asset, a step forward in the cognitive enterprise, not a step backward crushing their own roots.

Perceiving First-Level Causal Connections

We need to examine first-level generalizations, the axioms of induction, in greater depth, with particular emphasis on how we come to learn and objectively validate them.

Let us start by noting that all generalizations—first-level and higher—are statements of causal connection. All assert (or imply) that an entity of a certain kind necessarily acts in a certain way under a given set of circumstances, which is the essence of the law of causality. This is true on all levels of development, from "Pushing a ball causes it to roll," on through "A net force exerted on a body causes it to accelerate in accordance with the law $F = mA$," and beyond. In reality, there is nothing to unite two existents (such as pushing and rolling, or force and acceleration) universally, i.e., there is nothing to make any generalization true, except some form of causal relationship between the two.

The only justification for inferring the future from the actions of the past is the fact that the past actions occurred not arbitrarily or miraculously, but for a reason, a reason inherent in the nature of the acting entities themselves; i.e., the justification is that the past actions were effects of causes—and thus if the same cause is operative tomorrow, it will result in the same effect.

Any validation of generalizations, therefore, must answer the question: How—by what means—does man learn causal connections? The subsequent chapters of this book will answer this question for the higher-level generalizations that culminate in scientific theories. Here we will begin by considering how we grasp the causal relationships expressed in first-level generalizations.

An essential precondition of a man's discovery of particular causal connections is his grasp in some terms of the general law of causality. If anyone lived (or thought he lived) in the acausal universe described by empiricist philosopher David Hume, he could not raise or answer the question "Why?" about anything. Without the fact and the knowledge of the law of causality, there would be nothing but a flow of unconnected, random data.

Knowledge of the law of causality is first gained by a child in implicit form, in the early, preconceptual stage of cognition; it is grasped as a corollary—a self-evident implication—of the law of identity, one of the fundamental axioms of philosophy. The law of identity states that to be is to be something in particular, i.e., to have a nature; causality is the application of identity to the realm of action, i.e., it states that an entity must act in accordance with its nature. The (implicit) knowledge of both laws is necessary for any further cognitive development. Only when a man knows the law of identity can he go on to understand and ask the question: "What is this thing?" i.e., "What is its identity?" Similarly, only when he knows the law of causality, at least in implicit form, can he go on to understand and ask the question "Why?" i.e., "What is the cause?"

Assuming the necessary philosophic foundation, our question is: how does an individual come to discover particular causes? Specifically, how does a first-level inducer grasp his first causal connections (and thereby come to gain an explicit grasp of the concept "cause")? A child's first causal discoveries, I believe, flow from his experiences of his own personal efficacy. This is only a likely (and unoriginal) hypothesis; if not universally applicable, it indicates at least one possible pattern of development.

A toddler, say, pushes a ball and it rolls away. How do we formulate (in adult, conceptual terms) what the child actually perceives here without benefit of language? Here are three formulations: "I rolled the ball by pushing it"; "My pushing it made the ball roll"; "I caused the ball to roll by pushing it."

These three formulations are logically equivalent; each entails the others; each identifies the same self-evident fact (from slightly different perspectives). Only the third statement mentions the concept of "cause." But the content of that concept is already present in the others; it is present in the very meaning of "rolling" an object. To roll an object is to cause it to roll by a certain means. The experience of rolling a ball, therefore, is the experience of causing something to happen. It is a pure experience of causation, without which the concept of "cause" could never be reached.

The experience is directly perceptual. Just as one perceives an intransitive "rolling" directly (as in "The ball is rolling")—so, exactly so, in the case of a transitive "rolling" ("I rolled the ball"). And if such rolling is an object of direct experience, as it clearly is, then causing, too, is an object of direct experience.

Consider another example: a thirsty toddler drinks a glass of water and his thirst disappears. What does he perceive? "I stopped (got rid of, slaked, quenched) my thirst by drinking water. . . . My drinking water made my thirst go away . . . I caused my thirst to go away by drinking water . . ." Again, the content of "cause" is present in the experience itself. The quenching of one's thirst is an object of direct (introspective) experience. It is an experience of one thing causing another, since to quench is to cause a certain effect. Thus the experience of the quenching is the perception of the causing.

In these cases (and countless similar ones), a child, contrary to Hume, does experience a connection between certain events, not merely a conjunction. He experiences the connection between what he does and what it makes happen. This is the basis of a child's first-level generalizations—and it gives him the explicit knowledge of "cause" necessary for further progress.

When a child moves beyond these early experiences to discover causation in the external world apart from his own action, he uses the same method. Armed with an explicit concept of "cause" (of one thing "making" another happen), he is ready to perceive, all around him, further instances of it. "I make the ball roll" becomes, in due course, "The wind makes the leaves flutter," "The fire makes the paper turn into ashes," "The rain makes the ground wet." In all such cases, the causal connection is grasped from a single instance, because we directly perceive the causation as it is occurring. Just as we perceive, without the need of language, "*rolling* the ball," so we perceive "*blowing* the leaves," "burning the paper," "dampening the earth." All the underscored terms denote objects of experience which are causal processes, processes in which one thing makes another happen.

The primary method of grasping causal connection, therefore, is to perceive it. Building on this foundation, scientists develop more sophisticated, experimental methods of discovering causality, in higher-level cases where perception of the cause is not possible. The use of such methods requires an analysis of variables going far beyond the first level of cognition. In regard to first-level generalizations, however, direct perception of cause and effect is essential—and sufficient.

The sheer observation of a regularity, without any grasp of its cause, does not establish a generalization. For example, however often primitive man observes the daily and annual movements of the sun, he cannot, on such basis alone, conclude that the sun must always move relative to Earth in this particular way. His perceptions here are rather the first evidence he has for a generalization—which can be validated only by reference to later knowledge based on other methods (e.g., in this case, the knowledge and methods of Copernicus, Kepler and Galileo).

Here again we see that quantity of instances alone is irrelevant to induction. In first-level induction, a single instance is sufficient. By contrast, thousands of observations of an unconnected regularity establish at most a hypothesis worthy of investigation.

I have been assuming in the above a firm distinction between two forms of grasping causality: in personal terms, through one's own efficacy, and then, in regard to the external world, impersonally, without reference to human efficacy. But this distinction, so clear to us today, had to be learned across many centuries.

When they turn to cause and effect in the external world, primitives (and children left to themselves) typically continue to interpret the causal processes they perceive on the model of their early personal experience. Projecting their own pattern outward, they think of causal agents in the external world, some or all, as being personal entities, and they construe causation as the expression of inner desires or intentions. The obvious historical example of such anthropomorphism is the animist idea that even inanimate entities are ensouled things who act with ends in view. Theism maintains the same view of causality, merely consolidating the multitude of ensouled causal agents into a relatively few efficacious deities or even into a single omnipotent One.

In this respect, religion represents the mind and metaphysics of primitive man. Such a mind has little or no concept of an impersonal material world, one in which the action of external entities flows not from souls or desires, but from the law of identity, i.e., from the physical nature of the acting entities in the absence of any consciousness, immanent or transcendent.

The impersonal metaphysics was the great—and historically recent—achievement of the Greeks, specifically of Aristotle's secularism and advocacy of reason. It was this approach that led to the clear Greek distinction between the animate and the inanimate, which included the fact that consciousness can belong only to the animate. Once the Greek approach was embedded in the mind of the West (and leaving aside relapses such as the Middle Ages), causation could no longer be conceived in terms of the personal efficacy of supernatural agents. Thus did the objective view of cause and effect displace the anthropomorphic view that, at the beginning, had seemed to be merely an innocent extension to nature of men's own causal experience.

Western civilization broadened the concept of "cause," by regarding personal efficacy as merely a subtype of it. This was a crucial precondition of the development of modern science. It amounts to bringing causality for the first time fully into the realm of reality and identity—i.e., to breaking its primordial bonds to mysticism.

Conceptualizing First-Level Causal Connections

Percepts as such reveal concretes, not abstractions—Tom, Dick, and Harry, for example, not "man." By perception alone, therefore, the first-level inducer grasps causal connections only in concrete terms, as a relationship at a specific time and place between two or more particulars. He grasps, for example, that his act of pushing just now caused that ball to roll. Or he grasps that this morning the flames in the fireplace over there burned that particular piece of paper.

Such observations, though indispensable as the start of an inductive process, are not yet generalizations. What turns them into generalizations? What mediates the passage from a causal connection linking particulars to a universally applicable truth? The answer lies in man's distinctive means of dealing cognitively with particulars: his conceptual faculty. The essence of concept-formation is the passage from particulars to universals.

In the nature of the case, when a concept is formed, only some of the instances in the subsumed group have been perceived. New instances are conceptualized, i.e., placed under the appropriate concept, as and when they are encountered. This is man's method of connecting new percepts to previous ones, and thus of applying to them any knowledge already gained about the members of the group.

As a developing young mind, the first-level inducer is eager to use his simple vocabulary to name new objects that he recognizes. He identifies, in terms of the vocabulary available to him, the elementary causal connections he directly perceives. He is not content mutely to observe that the hot thing over there caused the other thing to blacken and disappear. He can name the entities and processes at work, by applying concepts he has already formed, such as "fire," "paper," "burning."

In utilizing concepts as his cognitive tools, he is thereby omitting the measurements of the particular causal connection he perceives. "Fire" relates the yellow-orange flames he perceives to all such, regardless of their varying measurements; the same applies to "paper" and to the process of "burning." Hence his first *statement* of his concrete observation: "Fire burns paper." This statement is simply a conceptualization of the perceived data—which is what makes it a generalization.

Notice that when our first-level inducer identifies a perceived causal connection in words, he does not do it as a description of unique concretes, even though that is all he perceives; he at once states a universal truth. His first remark is not "I see shimmering, yellow-orange smoke-emitting flames, about one foot high, turning that huge front page of the newspaper with its big headlines into a small pile of blackened ashes." The child at this early stage does not have the conceptual apparatus necessary to distinguish one instance of fire-burning-paper from another by means of words; first he must grasp that what he sees is an instance of "fire," "burning," "paper," i.e., of his earlier concepts. Only much later, when the vocabulary identifying specific measurements of these existents has been developed, can he use words in sophisticated combinations to describe the action of a unique fire. Logically, the generalization must come first; it is the direct product of applying one's conceptual apparatus to the perceived connection.

Similarly, a toddler sees a particular ball, but his identification of it is simply "ball." At this early stage, the child does not and cannot know any wider integrations or narrower subtypes or cross-classifications of "ball"; he cannot identify a ball as "a human artifact," or as "a yellow tennis ball," or as "a product of capitalist profit-seeking." To him, at the start of the conceptual process, the verbalized object is "ball," pure and simple. The same applies to the child's experience of himself as the particular pushing agent. His identification must be of "pushing" as such, not of "voluntary human action," nor of "exerting force," nor of "his own individual act of pushing"—since he does not yet know any such relatively more abstract terms; the concept simply denotes any and every act of pushing, regardless of the agent doing it. And, as to the time and place of his observation, this is par excellence an irrelevancy to the child (and to anyone). Inherent in forming and applying a concept is the understanding that what counts cognitively is only the identity of its referents. The mere passage of time or the mere change of location, assuming everything else remains the same, makes no difference to one's conclusions, because the concept of an existent subsumes all instances everywhere, past, present, and future.

Because of his simple, first-level conceptual structure, our inducer, in the very act of naming what he perceives, automatically drops the measurements of the perceived cause and effect and thereby gains knowledge transcending the given concrete. This is how he is able to grasp that the cause pertains to pushing as such, and the effect to balls as such, no matter where or when the ball is pushed.

If we judge by their actions, animals also have a direct experience of causation. They too perceive that various actions they take make certain things happen. But they cannot go on to infer any generalization from these perceptions. The crucial difference here is that animals have no conceptual faculty, no faculty of omitting measurements; so they cannot set aside the particularity of any perceived data. Thus they have no cognitive power to separate what counts in a causal situation (e.g., being a fire) from what does not count (the exact shade of the flame, the area of the paper, etc.). What does not count is the measurements, which, in an epistemological context, a conceptualizing mind discards (implicitly or explicitly) as irrelevant, mere detail, nonessential. Animals, as a result, cannot project from their percepts what future to expect. But this is what man does in the sheer act of conceptualizing a percept.

A generalization is the conceptualization of cause and effect; i.e., induction may be described as *measurement-omission applied to causal connections*. It is nothing more (or less) than an essential form of the method of concept-formation. Just as a concept, through measurement-omission, integrates an unlimited number of particular existents of a certain kind into a single word, so does a certain union of concepts integrate through measurement-omission an unlimited number of particular causal sequences of a certain kind into a single proposition that subsumes them all: a generalization.

Let us now sum up in regard to the axioms of induction. When a first-level inducer identifies his concrete experience of cause and effect in terms of words, his perceptual grasp of the causal relationship becomes thereby a conceptual grasp of it, i.e., a generalization. And since the application of first-level concepts is automatic and self-evident, the two aspects of a first-level generalization—the perceptual and the conceptual—are each, to a human mind, self-evident.

Hence the conclusion: There are, at the base of all future induction, absolutely certain first-level generalizations, which extend beyond all possible perception yet follow self-evidently from man's highly limited perceptual experience, as and when this is processed by his conceptual faculty.

The Structure of Inductive Reasoning

Let us now take a wider look at the process of induction, no longer restricted to the first level. Specifically, let us penetrate to the essence of inductive reasoning on any level.

In general, reasoning is the process of inferring a conclusion from earlier knowledge. In valid reasoning, one's premises are not the takeoff point for a flight of imagination: for a guess, a hypothesis, or an arbitrary "leap." In reasoning, the conclusion follows from the premises necessarily. If it does not follow necessarily, then the argument is a non sequitur, and the inference is invalid.

Rand defines logic as the "art of noncontradictory identification." If one denies the conclusion of a logical argument, one is contradicting the earlier information from which the conclusion was inferred, and is thereby violating the law of identity. But a contradiction is impossible; hence, if the premises are true, the conclusion in question must be true. This is the pattern and principle of all valid reasoning, whether deductive or inductive.

The application of this principle to deductive inference is straightforward. In applying a generalization to a particular case, we are making explicit in the conclusion information that was included implicitly in the premise from the outset. In this sense, a deductive conclusion contains nothing logically new. That is why, in deduction, it is self-contradictory to affirm the premises and deny the conclusion. For example, I could not reason "All men are mortal; Socrates is a man; therefore Socrates is not mortal." This is tantamount to stating, "All men are mortal—and here is one who isn't." In the valid syllogism, by contrast, when I conclude that Socrates is mortal, I am doing no more than remaining true to my premise.

But the situation in regard to induction is more complex. If I reason from the mortality of Tom, Dick, and Harry to the conclusion that all men are mortal, my conclusion here is something new. It is not implicit in the data about the named individuals; here it is not a matter of merely remaining true to what I have already laid down. Hence the problem:

Why is inference in this direction—i.e., from some to all, or from particulars to a generalization—necessary? Why must a generalization follow from information about one or more of its instances? What contradiction would we be embracing if we accepted the information regarding the observed individuals yet denied the generalization?

No satisfactory answer has ever been offered in the history of philosophy. As a rule, the attempt to validate induction has taken the form of attempting to reduce induction to deduction. Aristotle is a good example here. In his view, induction merely suggests generalizations, which, to be validated and thus become knowledge, must then be deduced from broader generalizations, a process that continues back until one reaches the broadest generalizations of all, which are supposedly self-evident. For example, our experience with Tom, Dick, and Harry merely suggests that all men are mortal. But one then proves this last by deducing it from the generalization that all living organisms are mortal. In this view, a general truth is known either as a self-evidency or by a process of deduction from such self-evidencies. Induction is not an independent form of reasoning or of proof.

This viewpoint (which is a Platonic element in Aristotle's thought) soon became the staple of the rationalists, many of whom discarded induction even as a suggestive preliminary. In reaction to all this, the empiricists justifiably denied, as floating and mystical, the rationalists' deductive castles, but nevertheless quickly came to agree with them that induction is not valid reasoning, but merely a blind "leap" in the dark that cannot be the foundation of reliable knowledge. So the empiricists ended as skeptics.

The challenge to logicians and philosophers is to identify a form of reasoning hitherto unacknowledged: a form of reasoning in which the conclusion follows from its premises necessarily, but not deductively. In this type of case, the conclusion does state something new—something that goes beyond all earlier knowledge. Yet that same conclusion, given the earlier knowledge, is inescapable, compelling the mind's acquiescence on pain of self-contradiction.

The lead to solving this problem may be found in our study of the process of reaching first-level generalizations. As we have seen, two elements are involved: the grasp in a concrete form of a causal process, and the conceptual identification of this process. This combination is what validates a first-level generalization. How might this pattern apply to complex, higher-level generalizations?

Let us examine a case typical of scientific induction, in which we do not directly perceive causal connections, and in which we are not restricted to a handful of first-level words, but rather depend for our identifications on a multitude of advanced concepts. The example I have chosen is Benjamin Franklin's famous kite experiment. It will serve to illustrate the pattern that we will see repeatedly in the next four chapters.

Franklin set out to prove that lightning is essentially electricity. Thunderclouds, he hypothesized, are electrically charged, and lightning is merely an electrical discharge, when this charge runs off to Earth. Scientists do not always have their explanation of events worked out as a hypothesis in advance of their experiments, but sometimes they do, and Franklin did in this case. He set up his apparatus accordingly.

He flew a kite during a storm, protecting himself inside a shed, holding the wet kite string by means of a nonconducting silk ribbon. A pointed wire jutted out from the top of the kite; at the bottom, a metal key was tied to the wet kite string and held close to a wire going down into a Leyden jar, a kind of condenser in which electrical charge can be stored. If Franklin was right, the electrically charged thunderclouds should cause the key to become charged, and this charge will flow into and accumulate in the Leyden jar. Of course, everything Franklin predicted turned out as he expected, and he concluded—from his experience of one thunderstorm—with a sweeping and necessary generalization describing the nature of lightning as such, true everywhere and always. Why did this prove his generalization?

First, what did Franklin actually see during this experiment? What concretes did he observe that could also have been observed by a child or a savage? Among other things, he saw sparks flying from the key to the wire in the Leyden jar. He saw pieces of the wet kite string become rigid and repel each other. He observed that if one holds a pointed metal object up to the jar, sparks are drawn out of it. And he found that if he held the jar with one hand while touching his finger to the wire entering it, he felt an unpleasant shock.

These concrete observations are essential to the experiment; you could learn nothing from it without them. Yet these observations would be meaningless to an ignorant person; a series of sparks and shocks would communicate no causal sequence to a child, or even to an ordinary educated adult at Franklin's time. There is a causal sequence at work here, but it is not perceivable as such. Another element, therefore, is necessary before Franklin can grasp the causal sequence and validate his generalization.

Besides his percepts, Franklin needed a series of sophisticated concepts; otherwise, he could neither have designed his experiment nor interpreted its results. For example, he would have been helpless without such concepts as "electricity," "discharge," "conductor," "insulator," and "Leyden jar." These concepts were made possible by and represent a wealth of earlier knowledge (which was also discovered by means of experiment). Without this *conceptual framework*, as we may call it, Franklin could only have stared uncomprehendingly at sparks and shocks. Given such a framework, however, he can at once identify what he is seeing: The kite apparatus is a long conductor, and thus the electrically charged thundercloud causes the key to become charged, and then the key discharges into the insulated Leyden jar.

Once Franklin can identify what he is seeing in such terms, his conclusion—the generalization—follows directly. The conceptual framework enables him to identify, with the concrete measurements omitted, the essential causal chain; nothing else known explains the observations. The conclusion must be that thunderclouds are electrically charged and therefore lightning as such is an electrical discharge—which is the generalization.

If one grasps the observations in this case, and knows that the conceptual framework is valid, then the generalization follows necessarily. Its denial under these conditions would involve a contradiction. One who denied Franklin's generalization would be contradicting either direct observations and/or a valid conceptual framework.

Whether we speak of first-level or advanced induction, therefore, the same two elements are involved: the grasp of a causal process through concrete observations, and the use of concepts to identify it. The main difference between beginner and scientist here lies in the complexity of the requisite conceptual framework.

The child knows only a handful of concepts, like "fire" or "paper," which he defines ostensively, and which are not yet logically connected to one another in his mind. But as concept-formation progresses beyond the first level, a cluster of unrelated concepts is no longer adequate. All concepts must eventually become aspects of one integrated conceptual framework. Knowledge is a sum, a unity, and no concept can be valid until it is integrated into that unity. A free-floating, disconnected concept would have no context in the rest of one's knowledge, and thus no tie to reality.

The conceptual framework essential to Franklin's experiment, therefore, extends far beyond the handful of technical electrical concepts I have so far mentioned. Precisely because all knowledge is integrated, electrical knowledge cannot stand in a vacuum as a self-contained cognitive compartment. In order fully to understand the electrical concepts he was applying—and in order to know that these concepts, as against any others known, are the only relevant ones, the only ones that explain the facts in this case—Franklin needed access to the total of his knowledge, including the vast body of information from other fields, outside of electricity and its manifestations.

It is instructive to recall here the origin of Franklin's hypothesis in regard to lightning. He began by listing twelve observed facts that related lightning to everything from all departments of his knowledge that were conceivably relevant to understanding its nature. These facts ranged all over the map of cognition—they related lightning to light, to color, to speed and direction of motion (and thus implicitly to dynamics), to the behavior of metals (and thus to the knowledge of different kinds of substances), to sound, to heat and temperature, to smell, and even to animal life and death. Having surveyed this vast, sprawling cognitive territory, Franklin found data everywhere suggesting that lightning was electrical. The next step to take, he concluded, was obvious: "Let the experiment be made."[12]

In order to interpret his observations in this experiment, he needed to survey the sum of his knowledge; he needed to integrate lightning to everything known that might be relevant to its nature, whether or not any given item of knowledge was formally included in the study of electricity. Integration is a requirement of logic, and therefore in higher-level induction the proper conceptual identification of a causal process requires the knowledge and use of one's total conceptual framework.

The structure of inductive reasoning, in general, on any level, is: observation; the application of one's total conceptual framework; and therefore, necessarily, a generalization.

Now we see the real contrast between induction and deduction. It has nothing to do with the notion that induction is merely probable, or that induction involves some kind of arbitrary leap.

Deduction is a simple form of reasoning. It starts with a causal connection already conceptualized and formulated as a generalization. In other words, it starts with a complex conceptual product regarded as established and unproblematic. The deducer is not as such concerned with the process of conceptualizing complex data. He takes for granted from the outset that we have solved all the difficult epistemological questions involved in forming and using concepts. He takes as a given that the conceptual faculty has been used to gain profound new knowledge, and that it has been used properly. He then proceeds to milk the new knowledge for its implications.

In contrast, an inductive argument is not a self-contained series of premises from which the conclusion follows as a matter of formal consistency. The reason is that the bridge from observation to generalization is not one premise, or even a hundred premises, but the total of one's knowledge properly integrated. This is why induction is so much more difficult and controversial than deduction, and why it is not reducible to the formalism of symbols.

Deduction says: Given one specific relation of concepts (e.g., "man" and "mortality"), X must follow. Induction says: Given the entire system of concepts, X must follow. In deduction the conclusion is necessary—otherwise you negate one specific product of the conceptual faculty, one specific generalization. In induction the conclusion is necessary—otherwise you negate the whole system of human concepts, i.e., the sum of knowledge gained by man's reason, i.e., the rational faculty as such.

The problem of induction has been insolvable for so long, because the nature of human consciousness has been misunderstood for so long. To solve the problem of deduction, one must grasp that A is A—which is Aristotle's monumental achievement. But to solve the problem of induction, one must grasp another monumental achievement: Ayn Rand's theory of concepts.

Deduction takes for granted the process of conceptualization. Induction is the conceptualizing process itself in action.

2.

Experimental Method

The scientific revolution of the seventeenth century was made possible by the achievements of ancient Greece. The Greeks were the first to seek natural (as opposed to supernatural) explanations and comprehensive theories of the physical world, and develop both deductive logic and advanced mathematics. However, their progress in physical science was impeded by the widely held view that higher knowledge is passively received rather than actively acquired. For many Greek thinkers, perfection was found in the realm of "being," an eternal and immutable realm of universal truths that can be grasped by the contemplative mind of the philosopher. In contrast, the physical world of activity was often regarded as a realm of "becoming," a ceaselessly changing realm that cannot be fully understood by anyone. The modern scientist views himself as an active investigator, but such an attitude was rare among the Greeks. This basic difference in mind-set—*contemplation* versus *investigation*—is one of the great divides between the ancient and modern minds.

Modern science began with the full development of its own distinctive method of investigation: *experiment*. "Experimentation" is the method of establishing causal relationships by means of controlling variables. The experimenter does not merely observe nature; he manipulates it by holding some factor(s) constant while varying others and measuring the results. He knows that the tree of knowledge will not simply drop its fruit into his open mind; the fruit must be cultivated and picked, often with the help of instruments designed for the purpose.

Precisely what the Greeks were missing can be seen by examining their closest approach to modern experimental science, which is well illustrated by Claudius Ptolemy's investigation of refraction. Ptolemy conducted a systematic study in which he measured the angular deflection of light at air/water, air/glass and water/glass interfaces. This experiment, when eventually repeated in the seventeenth century, led Willebrord Snell to the sine law of refraction. But Ptolemy did not discover the law, even though he did the right experiment and possessed both the requisite mathematical knowledge and the means to collect sufficiently accurate data.

Ptolemy's failure was caused primarily by his view of the relationship between experiment and theory. He did not regard experiment as the means of arriving at the correct theory; rather, the ideal theory is given in advance by intuition, and then experiment shows the deviations of the observed physical world from the ideal. This is precisely the Platonic approach he had taken in astronomy. The circle is the geometric figure possessing perfect symmetry, so Ptolemy and earlier Greek astronomers began with the intuition that celestial bodies orbit in circles at uniform speed. Observations then determined the deviations from the ideal, which Ptolemy modeled using mathematical contrivances unrelated to physical principles (deferents, epicycles, and equants). Similarly, in optics, he began with an a priori argument that the ratio of incident and refracted angles should be constant for a particular type of interface. When measurements indicated otherwise, he used an arithmetic progression to model the deviations from the ideal constant ratio.[1]

Plato had denigrated sense perception and the physical world, exhorting his followers to direct their attention inward to discover thereby the knowledge of the perfect ideas that have their source in a nonphysical dimension. Unfortunately, Plato explained, these perfect ideas will correspond only approximately to the ceaselessly changing and imperfect physical world we observe.

Ptolemy's science was superficially anti-Platonic in that he emphasized the role of careful observation. However, at a deeper level, his science was a logical application of Platonism; in astronomy and in optics, he started with the "perfect" model and then merely described without explanation the inherently unintelligible deviations from it. Thus Ptolemy regarded experiment not as a method of discovery but instead as *the handmaiden of intuition*; he used it to fill in details about a physical world that refuses to behave in perfect accordance with our predetermined ideas. This approach is a recipe for stagnation: The theory is *imposed on* rather than *derived from* sensory data, the mathematics is detached from physical principles, and, without an understanding of causes, the scientist is left with no further questions to ask.

The birth of modern science required an opposite view: Experiment had to be regarded as the essential method of *grasping* causal connections. The unique power of this method is revealed by examining how it was used by the geniuses who created the scientific era.

Galileo's Kinematics

Legend has it that modern physics began in a church.

On a Sunday in 1583, the nineteen-year-old Galileo let his attention wander from the sermon and focus instead on a hanging cathedral lamp that swung in the draft. As he watched, he noticed with surprise that swings through small arcs seemed to take the same time as swings through larger arcs. Using his pulse beat as a clock, he timed the oscillations and confirmed that the period seemed independent of arc size.

At this point Galileo had made an interesting observation and a crude measurement. But he had proven nothing. In order to prove the amplitude independence—and then go further to discover a law relating the properties of a pendulum to its motion—he had to design and perform a series of experiments.

He began by constructing two similar pendulums, both of the same length and with the same lead bob weights. He pulled both pendulum bobs from the vertical by different angles (for example, thirty degrees for one and fifteen degrees for the other), and released them at the same time. Galileo then observed that the two pendulums swung back and forth in nearly perfect unison despite their different amplitudes, and he noted that they continued to do so as he counted more than ten swings. With all other relevant factors held constant, doubling the amplitude had no discernible effect on the period.

The next steps of Galileo's investigation were guided by his thoughts concerning the cause of this surprising result. He realized that the pendulum bob gains speed only because it is falling toward Earth, i.e., only because of the *downward* component of its motion—and this component obviously increases as the amplitude of the swing is increased. Thus when the bob traverses a greater distance it does so at a greater speed; the two factors must compensate to keep the period constant.

But is this compensation exact for all amplitudes? Galileo approached the question in two ways: experimentally and mathematically. First, he repeated the above experiment using an amplitude of nearly ninety degrees for one pendulum and only ten degrees for the other. In this extreme case, he measured the period of the large swings to be about 10 percent greater than the period of the small swings. Despite the discrepancy, this result did not dissuade him from the "law of amplitude independence." He thought it likely that the relatively small increase in period is caused by the larger and faster swing encountering greater air resistance, and he was deliberately abstracting from the effects of such "impediments."

It was impossible for Galileo to directly determine by experiment the effects of air resistance; a vacuum pump would have enabled him to remove the air, but it was another half century before the instrument was invented. So, instead, he turned to mathematics for a proof of the amplitude independence. Starting from the idea that the pendulum bob's speed is proportional to the sine of the amplitude—because this factor isolates the efficacious, downward component of the motion—he attempted to prove that no matter where a bob is released along the circular arc it reaches the bottom at the same time.

Here Galileo encountered another obstacle: In general, the mathematical concepts and methods of his day were inadequate to deal with a moving body that continuously changes direction. So he simplified the problem by replacing the circular arc by a chord of the circle that terminated at the bottom. Now he had a problem that he could solve, and from a hypothesis relating speed to inclination angle he derived that frictionless movement down all such chords takes the same amount of time (see Figure 1).[2] The result was tantalizingly close to what he wanted, yet irreconcilably different: Motion down the chord is not the same as motion down the circular arc. But Galileo could not make any further progress with the analysis. In the end he decided to present the law of amplitude independence as valid while privately expressing his dissatisfaction with the lack of a proof.[3]

After eliminating amplitude as a relevant factor, he turned to consider properties that might affect the rate at which the pendulum swings. He asked: Does the material or weight of the bob affect the period? The question was easily answered by experiment. Starting with his two identical pendulums, he replaced the lead bob of one with a cork bob. He then pulled the bobs aside by twenty degrees or more and released them

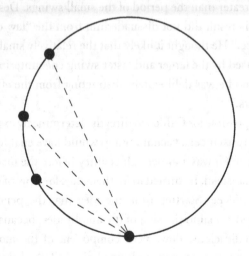

Figure 1. Frictionless sliding down any chord that terminates at the bottom of the circle takes the same time.

at the same time. The amplitude of the cork pendulum diminished more rapidly, and he correctly attributed this difference to air resistance. Given the results of his earlier experiments, he could disregard the amplitude difference because it has a negligible effect on the period. The crucial observation was that the lead and cork bobs continued to swing back and forth in nearly perfect unison. Galileo confidently and logically generalized from this result, concluding that in *all cases* the material and weight of a pendulum bob have no effect on its period.

Since the pendulum bobs in the above experiment swung with the same period, the same cause must have been operative. It appears that the only relevant property the two pendulums have in common is length, and therefore length must be the causal factor determining the period. A little reflection shows that this idea integrates with a wealth of common observations; for example, a child's swing hanging from a high tree branch takes more time to go back and forth than a shorter one hanging from a lower branch, and a long vine sways more slowly in the breeze than a short one. But precisely how does the length affect the period? Galileo discovered the answer by conducting a series of experiments in which he varied the length of a pendulum across a range from about two to thirty feet. He measured the period by comparing it to that of another pendulum of constant length or by using a water clock (a device that measures time by marking the regulated flow of water through a small opening). His data established an exact mathematical relationship between length and period, which he immediately generalized to a law applying to all pendulums anywhere on Earth in any era: The length is proportional to the square of the period.

It is instructive to note the experiments that Galileo did *not* perform. He saw no need to vary every known property of the pendulum and look for a possible effect on the period. For example, he did not systematically vary the color, temperature, or smell of the pendulum bob; he did not investigate whether it made a difference if the pendulum arm is made of cotton twine or silk thread. Based on everyday observations, he had a vast prescientific context of knowledge that was sufficient to eliminate such factors as irrelevant. To call such knowledge "prescientific" is not to cast doubt on its objectivity; such lower-level generalizations are acquired by the implicit use of the same methods that the scientist uses deliberately and systematically, and they are equally valid. Given such a context, Galileo quickly concluded that the period of a pendulum depends *only* upon its length.

In reaching this conclusion, he did overlook one relevant factor: the pendulum's location. He knew that a pendulum swings because the bob falls toward Earth. He also knew that the moon does not fall to Earth, which might have suggested to him that Earth's gravity must diminish with increasing distance. So why not carry a pendulum to the top of a high mountain and see if it swings more slowly?

In Newton's era, momentous consequences would follow when scientists used pendulums to discover such gravitational variations. But this possibility never occurred to Galileo because he lacked Newton's concept of "gravity." Galileo still thought in terms of the simpler concept of "heaviness," which merely referred to the property of earthly objects that causes them to press downward and fall to Earth. He lacked the idea of an unseen *interaction* between the object and Earth. Given this modern idea of force, it is reasonable to think of the interaction weakening with increasing distance between the bodies. If, however, one thinks only of a "natural tendency" of the heavy object, the factor of distance to the Earth's center cannot be grasped as relevant. The more advanced idea of "gravity" was necessary before scientists could discover that a pendulum's period varies slightly with location—and then go further to discover all that this implies. Here we see how the lack of a crucial concept can halt progress, and how the concept's formation can pave the way to further knowledge.

The pendulum provided Galileo with an excellent introduction to the experimental study of motion; the measurements were relatively easy because the bob stayed in one area while slowly repeating its motion for a long time. However, as Galileo discovered, the analysis of the motion was complicated by the fact that the bob continuously changed direction. By contrast, the simplest case of a body exhibiting its natural tendency to move toward Earth is that of the body falling straight down.

Early in his career, when he was mathematics professor at the University of Pisa, he began his investigation of free fall by addressing an old question that was still a key point of confusion: How does the weight of a body affect the rate at which it falls? Galileo demonstrated the answer with his characteristic dramatic flair. He climbed to the top of the famous Leaning Tower and, from a height of more than fifty meters, dropped two lead balls that differed greatly in size and weight. The students and professors assembled below saw both objects hit the ground at very nearly the same time. Contrary to the common assumption, the rate at which a body falls is independent of its weight.

Galileo then asked the next logical question: Does the rate of fall depend upon the material of the body? He repeated the experiment using one ball of lead and another made of oak. Again, when dropped simultaneously from a great height, they both hit the ground at very nearly the same time. Thus Galileo arrived at a very broad generalization: All free bodies, regardless of differences in weight and material, fall to Earth at the same rate.

On the surface, it seems too easy. It appears as though Galileo arrived at this fundamental truth of physics—one that had eluded the greatest minds in ancient Greece—merely by doing a few experiments that any child could perform. But a closer look reveals that Galileo's reasoning was not so simple; it depended on his pioneering use of one valid concept and his rejection of certain widely accepted invalid concepts.

First, notice that the objects he dropped were not selected randomly. If Galileo had thrown a bale of hay and a straw hat off the top of the Leaning Tower, the event would not have been a landmark in the history of physics. Yet these objects are made of similar material and have greatly different weights, just like the two lead balls he actually used. Or consider Galileo's second experiment: Imagine that he attempted to drop the lead and oak balls through water instead of air, perhaps thinking that it would be easier to investigate a slower motion. Again, the result would not have led to any important discovery. On the contrary, such experiments are easily misinterpreted as evidence that weight is always an essential factor in determining the rate of fall.

Galileo chose the conditions of his experiments with a crucial criterion in mind: He wanted to minimize the effects of *friction*. "Friction" is the force that resists the relative motion of two bodies in contact. It is sometimes said that Galileo ignored this force, because the laws he discovered describe frictionless motion. But this is the opposite of the truth. In fact, he thought deeply about air resistance and other forms of friction, and he carefully distinguished the cases in which friction plays a minor role from the many cases in which it plays an essential role. Without this distinction, it is impossible to arrive at any law of motion; with it, Galileo successfully discovered the law of free fall.

Enrico Fermi, another great Italian physicist, paid tribute to this achievement with the following comment:

> [I]t was friction itself that for thousands of years had kept hidden the simplicity and validity of the laws of motion. In other words, friction is an essential element in all human experience; our intuition is dominated by friction; men can move around because of friction; because of friction they can grasp objects with their hands, they can weave fabrics, build cars, houses, etc. To see the essence of motion beyond the complications of friction indeed required a great insight.[4]

A contemporary physicist sees the effects of friction everywhere around him. That is because he has been raised on the truths discovered by Galileo and Newton. Prior to the seventeenth century, natural philosophers viewed the motions they observed from a different perspective, a perspective tainted by the errors contained in the old Greek physics. For example, when Leonardo da Vinci studied pendulums, he did not grasp that the amplitude gradually diminishes because of air resistance. Instead he analyzed the arc into a "natural" downward portion and an unnatural, or "accidental," upward portion. He then invoked the widely accepted dogma that *accidental motion will always be shorter than the natural* to explain the damping of the swings. It never occurred to him to abstract from this effect, since he regarded it as fundamental to the nature of motion.

Just as valid concepts such as "friction" can propel science forward, invalid concepts can stop it. Da Vinci's mistaken analysis of pendulums rested on the Greek concepts of "natural" and "violent" motion, which were formidable barriers to progress in physics. At the root of this distinction was the false idea that motion requires a mover, i.e., a force. Rocks falling, smoke rising, and the moon circling were regarded as cases of natural motion in which the body is moved by an internal force inherent in its nature. Rocks thrown upward, smoke blown horizontally, and birds flying were regarded as cases of violent motion in which the body is moved by external pushes against other bodies. Natural motions were held to be the true province of the physicist, since they resulted from the nature of the body; violent motions were typically dismissed as less interesting.

Like square pegs in round holes, the facts resisted attempts to fit them into these invalid categories. Consider the simple case of a man throwing a rock. Why does the rock continue to move after leaving the thrower's hand? As it flies through the air, where is the mover? Since a violent motion requires an external force, the proponents of the Greek theory were compelled to give an unconvincing answer: The thrower allegedly passes his motive power to the air, and then air currents push on the rock to cause its continued movement. According to this view, the primary role of air is not to resist such violent motions but to cause them.

During the Middle Ages, some thinkers began to reject the implausible claim that air pushes a projectile along its path. In discussing the case of a long jumper, fourteenth-century philosopher Jean Buridan wrote: "The person so running and jumping does not feel the air moving him, but [rather] feels the air in front strongly resisting him."[5] But nobody was yet ready to give up the idea that motion requires a force. So they "internalized" the force; they claimed, for example, that the thrower of a rock transfers his motive power directly into the rock, giving it a property called "impetus." Despite their acceptance of a false premise, these philosophers did achieve a partial break with the errors of the past. They abandoned the distinction between natural and violent motion; in effect, their view transformed violent motions into natural ones by claiming that such motions are caused by the internal impetus of the body.

The medieval proponents of "impetus" supplied an answer to the Greek quandary about what makes a projectile go—but then they faced the question: Why does the projectile ever slow down or stop? What happens to its impetus? One response was to claim that impetus naturally dissipates over time. But this answer was inadequate; among other problems, it gave no clue as to why the rate of dissipation depends on the medium through which the body travels. So it was suggested by Buridan that a body loses impetus only when it works to overcome resistance. Buridan's idea contained an important element of truth insofar as it identified the role of friction in opposing motion.

But it was Galileo who took the crucial step by combining this appreciation of friction with the experimental method. He did not merely acknowledge the existence of friction; he actively sought to control and minimize it. This is what enabled him to abstract from the effects of air resistance and thereby discover that all free bodies fall with the same motion.

The next reasonable question was: What is the nature of this motion? In particular, Galileo wondered how the speed of a falling body increases with time and with distance. Of course, he had no way to directly measure the speed. However, he realized that there was a closely related measurement that was difficult but not impossible: He could measure how the distance fallen varies with the elapsed time.

Using his water clock, Galileo timed a fall from about six feet and another fall from twice that height. He found that doubling the height increased the time of fall by less than 50 percent. This result suggested that the distance fallen might be proportional to the time squared, just as the length of a pendulum is proportional to its period squared.

Galileo then realized that he could use the pendulum to check this idea. He devised a pendulum of easily adjustable length in which the bob impacted a fixed board placed at the bottom of its swing. He then measured the time of free fall from a particular height, and adjusted the pendulem length until it swung to the vertical in the same time. He found, for example, that a weight will fall nearly five feet in the time that a four-foot pendulum swings to the vertical. (Galileo seems to have used time measurements with the water clock, although it would have been possible to compare the distances directly.) By repeating the procedure for several different values, he proved that the ratio of height fallen to pendulum length is always the same. Since the pendulum length varies as the square of the elapsed time, the distance traversed in free fall must also be proportional to the time squared. In this way, using his prior knowledge of pendulums and the experimental method, Galileo arrived at a generalization of impressive scope: For all free bodies on Earth, the height fallen is equal to the square of the elapsed time multiplied by a specific constant (the value of which depends on the particular units).

He realized the implications of his time-squared law. Since the height fallen is equal to the average speed of fall multiplied by the elapsed time, the height can be proportional to time squared only if the speed is directly proportional to the time. Thus Galileo had found the answer to his original question about the increase of speed during fall: The speed increases in direct proportion to the elapsed time, i.e., it increases by equal increments in equal time intervals. In familiar English units, we say that the speed increases by thirty-two feet per second during each second of fall.

In addition to the concept of "friction," this discovery depended on Galileo's prior development of two key concepts of motion. Throughout the above reasoning, he was using concepts of "speed" and "acceleration" that differed profoundly from those in common use at the time. Stillman Drake, a leading Galileo scholar, points out that "the Italian word 'velocita' . . . just meant swiftness, a vague qualitative concept. . . ."[6] The alternative was the Latin word "velocitas," then used by natural philosophers to mean "intensity of motion." Galileo recognized that such qualitative ideas are dead-ends in physics; the science of kinematics requires quantitative concepts of motion that are defined mathematically and can be identified by measurements.

Galileo faced two obstacles that prevented him from developing fully adequate concepts of motion. First, the Greek theory of proportions restricted him to ratios of "commensurable quantities," for example, ratios of distances, or of times, or of speeds. An overly narrow concept of "number" had led the Greeks to reject ratios of "unlike quantities" such as distance over time or speed over time. Second, the crucial ideas of instantaneous speed and instantaneous acceleration are impossible without the mathematical concept of "limit," which was not yet developed. As a result, he could offer mathematically rigorous definitions only for motion at constant speed or for motion at constant acceleration.

Despite these restrictions, Galileo's new concepts of motion were a crucial advance over those of his predecessors, and they were adequate for his purposes, since free fall occurs with a simple uniform acceleration. However, his direct experimental evidence for the law of free fall was open to one criticism: It was difficult to obtain repeatable and accurate measurements of such short time intervals. One could more easily investigate the acceleration of fall if there were a way of slowing it without changing its nature. This was the motive behind Galileo's inclined-plane experiments.

In the case of a ball rolling down an inclined plane, the movement is caused by the downward component of the heavy ball's constrained motion. Galileo reasoned that since the cause of the motion is the same as in free fall and the ball's direction is constant, the acceleration down the plane should be of the same nature as in free fall, but merely attenuated by the ratio of the height fallen to the total distance traversed. Thus rolling balls down a plane inclined at a small angle from the horizontal provided a way to study the acceleration of a falling body in a form that was greatly reduced in magnitude and therefore easier to measure.

Galileo rolled a bronze ball down a smoothly polished groove carved in a straight wooden plank that was about eight feet long. Using an angle of inclination of almost two degrees, it took more than four seconds for the ball to roll down the plank. He then had an ingenious idea. He tied eight very thin strings around his plank. When the ball rolled over a string, it made a slight but audible bumping sound. As he repeatedly rolled the ball down the plank, he adjusted the location of the strings until the sounds occurred at regular intervals of a little more than a half second. Galileo was quite knowledgeable about music and he knew that the regularity of such beats can be judged very accurately (most people can detect a deviation of one sixty-fourth of a second). The positions of the strings that produced the regular beats were a record of the distance traveled by the ball as a function of time. His results proved that the distance is proportional to the square of the time, and therefore motion down an inclined plane is uniformly accelerated. He later confirmed this law with additional experiments in which he used longer inclined planes and made time measurements with his water clock.

Galileo also grasped some crucial implications of his idea that the ball's acceleration down the plane is proportional to the sine of the inclination angle. First, he mathematically deduced that the final speed of the ball at the bottom of the plane depends only on its initial height, not on the length of the plane or its degree of inclination. The height of the plane, he showed, is proportional to the square of the ball's final speed. Second, the acceleration of the ball must approach zero as the inclination angle approaches zero, implying that *free horizontal motion must occur at constant speed.*

Galileo designed an experiment that made use of the first implication in order to test the second. His inclined plane was mounted on a table about three feet high. At the bottom of the incline he devised a curved deflector so that the ball made a smooth transition to roll briefly along the horizontal tabletop before flying off and hitting the ground some distance away (see Figure 2). He chose an initial height of the plane and then measured where the ball landed. Armed with his knowledge of the relationship between height and speed and with his hypothesis of constant horizontal speed, Galileo could then calculate where the ball would land for any height of the inclined plane. He made his calculations, performed the experiment, and found that his predictions agreed with his measurements.

The inclined plane provided Galileo with a bridge between vertical and horizontal motion, and it cast light upon the nature of both. He used it to study acceleration of a falling body and to provide a projectile with known and easily variable horizontal speed. The results of his

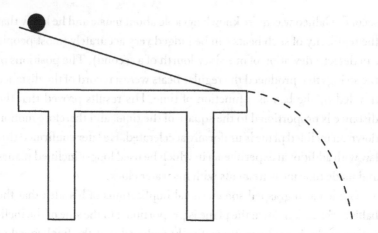

Figure 2. A ball moving with constant horizontal speed and constant vertical acceleration traces out a semiparabola.

experiments led inexorably to the crowning generalization of his kinematics: Free vertical motion occurs with constant acceleration, whereas free horizontal motion occurs with constant speed.

The experiment described above led to yet another crucial discovery. Galileo had not merely measured the distance from the table to the ball's impact point; he had also observed and carefully drawn the trajectory of the ball through the air. He had an intimate knowledge of Greek geometry, and therefore the shape of the trajectory struck him as familiar: It looked like a semiparabola. This observation started a chain of thought that led to the realization of why the trajectory is necessarily a parabola.

He had proven that a free body falls through a vertical distance that is proportional to the square of the elapsed time. He had also proven that the horizontal distance traversed by a free body is directly proportional to the elapsed time. Furthermore, his experiment showed that the horizontal motion is unaffected when the body is simultaneously falling. Thus the vertical and horizontal motions occur independently, each rigorously following its own law while remaining oblivious to the other. By combining the two separate laws, Galileo derived the conclusion that the change in the height of a projectile is proportional to the square of the change in horizontal position—and he knew that this relationship describes the curve of a parabola. Without any of the hand-wringing and arbitrary doubting of a skeptic, he concluded that *all free projectiles follow parabolic trajectories.*

Rand's theory of concepts, as we saw in Chapter 1, led her to issue a challenge to skeptics: Those who deny the validity of concepts must first prove the invalidity of algebra. Here we are dealing with inductive generalizations, but a similar challenge applies: Those who deny the validity of induction by declaring that it is impossible to find "all" in the "some" must first prove the invalidity of kinematics by declaring that it is impossible to find a causal connection between the referents of the concepts "projectile" and "parabola." Such skeptical arguments are futile, since Galileo found just that connection.

Galileo thought of a simple way to demonstrate the above principle. When a ball is rolled across a smooth *inclined* tabletop, it moves with constant speed across the table and with constant acceleration down the table—and hence it traces out a parabolic path. He immediately put the principle to practical use by solving several long-standing military problems; for example, he showed how a cannon's range depends upon its firing angle, and how to calculate the firing angle for a target at some specified height above the ground.

It was a feat of genius to grasp that projectile motion could be analyzed into independent horizontal and vertical components. Stillman Drake points out that Galileo's predecessors had thought quite differently:

> Medieval impetus theory, like Aristotelian physics, supposed that when two different tendencies to motion were present in the same body, only the stronger would determine its actual motion. When the stronger tendency was violently imparted, as in a ball thrown horizontally, it was assumed that conflict between this and the natural tendency to fall weakened the horizontal motion until the constant vertical tendency became stronger and brought the ball to earth.[7]

Even today, this false view remains influential. Consider an untutored man who is told that a bullet will be fired horizontally from the muzzle of a gun while a second bullet is dropped simultaneously from the same height. When asked to guess which bullet will hit the ground first, the man will invariably choose the dropped bullet. Galileo was the first to grasp that the horizontal motion of the fired bullet is irrelevant and therefore both bullets hit the ground at the same time (assuming, of course, that the Earth's surface can be approximated as flat).

Galileo's analysis led to a new synthesis. According to the old medieval view, two causes are necessary to explain the rise and descent of a projectile. Once the projectile is in the air and moving freely, its rise is caused by the upward impetus that has been imparted to it. After this impetus dissipates, a second cause becomes operative: the body's natural tendency to fall toward the Earth. In contrast, Galileo recognized that the same cause and the same effect are operative throughout the trajectory: The projectile is always accelerating toward the Earth at the same rate while simply conserving its horizontal speed.

Experiments enabled Galileo to reach and validate his mathematical description of motion and thereby achieve a perspective that was more abstract and more integrated than that of his predecessors. His abstraction from the effects of friction, his analysis of motion into horizontal and vertical components, his mathematically precise definitions of uniform speed and uniform acceleration, his application of the Greek knowledge of parabolas—these were among the key conceptual steps that raised him to a height from which he could see the same principles at work in many superficially different motions. From this new perspective, he saw a swinging pendulum, a falling apple, a ball rolling down a hillside, and a cannonball rising in the air as variations on the same theme: the constant acceleration of heavy bodies toward the Earth. One historian of science puts it this way:

> Galileo introduced a classificatory system where very different looking things . . . were regarded as all belonging to the same category, and hence were analyzable in a coherent and comparable

manner. They were seen as instances of the same thing, in much the same way as a moving compass needle, patterned iron filings, and induced current in a moving conductor—observationally all very different—are seen as indicators of one thing, a magnetic field.[8]

The various motions Galileo studied were not related merely in hindsight, as a result of his laws; as we have seen, they were connected during the discovery process, and the connections were essential to discovering the laws. At each step along the way, Galileo made use of the full context of knowledge available to him. The pendulum played a crucial role in the study of free fall, and then both pendulum and free-fall investigations led to the study of inclined-plane motion, which in turn led to the understanding of projectile motion. Galileo's kinematics was developed and validated not as a conglomeration of separate pieces, but as *a unified whole*.

Integration is the process of uniting a complexity of elements into a whole. Cognitive integration is the very essence of human thought, from concept-formation (an integration of a limitless number of concretes into a whole designated by a word), to induction (an integration of a limitless number of causal sequences into a generalization), to deduction (the integration of premises into a conclusion). An item of knowledge is acquired and validated by means of grasping its relation to the whole of one's knowledge. A thinker always seeks to relate, grasp hidden similarities, discover connections, unify. A conceptual consciousness is an integrating mechanism, and its product—knowledge—is an interconnected system, not a heap of isolated propositions.

Galileo integrated his knowledge not only within the subject of physics but also between physics and the related science of astronomy. Copernican astronomy claimed that the Earth spins rapidly about its own axis and hurtles around the sun at astonishing speed. According to the old views regarding motion, this claim was simply preposterous. If the Earth is moving, people asked, what would happen when a rock was tossed straight up in the air? The Earth would move underneath it, and, contrary to experience, the rock would come down miles away. Furthermore, what is causing the alleged motion of the Earth? There is nothing pushing it, and the materials on Earth exhibit no natural inclination to revolve in circles. The only motion natural to heavy bodies is to fall straight down. If the Earth were not already in its natural place, it would simply fall toward that place. And since the Earth is very heavy it would fall very quickly; any lighter bodies that were not fastened down—including ourselves—would be left behind! Galileo's theory of motion nullified these objections, and thus it served as the foundation for his defense of the new astronomy. This crucial integration had the inverse benefit as well: Galileo could point to the abundant observational evidence in favor of the heliocentric theory (see the next chapter) as further support for his kinematics.

Now let us turn from Galileo's triumphs to mention the problems that he confronted but could not solve. Today, the errors of great scientists are often cited as reasons for doubting the validity of scientific method. If even the best practitioners of this method make mistakes, it is argued, how can we trust any scientific results? In order to see that such doubts are baseless, it is worth examining Galileo's errors. We will see that they provide no foothold for skepticism; on the contrary, they illustrate that a rational process is self-correcting.

Let us start with the analysis of pendulum motion. Later scientists proved that the slightly greater period of a pendulum swinging in a larger arc is not caused by air resistance, as Galileo had supposed. Even when the air is removed, the period of a pendulum bob swinging along a circular arc is more than 10 percent greater for very large swings than for small swings. Galileo did not have the experimental or mathematical means to identify the cause in this case. Ideally, he should have openly acknowledged the small amplitude dependence he had discovered, and then merely suggested air resistance as a possible cause.

But the mistake was of little consequence. The conditions for a truly isochronal pendulum were discovered one generation after Galileo published his theory of motion. In 1659, Christian Huygens proved that the period of a pendulum is independent of amplitude when the bob moves along the arc of an inverted cycloid rather than a circle (a cycloid, shown in Figure 3, is the curve traced by a point on the rim of a rolling wheel). In order to solve the problem that had stumped Galileo, Huygens made use of two new developments in mathematics: the recently discovered properties of the cycloid and the technique of "infinitesimals." By starting with Galileo's law of inclined-plane motion and then treating the curved path of the pendulum bob as a series of infinitesimally small inclined planes, he demonstrated that the bob always descends in the same time only when the curve is a cycloid. Thus the very knowledge that Huygens inherited from Galileo—when combined with the new mathematics—enabled him to correct Galileo's mistake.

The same point is illustrated by an oversight in Galileo's analysis of inclined-plane motion. His bronze ball moved down the inclined plane by rolling—rather than sliding—because of the friction between the ball and the wood surface. He never suspected that the acceleration of a rolling ball is about 28 percent less than that of a sliding ball. His theorem relating the acceleration on an inclined plane to the acceleration of free fall is true only for frictionless sliding, yet he implied that it is true for the rolling balls used in his experiments. This was an understandable error

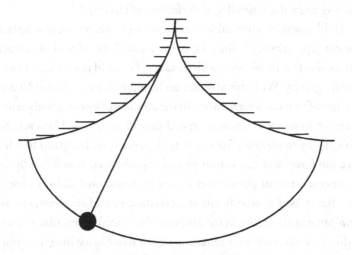

Figure 3. The period is independent of amplitude when the pendulum bob is constrained to move along the arc of an inverted cycloid.

on a subtle point. The mechanics of rolling balls is complex; Galileo lacked the dynamical and mathematical concepts that are required to grasp the subject. Eventually, in the eighteenth century, it was the powerful combination of Newton's dynamics and Euler's mathematics that rendered the behavior of rotating bodies fully intelligible. Again, scientists stood on Galileo's shoulders in order to reach a height from which his error was seen and corrected.

The fundamental error in Galileo's physics is found in his treatment of horizontal motion. His evidence that free horizontal motion occurs with constant speed came primarily from laboratory experiments and secondarily from field observations of short-range projectiles. Thus the evidence was limited to a domain of short distances over which the Earth can be approximated as flat. However, Galileo speculated about how his principle would apply to motions over very large distances. He argued that in such cases "horizontal motion" can only mean motion at constant altitude, from which he deduced that free horizontal motion is ultimately circular motion around the spherical Earth. This was his concession to the Greek idea of "natural circular motion," and he supported it with an a priori argument handed down from Plato (an argument based on nothing more than the alleged perfection of circles).[9]

Galileo was left vulnerable to committing this error because he lacked the concept "gravity." Since he never formed the idea of an attractive interaction that diminishes with distance, he could not abstract from the Earth's gravity. With this abstraction he might have arrived at Newton's first law of motion, which states: In the absence of forces, a body remains at rest or moves with constant speed *in a straight line*. However, Newton's ability to abstract from gravity depended on his grasp that it is a variable force that can diminish to insignificance at sufficiently large distances; such an abstraction makes no sense on Galileo's view that free, heavy bodies simply fall at a constant rate of acceleration—as an omnipresent effect. So, in the absence of a crucial prerequisite concept, Galileo's mind could only remain at rest or move in a wrong direction on this issue; he could not arrive at the principle that later became Newton's first law.

Earlier we saw Leonardo da Vinci make a similar error in his analysis of pendulum motion. Dismissing the air as an omnipresent background, he did not identify or abstract from the effects of air resistance on pendulum motion. As a result, he was unable to explain the damping of the pendulum, and he filled the void in his understanding by appeal to an arbitrary dogma. In a parallel way, Galileo did not identify and abstract from the effects of gravity, and he filled the void in his understanding by appeal to a baseless Platonic argument.

Galileo erred on other issues that cannot be understood without the idea of gravity. An obvious example is his attempt to explain the ocean tides without reference to the gravitational force of the moon and the sun. Less obvious examples are his failure to accept Kepler's law that planets move in elliptical orbits, and his suggestion that comets might be atmospheric phenomena rather than celestial bodies. Both of these latter errors were caused by Galileo's concession to "natural circular motion," which I have argued was a consequence of his inability to abstract from the effects of gravity. On one topic after another, Galileo was stopped by the same barrier. We can see why Newton's concept of gravity was so central to the development of modern physics.

Of course, it was Galileo who paved the way for his successors—not merely by presenting the knowledge he discovered but also by providing insight into the proper method of discovery. The latter was the most valuable part of his legacy. The old adage applies here: "Give a man a fish and he eats for a day; teach him to fish and he eats for a lifetime."

Regrettably, Galileo's published works do not give an entirely accurate portrayal of his discovery process. It is often the case that a scientist presents his theory in a form that obscures the steps by which he arrived at it. Galileo occasionally created a misleading impression of his method by presenting deductive arguments from "plausible first principles" or from thought experiments, while giving less emphasis to inductive arguments from actual experiments. In regard to method, his practice was better than his presentation. Thus he did not take full advantage of the opportunity to teach his successors how to acquire scientific knowledge.

As a result, the role of experimentation was not adequately grasped by the generation of scientists who followed Galileo. This left the door open for René Descartes, who led a Platonist revival. Descartes explicitly rejected the method of inducing causes by observing their effects, and he criticized Galileo for using such an approach. "He seems to me very faulty in . . . that he has not examined things in order," Descartes wrote, "and that without having considered the first causes of nature he has only sought the reasons of some particular effects, and thus he has built without foundation."[10] In contrast, Descartes explained that his goal was "to deduce an account of effects from their causes."[11] How do we know the fundamental causes? With Plato, Descartes claimed that he had direct access to them by means of "clear and distinct" innate ideas.

Thus even Galileo's spectacular achievement was not enough to institutionalize the experimental method and discredit Platonism among scientists. That task was left to the man who completed the scientific revolution: Isaac Newton.

Newton's Optics

When Newton began his battle to establish a proper inductive method in physics, he was working in the field of optics, not kinematics or astronomy. In his early years, well before the *Principia* brought him fame, he conducted a study of light and colors that has been described as "the preeminent experimental investigation of the seventeenth century."[12]

We live in a colorful world. Typically, the colors we see are produced by reflection of ordinary (white) light from bodies, and the specific color reflected depends on the nature of the body. By the second half of the seventeenth century, it was also known that colors can be produced by refraction. While an undergraduate at Trinity College, Newton learned about the sine law of refraction (discovered by Snell in 1621), about colors that result from white light passing through wedges of glass (prisms), about the idea that rainbows are somehow caused by light refracting within raindrops, and about the fact that refracting telescopes produce blurred images with colored edges.

Newton's early interest in the subject is evident from his detailed study of Robert Boyle's book *Experiments and Considerations Touching Colors* (1664). Two scholars offer the following description of Newton's notes on the book:

> [The notes] comprise data concerning the ways in which the colors of objects are changed under a wide variety of circumstances. They record the effects of heat, the characteristics of various sublimates, acids, and precipitates, the ways objects change in various lights and positions, the effects of dyes, of solutions, and salts, and the changes wrought on colors by various combinations of these "instruments." Although Newton's aim is to increase his basis of information, the entries are more than a haphazard miscellany. Each bit of information pertains in some way to either the difference in the appearance of a body's color when it is looked on, in contrast to when it is looked through, or the ways in which a body's color can be changed.[13]

During these undergraduate years, Newton kept a notebook titled "Certain Philosophic Questions," in which he recorded his questions and first groping thoughts about a wide range of topics in physical science, including the topic of light and colors. For example, he asked why materials differ in transparency, why refraction is slightly less in hot water than in cold water, why coals are black and ashes are white. He asked whether light moves with a finite speed, whether rays of light might move a body "as wind does a sail," and whether refraction at glass surfaces is the same when the surrounding air is removed. The questions show an extraordinarily active mind that had absorbed the available knowledge of the subject.

In his notes on colors, Newton referred to some of the proposed explanations that he encountered in the literature. He wrote: "Colors arise either from shadows intermixed with light, or by stronger or weaker reflections. Or, parts of the body mixed with and carried away by light."[14] He then quickly ruled out the first possibility, simply by citing many cases in which black and white are mixed without producing any color, and by pointing out that the edges of shadows are not colored. At this early stage, he had no theory of his own—and he was realizing that nobody else had one, either (despite a few boastful claims by others to the contrary).

It was not long before Newton purchased a prism and began his own investigation. He started by looking at various objects through the prism. His first important observations were of colors that appear along the boundaries between light and dark objects. For example, when a thin strip of white paper is placed against a dark background and viewed through a prism, one edge of the paper will appear blue and the other edge red.

From the observation of rainbows and light refracting through prisms, it was widely known that blue and red were on opposite sides of the color spectrum. Some scientists proposed that when a beam of white light enters water or glass at an oblique angle, one edge of the beam is affected differently than the other, causing the light on one side to turn blue while the light on the other side turns red. However, another possibility occurred to Newton: It struck him that rainbows and "boundary colors" might result if blue light were refracted slightly more than red light. In other words, he thought to ask: Are blue and red light seen on opposite sides not because they originate from different locations within the beam but instead because they are bent at different angles by the water or glass?

The question could be answered only by experimentation. Newton took a thread and colored half of its length blue and the other half red. When he laid the thread in a straight line against a dark background and viewed it through a prism, the blue and red halves looked discontinuous, with one appearing above the other. The prism shifted the image of the blue half of the thread more than it shifted the red half. From this one experiment, Newton reached a universal truth: Upon refraction, blue light is bent more than red light.

Since the various colors of light emerge from the prism at slightly different angles, the color spectrum will spread out as the light moves farther away. This thought led Newton to another experiment. With the windows of his room shaded, he allowed sunlight to enter through one small hole. He placed a prism near the opening so the light would pass through it and be displayed on the far wall about twenty-two feet away. He observed that the narrow, circular beam of white light was bent by the prism and transformed into a full, elongated spectrum of colors in the order red, orange, yellow, green, blue, and violet. The spectrum spread out in the same direction that the glass bent the light, and it was five times as long as it was wide.[15]

After observing this striking change in a beam of incident white light, it was natural to ask what effect a prism has on an incident beam of colored light. To find the answer, Newton performed a series of experiments in which he generated a spectrum with one prism and then passed the individual colors one at a time through a second prism. In contrast to white light, he found that only the direction of the colored light was altered. His measurements confirmed that blue light was bent more than red light, as he expected. More important, however, was the crucial new fact that the color is always unchanged and the beams are not spread out by the second prism.

Apparently the individual colors are redirected but otherwise unaffected by prisms. But if prisms do not affect colors, then how can they create them from a beam of white light? Perhaps, Newton thought, the colors are not created by the prism; perhaps they are in the white light and merely separated by their variable angle of refraction. In other words, he was struck by a radical idea: Maybe a mixture of all the colors is experienced by us as white light.

He knew that in some cases a mixture of two colors is seen as a different color. In his early notes, he had recorded his observation that a yellow candle flame viewed through blue glass appears green. He also knew that white light viewed through a combination of red glass and blue glass appears purple. Such evidence had already convinced him that a mixture of colors can appear quite different than any of its components. However, it was a bold step to suggest that whiteness—which had long served as the very symbol of "purity"—was in fact a mixture of all the colors in the spectrum. It was bold, but nevertheless grounded in observational evidence.

Newton was never satisfied with merely suggesting a possibility—he settled for nothing less than experimental proof. If white light is composed of all the colors, then it should be possible to bring the separated colors back together and form white light once again. He realized that this can be done by using a combination of prisms or a focusing lens, and he showed that when the entire color spectrum is made to converge, it appears white. Furthermore, when the spectrum is allowed to continue through the focal point and diverge again on the other side, the colors reappear in the reverse order. The conclusion was now inescapable: The individual colors are the "pure" and simple components, whereas white light is a mixture of them.

He next applied this new insight to understand why objects around us appear with their characteristic colors. The basic implication of his theory was clear: When an object is illuminated by white light and yet it appears some particular color, the reason must be that the object reflects that color strongly while absorbing or transmitting much of the light in the rest of the spectrum. Based on his prior discoveries, Newton did not expect colors to be created or changed by reflection; they should merely be separated to the extent that one color is reflected more than the others.

In order to test this experimentally, he took a piece of paper and painted the left half blue and the right half red. In a shaded room, he illuminated the paper with only the blue light from a prism. As he expected, the entire paper appeared blue, but the color was intense on the left half and faint on the right half. When the paper was illuminated with red light from the prism, he again saw the expected result: The entire paper was red, but now the left half was faint and the right half intense. Colors are not changed upon reflection; blue paint reflects blue light strongly and red light weakly, whereas red paint reflects red light strongly and blue light weakly. These observations were a simple yet powerful confirmation of his theory.

He offered other convincing demonstrations that the colors composing white light are separated by unequal amounts of reflection or transmission at surfaces. For example, he darkened his room and then allowed a beam of white light to illuminate a very thin gold foil. He found that the reflected light on one side was the usual brownish yellow color of gold, whereas the transmitted light on the other side was a greenish blue color.

Newton's theory of colors integrated and explained an enormous range of observations. For instance, he was able to explain all the essential properties of rainbows, such as the greater brightness of the sky within the rainbow, the angular position and width of the primary and secondary rainbows, and the reversed order of colors in the two rainbows. The theory also enabled him to understand why simple refracting telescopes produce blurred images with colored edges. Since the colors in white light are refracted at slightly different angles, they do not converge to form a sharp image. He solved the problem by inventing a new type of telescope that focused the light by means of reflection from mirrors rather than by refraction through glass. Thus he wasted no time putting his theory to practical use, and the superior performance of his reflecting telescope provided further confirmation of his theory.

His predecessors had assumed that colors were the result of some modification of "pure" white light. Then, without any supporting evidence, they speculated about the specific nature of the modification. Descartes had claimed that light was a movement of certain small particles, and that colors are caused by rotation of the particles: The light particles that rotate most rapidly are allegedly seen as red, while those that rotate most slowly are seen as blue. The prominent English scientist Robert Hooke offered a different theory. He supposed that white light was a symmetrical wave pulse, and he claimed that colors result when the pulse becomes distorted. According to his theory, light is red when the leading part of the wave pulse is greater in amplitude than the trailing part and it is blue when the reverse is true. He assumed that the other colors were a mixture of red and blue.

Newton saw these "theories" for what they were: fictions based only on the fertile imaginations of their creators. He rejected their speculative approach and refuted their basic assumption. He proved that colors do not result from any modification of white light; rather, they are the elementary components of white light.

The most radical aspect of Newton's theory did not consist of what he said, but of what he refrained from saying. He presented his results and conclusions without committing himself to any definite view regarding the fundamental nature of light and colors. He reasoned as far as the available evidence could take him—and no further. Many scientists reacted to Newton's original paper with surprise and confusion because they were accustomed to the Cartesian method of deducing conclusions from imagined "first causes." Here was a paper about colors in which the author simply ignored the controversy about whether colors were rotating particles or distorted wave pulses or something else. Were some pages missing? they wondered.

Rather than omitting anything, Newton had supplied what was omitted from the method of Descartes: objectivity. Newton induced his conclusions from the observed results of experiments; he did not deduce them from "intuitions." He was careful to identify the epistemological status of his ideas, and to distinguish clearly between those he regarded as proven and those based on evidence that was inconclusive. He knew only too well the painstaking effort that is required to discover basic truths about nature, and he had no patience for those who attempted to shortcut the process with empty speculation.

Newton once said that he "framed no hypotheses," a statement that became both famous and widely misunderstood. Explaining his terminology, he wrote: "The word 'hypothesis' is here used by me to signify only such a proposition as is not a phenomenon nor deduced from any phenomena, but assumed or supposed—without any experimental proof."[16] Unfortunately, this did not make his meaning entirely clear. He did not intend to reject out of hand all hypotheses that lacked full experimental *proof*; in actual fact, he used the term "hypothesis" to refer to an arbitrary assertion, i.e., a claim unsupported by any observational *evidence*.

Newton understood that to accept an arbitrary idea—even as a mere possibility that merits consideration—undercuts all of one's knowledge. It is impossible to establish any truth if one regards as valid the procedure of manufacturing contrary "possibilities" out of thin air. As he explained in a letter to a colleague:

> [I]f anyone may offer conjectures about the truth of things from the mere possibility of hypotheses, I do not see by what stipulation anything certain can be determined in any science; since one or another set of hypotheses may always be devised which will appear to supply new difficulties. Hence I judged that *one should abstain from contemplating hypotheses, as from improper argumentation.* . . . [17] (Italics added.)

Here, while defending his theory of colors, he introduced a crucial new principle of inductive logic. It is the proper response to most of the claims made by Descartes and his ilk, the only response they warrant: outright dismissal. Newton recognized that the attempt to refute an arbitrary assertion is a fundamental error. To grasp the nature of the world, one's thinking must begin with information received from the world, i.e., sensory data. But an arbitrary idea is detached from such data; to consider it is to leave the realm of reality and enter a fantasy world. No knowledge can be gained by taking such an excursion. One cannot even achieve the misguided goal of disproving an arbitrary idea, because such claims can always be shielded by further arbitrary assertions. Upon entering the fantasy world, one is caught in a proliferating web of baseless conjectures, and there is only one way out: to dismiss all such claims as noncognitive and unworthy of attention.

The senses provide our only direct contact with reality. Without such contact, there may be brain action but there is no thought. The mental gyrations of Cartesian physics are like the spinning wheels of an elevated car—despite the motion, there is no chance of taking the road anywhere. As to those scientists who agree with Plato and Descartes and therefore reject the road because it is dirty and noisy and degrading to their elevated tires, they forfeit their means of ever going anywhere.

Newton's theory of colors received a hostile reaction from such scientists. At first Newton patiently reiterated how to conduct the experiments and what conclusions could be inferred with certainty from the results. Finally he laid down an epistemological law in his effort to preempt all discussions that were not based on the observed facts. He declared that any valid criticism of his theory must fall into one of two categories: Either it argues that his observations are insufficient to support his conclusions, or it cites further observations that contradict his conclusions. As he put it:

> The theory which I propounded was evinced to me, not by inferring it is thus because not otherwise, that is, not by deducing it only from a confutation of contrary suppositions, but by deriving it from experiments concluding positively and directly. . . . And therefore I could wish all objections were suspended from hypotheses or from any [grounds other] than these two: of showing the insufficiency of experiments to determine these queries, or prove any other parts of my theory, . . . or of producing other experiments which directly contradict me, if any such may seem to occur.[18]

Galileo had fought the Church in order to expel religious faith from the realm of science; Newton fought his fellow scientists in an effort to expel the arbitrary as such, including secular claims.[19] The appeal to faith is the demand that ideas be accepted on the basis of emotion rather than evidence, and it is therefore a species of the arbitrary. It makes little difference whether the idea is in the Bible; for example, whether one is asked to accept that Joshua lengthened the day by commanding the sun to stand still, or whether one is asked to accept that particles of white light become colored when they rotate. There is no evidence for either claim, and to consider either is to reject the mind's only means of knowledge: reasoning from observed facts.

Although Galileo pioneered the experimental method, Newton was the one who established its fundamental role in modern physics. As two historians of science note, "Experiment became a principle as well as a method with Newton, who came to see the experimental foundation of his philosophy as the feature that set it apart from other natural philosophies and made it superior to them."[20] His experimental work in optics serves as a model of how physical science ought to be done.

The Methods of Difference and Agreement

As we saw in Chapter 1, our first generalizations are based on causal connections that are directly perceived. For example, the first step toward the modern physicist's understanding of gravitation is the generalization: "Heavy things fall." A child grasps the idea of "heaviness" by holding objects and feeling the downward pressure they exert against his hand. He notices that some things press down more than others; he implicitly omits the measurements, and calls the attribute "heaviness." The concept "fall" is also based directly on perceptual data: It refers to the downward motion of things that occurs spontaneously, without pushing. When a child feels the heaviness of a thing and then lets it go and sees it fall, he immediately grasps: "Its heaviness [that which made it press down on his hand] is what made it fall."

No deliberately applied method is required to grasp such first-level generalizations. The measurement-omission process is subconscious and automatic, and the causal connection is given in the perceptual data. The need for a method arises when we attempt to establish relationships that involve higher-level concepts.

Recall Galileo's study of pendulum motion. In contrast to the connection between the heaviness of a pendulum bob and its descent, we do not directly perceive the causal connection between the pendulum's length and its period. "Length" is a first-level concept, but "period" is not. The application of the concept "period" in this context presupposes knowledge that a pendulum engages in repetitive motion that can be related quantitatively to other motions by means of a unit of time. Here we need prior conceptual integrations—and an explicit method.

In this case, Galileo discovered the causal relationship when he built and compared two pendulums that differed in only one relevant factor—the length of their arms—and he then measured the resulting difference in their periods. By isolating and varying the length, he created a situation in which the difference in length could be identified as the only possible cause of the difference in period. This is the same method he had used earlier to eliminate other possible causal factors. For example, he observed that two pendulums have the same period when they differ only in the weight of their bobs or in the amplitude of their swings. In these experiments a single difference was introduced, but with negative results—the difference made no difference in the period, and therefore the varied factor is causally irrelevant.

Following the terminology of John Stuart Mill, this method of identifying causal factors is called the "method of difference." The investigator introduces one new factor (A) and as a result he sees the effect (B), which was absent prior to the introduction of the new factor. The method rests on the fact that the isolated factor is the only relevant difference. All other factors are eliminated as the cause because they are present even when the effect is not. When using this method, a scientist identifies the difference among all the similarities—the difference A that stands out as making the difference B. Assuming he has not overlooked a relevant factor or condition, he can conclude: A caused B. And then, upon identifying the causal connection conceptually, he arrives at the generalization: cases of A lead to cases of B. (I make no basic distinction between the method of difference and what Mill called the "method of variations," i.e., between a case in which the causal factor can be entirely eliminated and a case in which it is merely varied in magnitude. In both cases, we see a difference in the causal factor that stands out as leading to a difference in the effect.)

Most experiments employ the method of difference (with positive or negative outcomes). All of Galileo's free-fall experiments used this method: He isolated and varied the weight and then the material in order to prove that these properties did not affect the rate of fall, and then he isolated and varied the height in order to establish its relationship to the total time of the fall. He used the same approach in his investigation of free horizontal motion: He introduced differences in a single variable—the initial horizontal speed—and then he measured the corresponding differences in distance traversed during a constant time interval.

Newton too used this method throughout his experimental investigation of colors. He began by introducing a difference in the color of a thread and then he observed through a prism the resulting difference in the thread's image location. His later experiments directly revealed the causal relationship between an isolated change of color and the subsequent change in angle of refraction. Similarly, in his experimental investigation of reflection, Newton held constant the color of incident light while introducing a change in the color of the reflecting body, and as a result he observed a change in the intensity of reflected light.

The explicit statement of the method of difference is not known to most people, any more than they know explicitly the laws of logic or the law of causality. But just as people know causality implicitly, and (much of the time) think and act on its basis, so they know the method of difference implicitly, because it is a corollary of cause and effect. When a child observes that a thing is changed in a single respect (while surrounding conditions are unaltered) and then sees a change in the thing's action, he concludes that the first change caused the second. This is how a toddler discovers that a lamp switch causes the light to turn on and off (in this case, the toddler will repeat the action several times, thus eliminating the possibility of a mere coincidence). We all perform such simple "experiments" and use such reasoning throughout our lives. At an advanced stage of knowledge, it may require an enormous effort from an ingenious scientist to create the crucial experiment that reveals a causal connection. However, whether it is a child or a scientist who uses the method of difference, the situation of interest is always one in which he observes an isolated difference against a background of similarities and then sees its effect.

The other fundamental method used to identify causal relationships is called the "method of agreement." Here we seek to discover the *similar* factor in two or more cases that stands out (against a background of differences) as leading to the *similarity* in effect.

When using the method of agreement, we observe that two or more cases of a certain effect (B) *agree* in only one relevant antecedent factor (A). The factor A can then be identified as the cause of B; all other factors are eliminated because the effect occurs even when they are absent (or the effect remains constant even when they are varied). And then, assuming that we have formed the relevant concepts properly, we can arrive at a universal truth: Cases of A lead to cases of B.

For example, recall that Galileo compared two pendulums that differed in all the potentially relevant factors except length, yet the period remained the same. By the method of agreement, he concluded that length is the causal factor determining the period. Or consider an experimental investigation seeking to discover the cause of the final speed of a ball rolling down an inclined plane. The weight, size, and material of the ball, as well as the length and angle of the plane, are varied while a single factor is held constant: the initial height of the ball. The final speed of the ball is always found to be the same, and therefore the height through which the ball descends is the causal factor determining its speed.

Galileo's study of free fall also illustrates the method of agreement. Considered separately, each of his experiments used the method of difference; however, when the series of experiments are considered together we see that he varied many factors (e.g., the weight, size, density, and horizontal speed of the body) while holding a single factor constant: The heavy body was always free to fall unimpeded toward the Earth. The observed result was always the same, leading to the generalization that all free bodies fall to Earth with the same constant acceleration.

The same procedure was used by Newton to support the broad generalization that integrated his observations in optics. Many factors differed in his various observations involving white light interacting with prisms, lenses, raindrops, and reflective surfaces. From case to case, the total angular deflection of the light beam, its intensity, and the distance through which it traveled all changed; furthermore, sometimes the light was refracted through glass or water, whereas other times it was reflected and traveled through only air. Nevertheless, a similarity unites all these very different instances: One initial factor remained constant—the light was white—and one aspect of the outcome remained constant—the white light was decomposed into colors. By the method of agreement, this vast range of data led to the conclusion that white light is a mixture of elementary colors that can be separated by means of refraction or reflection.

The methods of difference and agreement often work hand in hand. Typically, one observes a difference making a difference, thus isolating some X factor as causal; and then one observes that the X factor alone is present in two or more of the observed cases of the effect. Of course, it can happen in the reverse order, when one first identifies a causal similarity against a background of differences and later observes that removing the cause eliminates the effect. In either case, the two methods are used to complement and confirm each other. However, this conjunction of methods is not always necessary. Either method alone, properly performed, is conclusive.

In the experimental work of Galileo and Newton, one striking feature is the *speed* with which they arrived at generalizations. Galileo did not conduct a laborious study of a hundred different pendulums or projectiles before reaching his conclusions; Newton did not find it necessary to experiment with dozens of different prisms, lenses, or light sources. It is obvious that the validity of induction has nothing to do with the number of instances one observes. We can now see what induction does depend upon: *the grasp of similarities and differences in a causal context.* When using the method of agreement, this may be possible on the basis of only two cases; when using the method of difference, only one instance of the effect may be needed. Always, what counts is the grasp of a uniquely effective similarity or difference. Here the process of generalization parallels the process of concept-formation; one does not need to see a hundred tables in order to form the concept "table"—one can grasp the necessary pattern of similarities and differences merely by seeing two tables in contrast to a chair.

In concept-formation, the grasp of differences and similarities in relation to each other is the starting point and base of every concept; it is essential at every level of the hierarchy. In Chapter 1, we saw that generalization is a form of conceptualization: It is measurement-omission applied to causal connections. Therefore the process of generalizing also rests on the grasp of differences and similarities; above the first-level, it proceeds by the methods of difference and agreement. The very type of relationship that makes possible concept-formation is what makes possible the grasp of causal relations and thus of generalizations.

The validity of the methods of difference and agreement should be regarded as beyond dispute. The correct application of the methods may be difficult in a complex case, but the methods themselves follow as self-evident implications of the law of causality. Yet their validity has been widely attacked and rejected by contemporary philosophers of science. The most common criticisms derive from a failure to understand the two essential components in the inductive proof of any high-level generalization: the role of perceptual evidence and the role of the conceptual framework.

First, it is crucial to grasp Newton's point that some evidence—grounded in observation—is required before one is entitled to suggest a factor as a *possible* cause. In the absence of such evidence, the assertion of a possibility must be dismissed without contemplation. Otherwise, skepticism is unavoidable.

Today, many intellectuals manufacture arbitrary possibilities just as a counterfeiter manufactures money. They are actually worse than counterfeiters, who at least acknowledge the existence of and try to imitate real money; the intellectuals who traffic in the arbitrary deny the existence of real knowledge. For example, the authors of a standard text on scientific method have this to say about Galileo's law of constant gravitational acceleration: "[T]he evidence for the acceleration hypothesis always remains only probable. The hypothesis is only probable on the evidence because it is always logically possible to find some other hypothesis from which all the verified propositions are consequences."[21] This is offered as a bald assertion. The authors do not even suggest another "logical possibility," much less give evidence in support of one; rather, they imply that the reader is free to dream up any "possibility" he wishes without the responsibility of citing evidence. It comes as no surprise when these authors ultimately conclude that the methods of difference and agreement "are not therefore capable of *demonstrating* any causal laws."[22]

The epistemological state of a scientist is not what such skeptics would have us believe. When a scientist confronts some aspect of nature, he does not do so as a helpless newborn; he enters his investigation armed with a vast context of knowledge that precisely delimits the possibilities. A factor qualifies as relevant to his investigation only if there is some *reason* to suspect that it plays a causal role, a reason based on the generalizations that he has already reached, which are ultimately reducible to evidence given directly by the senses.

This brings us to the second criticism that is often brought against the methods of difference and agreement. Some philosophers charge that the methods are invalid *because* they depend upon a prior cognitive context. For example, while discussing these methods, the above-quoted authors write:

> This canon [requires] the antecedent formulation of a hypothesis concerning the possible relevant factors. The canon cannot tell us what factors should be selected for study from the innumerable circumstances present. And the canon requires that the circumstances shall have been properly analyzed and separated. We must conclude that it is not a method of discovery.[23]

According to this view, the methods would qualify as methods of discovery only if they could be applied by rote. The need of an "antecedent hypothesis" and a "proper analysis" is what invalidates them—in other words, the need of knowledge and thought is what invalidates any discovery process.

These criticisms form a one-two punch against inductive inference. The skeptic leads with the claim that there are countless possibilities that cannot be eliminated, and therefore we cannot know any general truths (except this generalization itself, which is treated as an unquestionable absolute). When a rational man answers that the possibilities are delimited by his framework of prior conceptual knowledge, the skeptic asserts that such use of one's conceptual framework is outside the realm of logic. His underlying assumption is that one's conceptual framework is necessarily subjective; i.e., it was not derived from sensory evidence and its elements cannot be reduced back to such evidence. Thus, ultimately, the skeptic's attack on the validity of induction is based on his subjectivist view that concepts themselves are detached from reality.

A rational man must counter the skeptic's first punch with the principled rejection of the arbitrary; he must counter the second with an objective theory of concepts and generalizations. All thought begins with perception; without our only direct contact to existence, there is nothing to think about. Our entire interconnected framework of concepts can be nothing else but integrations of percepts. This is the cognitive whole that the scientist uses to delimit the relevant factors in his investigation and guide his analysis; it is precisely what enables him to use the methods of difference and agreement—and what makes his reasoning valid.

Induction as Inherent in Conceptualization

Concepts are what make induction possible and necessary.

Consider the concepts of "horizontal" and "vertical," which played such a crucial role in the development of Galileo's kinematics. Although relatively simple, these concepts are integrations of earlier concepts. We start with concepts of specific directions that we can indicate by pointing. Thus we begin with "up" and "down" and only reach the abstraction "vertical" at a much later stage; similarly, we start with concepts of specific horizontal directions (e.g., forward or backward, toward the sunrise or the sunset) long before we abstract to form the concept "horizontal." It is our quest to understand the actions of bodies that gives rise to the need for these more advanced abstractions. After observing that heavy bodies fall and light bodies rise and that such spontaneous motion does not occur in other directions, we eventually recognize that "up" and "down" are similar in an important respect and fundamentally different than any perpendicular direction.

Clearly, Galileo's discoveries would have been impossible without these wider abstractions; his law of constant acceleration is a generalization about free *vertical* motion and his law of constant speed is a generalization about free *horizontal* motion. Moreover, the formation of these concepts was itself an enormous step toward the discovery of the laws. The concepts were formed on the basis of grasping an essential difference in the way bodies move vertically versus the way they move horizontally. Armed with these and other key concepts (e.g., "friction," "speed," "acceleration," "parabola"), Galileo could then ask specific questions and formulate the quantitative answers that he found by means of his experiments.

Key concepts played a similar role in Newton's optics. The question that led to his first major discovery was: Is blue light refracted more than red light? Obviously, the question is impossible without the concept "refraction." This concept is an integration of *all cases* in which light bends at an interface between two materials. Such an action can depend on only the nature of the light and the materials, which are also identified in conceptual terms (e.g., *all* light of a particular color, *all* glass of a given type). Thus when Newton varied only the color of light and saw the subsequent change in the angle of refraction, he simply identified his observation conceptually in order to reach the generalization that blue light is refracted more than red light.

Or consider his investigation of why bodies appear colored. Newton knew that when sunlight shines on a body, the light is reflected, absorbed, or transmitted. Without conceptualizing the various possible actions of light, he could not have understood how colors are separated by reflection. With these concepts, his experiments led inexorably to the conclusion that colors arise when part of the spectrum is reflected more strongly than the rest, which is absorbed or transmitted.

When we have a properly formed concept, one that unites concretes by clearly defined essentials, we are often in a position to know at once when an attribute discovered by study of some instances is applicable to all instances. Using Rand's analogy between a concept and a file folder, we can say that such generalization about the referents of a concept is implied in the very act of placing each new item of knowledge in the file folder. By doing so, one is claiming: "This is now part of my knowledge of X, i.e., this is true of all X's—including the vast majority of them that I will never encounter."

A person who refrained from induction would find that his words did not designate concepts at all; they would be reduced to sounds. In the case of first-level concepts based on perceptually given similarities, he could apply a name to some referent he encountered, but without induction he could not apply any of his prior knowledge about such referents. So the name would not serve any cognitive function; he would remain in the state of an ignoramus confronting each new object from scratch.

Consider an infant who begins with the implicit definition of man as "a thing that moves and makes sounds." By further observation of specific men, he eventually discovers that when men make sounds, they are communicating messages to each other, and that when they move, they are doing it purposefully, in order to satisfy various desires. Now this child goes to the next block and sees more men who move and make sounds. However, when he is asked, "Why do you think they are moving and making sounds?" he answers: "I have no idea; I have never seen these particular men before." *This* would be an example of holding a concept minus induction.

Imagine the other bizarre behavior of such a child. His parents would continually hear responses such as: "I didn't know that this particular glass would fall when I dropped it"; "I didn't know that this particular fire would burn me"; "I didn't know that this particular water would quench my thirst"; and so on.

We would not conclude that this child was cautious about leaping to generalizations—rather, we would conclude that he suffered from some incapacitating mental disease. He would be the missing link between animals and men, able to apply a word, but uselessly, because he could not apply the knowledge previously gained about the things named by the word. Thus his words would be nothing more than concrete symbols associated with a few observed particulars, and therefore he would entirely lack the human capacity for thought.

A concept is a commandment to go from some to all—*it is a "green light" to induction*. The rules of the road mandate that we move forward through a green light; the rules of human cognition mandate that we generalize among the referents of our concepts. When we do so, we move forward by means of a unique mechanism (the conceptual faculty) not possessed by other animals, an integrating mechanism designed to take us from particular instances to universal generalizations.

When Newton discovered that the sun, the moon, Earth, apples, and comets all exert a specific type of attractive force ("gravity"), he was compelled to ascribe this force to all bodies. By doing so he integrated astronomy and mechanics and ushered in the modern scientific era; he was able to explain the planetary orbits, the fall of terrestrial bodies, the ocean tides, the motion of comets, the shape of the Earth and the motion of its spin axis—in short, he was able to present an intelligible, integrated universe for the first time. His generalizations followed precisely because he was able to relate the new concept of "gravity" to the whole framework of prior knowledge (see Chapter 4).

In optics, we have seen how Newton discovered that ordinary white light is a mixture of colors that form a "spectrum," i.e., an ordered array made up of red, orange, yellow, green, blue, and violet. Like "gravity" in mechanics, the concept "spectrum" is a key integration that made possible many further discoveries in optics. For example, when scientists found that heat existed beyond the red end of the spectrum and photographic paper was blackened beyond the violet end, they were compelled to extend the concept to include nonvisible infrared and ultraviolet light. This in turn was a key step toward the discovery that light is an electromagnetic wave, a discovery that achieved the grand-scale integration of optics with electromagnetism. Such is the power of concepts and the inductive reasoning that they necessitate.

Of course, the truth of our generalizations is dependent upon the validity of our concepts. *An invalid concept is a red light to induction*; it stops the discovery process or actively leads to false generalizations.

Recall the concepts of "natural" and "violent" motion in Greek physics. These concepts made a fundamental distinction between motions that are in fact similar; for example, smoke rising in air is regarded as "natural" but wood rising in water is regarded as "violent," and a ball swung around on the end of a rope is moving "violently" but the moon orbiting Earth is moving "naturally." On the other hand, they group together motions that are very different; for example, rising smoke and falling rocks are both moving "naturally," and a ball swung in circles and another ball with constant horizontal velocity are both said to move "violently."

Such concepts cannot be reduced back to observed similarities and differences. They are juxtapositions rather than valid integrations, and therefore it is impossible to reach true generalizations among their dissimilar referents. When the Greeks tried to generalize, they were led into a series of falsehoods. For example: "The violent horizontal motion of a projectile is caused by the air pushing on it"; "Celestial bodies are made of an unearthly material called 'ether' that moves naturally in circles around the Earth"; "In the absence of external forces, all heavy bodies move toward their natural place at the center of the Earth"; and so on. The science of physics was stopped at this red light until the concepts of natural and violent motion were rejected.

The concept "impetus" provides an excellent example of a more complex, mixed case. As we saw, this concept was based on a false premise but it was nevertheless a first attempt at a valid and important integration. Buridan was correct in thinking that something about a freely moving body remains the same in the absence of frictional forces, and dissipates as a result of such forces. However, because he thought that a force is necessary to cause motion, he misidentified the nature of the conserved property. He proposed an intrinsic attribute of the body that supplies the internal force propelling it and he called that attribute "impetus." Since there is no such attribute, all generalizations referring to it are false. Yet physicists found that the facts regarding motion could not be integrated without some such idea, and therefore "impetus" eventually had to be reformed and replaced rather than simply rejected outright. After Galileo identified and eliminated the underlying false premise, it was Newton who finally grasped the concept of "momentum" that had been out of Buridan's reach.

Although a valid conceptual framework does not guarantee the truth of subsequent generalizations, the errors of generalization committed by scientists can usually be traced to some inadequacy in their conceptual framework. When scientists overgeneralize (i.e., extend their conclusion beyond its legitimate range of validity) it is often because they lack the concepts necessary to identify important distinctions. We saw Galileo struggle with this problem in several cases. His claim that a circular pendulum is isochronal for all amplitudes was an unlucky guess on an issue that he could not resolve without the concepts of "infinitesimal" and "limit"; when he mistakenly extended his analysis of frictionless motion to rolling balls it was because he lacked the dynamical and mathematical concepts necessary to grasp the effects of rotation; and when he assumed that his law of constant vertical acceleration applied even at large distances from the Earth's surface it was because he lacked the concept "gravity." However, we also saw that such missteps are corrected in the normal course of pursuing science by means of a rational method. Once the requisite concepts were formed, scientists were immediately able to qualify Galileo's conclusions in ways that he could not.

One final point will lead us to the topic of the next chapter. We have seen that a concept can function as a green light to induction only if it is defined precisely—and, in physical science, *the required precision is mathematical*. Recall that Galileo had to define the concepts of "speed" and "acceleration" in mathematical terms before he could arrive at his theory of motion. A similar development can be seen in optics. Prior to Newton, the topic of colors had been treated in a way that was almost entirely qualitative, and as a result there was very little progress. An essential aspect of Newton's achievement was to transform the subject into a quantitative science. He began by measuring the different angles of refraction for each color, and he ended triumphantly by associating each color with a precisely calculated wavelength in his analysis of the famous "rings" experiment. As we shall see more fully, the cognitive integration necessary to validate a high-level generalization in physics is made possible only because the discoveries and laws are formulated in quantitative terms. Thus progress requires that the key concepts be defined in terms susceptible to *numerical measurement*.

Induction in physics is essentially dependent on two specialized methods: Experimentation is the means to mathematics, and mathematics is the language of physical science.

3.

The Mathematical Universe

In order to discover the nature of the physical world, man must be able to relate any fact to what he can directly perceive. Historically, the method that makes this possible was first applied to astronomy.

We begin on the scale of our perception. Thus prescientific man viewed Earth as the enormous centerpiece of the universe, surrounded by much smaller objects that move from east to west across the sky. Nearly all of these objects appear as mere points of light that decorate the night sky and serve to orient us on Earth. Attention to their movements led men to divide these points of light into two categories: the many hundreds of visible "fixed stars," with relative positions that do not change; and five "wandering stars," or "planets," which move in complex ways relative to the fixed stars. In addition to the stars, two objects stood out: the sun and the moon, both roughly the same in apparent size.

In the fifth century B.C., the philosopher Anaxagoras suggested that the sun might be about the size of the Greek peninsula. Most people of the time thought it implausible that the sun could be so large. But since distances to the celestial bodies were unknown and seemingly unknowable, nobody saw a way to settle the issue.

Two centuries later, however, a mathematical astronomer found a way. Aristarchus began by grasping that trigonometry, the branch of mathematics that studies triangles, provided a method of comparing the Earth–sun distance to the Earth–moon distance. When the moon is exactly half full, the line from the sun to the moon must make a ninety-degree angle with the line from the moon to Earth. So, during a half-moon, Aristarchus measured the angle between the line of sight to the moon and the line of sight to the sun. Using the known relationships between the lengths of the sides and the angles of a right triangle, his result of eighty-seven degrees implied that the Earth–sun distance is about twenty times the Earth–moon distance. Since both objects are of the same apparent size, he concluded that the sun's diameter must be about twenty times larger than the moon's diameter. (This method is highly sensitive to small errors in the measured angle, and thus Aristarchus greatly underestimated the sun's distance and size.)

This result said nothing about how the sun or moon compared in size to Earth. To obtain that information, Aristarchus applied mathematical reasoning to the observation of a lunar eclipse. First, he made measurements during such an eclipse that enabled him to compare the size of the moon to the size of Earth's circular shadow on the moon. Second, starting from his calculated values for the relative distances and sizes of the sun and moon, he used trigonometry to relate the size of Earth's shadow to the size of Earth itself. Putting all this together, he concluded that the moon's diameter is about one-third that of Earth, and therefore the sun's diameter is about six or seven times that of Earth.

The powerful combination of observation, measurement, and mathematics provided yet more results. The apparent sizes of the sun and moon had been measured; both bodies subtend an angle of about one-half degree in the sky. So, once their actual sizes (relative to Earth) were calculated, their distances from Earth could be determined. The distance to the moon was found to be about thirty Earth diameters, implying that the distance to the sun is about six hundred Earth diameters.

There remained the problem of relating these measurements to distances that we can perceive, since nobody can see an Earth diameter. The solution was provided by Eratosthenes, the leading Greek astronomer in the generation after Aristarchus. Again, trigonometry played a key role in providing the answer. Eratosthenes knew that at noon on June 21 the sun was directly overhead in the Egyptian town of Syene. Thus a vertical pole placed in the ground cast no shadow at this time. He also knew that the town of Alexandria was 500 miles directly north of Syene (using modern English units for convenience). He placed a vertical pole in the ground at Alexandria, and at noon on June 21 he measured the length of the shadow and compared it to the length of the pole. From his knowledge of right triangles, he deduced that the sun's rays made a 7.2-degree angle with the vertical. He could then calculate the circumference of Earth by means of a simple proportion; 500 miles divided by the circumference is equal to 7.2 degrees divided by 360 degrees. He arrived at the correct result of 25,000 miles for the Earth circumference, implying that the diameter of Earth is about 8,000 miles. And a mile, of course, has a known relationship to a perceivable unit, the foot.

The Greeks applied mathematics more extensively to astronomy than to any other science. As a result, astronomy became the most advanced physical science in antiquity. In contrast, relatively little progress was made in physics. The influence of Platonism convinced many Greek thinkers that the physical changes and motions of earthly materials are not fully intelligible, and therefore not susceptible of mathematical treatment. But the heavenly bodies were thought to possess a greater degree of perfection, and therefore the Greeks were more confident in applying mathematics to this realm.

Unfortunately, they were not able to sustain that confidence. Here, too, Platonism took its toll. At the beginning, the Greeks had based their mathematical astronomy on physical ideas. The Earth was by its nature regarded as immobile at the center of the universe; the heavenly bodies were either carried around by uniformly rotating spheres, or they moved on uniform circular paths simply because of the physical nature of their material (the "ether"). Before long, however, the observed movements of the sun, moon, and planets forced departures from these principles. Rather than searching for new principles, the Greeks gave up the goal of understanding the heavens and instead settled for "describing the appearances." The result was Ptolemy's theory, which employed mathematical devices (eccentric distances, epicycles, and equant points) that were inherently devoid of any reference to physical causes. Thus mathematics broke loose from its moorings in physics—and, consequently, astronomy drifted in stagnant waters for the next fourteen centuries.

Mathematics is not a "pure," isolated string of abstractions and deductions—and if it were, it would be nothing but a useless game. Rather, it is the science of relating quantities to one another, quantities that are ultimately related to perceivable objects. As we shall see shortly, it is by means of relating quantities that scientists grasp and express causal relationships.

The Birth of Celestial Physics

Aristarchus was first to propose the idea that would eventually lead to the integration of physics and astronomy. Our typical experience is that a relatively small object is more easily moved than a huge object. Thus when Aristarchus discovered that the sun is much larger than Earth, he suggested that Earth moves around the sun rather than vice versa.

The heliocentric idea was left as a mere suggestion, undeveloped by Greek astronomers. Indeed, there were major obstacles to its full development. First, the idea ultimately required for its foundation an entirely new physics. Second, it required the experimental and mathematical methods necessary to discover the new physics. And, more generally, it required the absolute conviction that the universe—from Earth to the farthest reaches of the cosmos—can be grasped by means of such rational methods. This latter conviction has its origins in ancient Greece, but it waned and then vanished entirely as the West descended into Christian mysticism.

With the rediscovery of Aristotle in the early Middle Ages, confidence in the power of reason began to reemerge. One consequence was a growing dissatisfaction with Ptolemaic astronomy. Averroes, the twelfth-century Aristotelian philosopher, identified the essence of the problem when he wrote: "Ptolemy was unable to see astronomy on its true foundations. . . . We must, therefore, apply ourselves to a new investigation concerning that genuine astronomy whose foundations are principles of physics. . . . Actually, in our time *astronomy is nonexistent; what we have is something that fits calculation but does not agree with what is*" (italics added).[1]

Nicolaus Copernicus was the first to respond to Averroes' call for a "genuine astronomy," i.e., an astronomy that attempted to explain the observations by identifying the true motions. He resurrected Aristarchus' heliocentric idea and developed it into a full mathematical theory. With the sun fixed and all the planets—including Earth—revolving around it, he was able to *explain* aspects of planetary motion that Ptolemy could only describe using artificial mathematical devices. Thus the Copernican theory, published in 1543, was the first key step toward restoring mathematics to its proper role as a tool for grasping reality, rather than merely for predicting "appearances."

The heliocentric perspective enabled Copernicus to recognize that the observations contained more information than Ptolemy had thought. In the geocentric theory, only the angular position of the planets could be calculated; the relative sizes of the orbits could not be determined. However, if all the planets orbit the sun and our vantage point varies as Earth moves, then carefully selected observations combined with the power of geometry enable one to calculate the relative sizes of the orbits. Copernicus carried out these calculations with impressive accuracy.

His results provided evidence for the sun-centered theory. Knowing the size of the orbits enabled him to compute the relative speed of each planet. He found that the farther a planet is from the sun, the slower it moves. This correlation between distance from the sun and speed strongly suggested a causal relationship. Copernicus wrote: "[T]he sun, as if resting on a kingly throne, governs the family of stars which wheel around. . . . [I]n this ordering we find . . . that there is a sure bond of harmony for the movement and magnitude of the orbital circles such as cannot be found in any other way."[2] The exact mathematical relationship, which he did not discover, would later play a key role in the development of celestial physics.

Knowledge of the relative distances and speeds of the planets—including Earth—enabled Copernicus to explain phenomena that are utterly mysterious on the geocentric view. For example, it had been known for millennia that the direction of a planet's motion across the night sky changes periodically. Mars, for example, usually drifts slowly eastward relative to the background of stars. However, every 780 days it reverses direction and drifts westward for about two months before reversing again and continuing its eastward course. This seemingly erratic motion is one reason for the name "planet," which derives from the Greek verb meaning "to wander." Ptolemy modeled the backward, or "retrograde," motions by means of a second smaller circle called the epicycle. Each planet moves around its epicycle, while the center of the epicycle moves in a larger circular orbit (see Figure 4). The epicycles were successful as a mathematical device for describing and predicting the observed angular positions, but no physical reason was ever offered to explain *why* the planets would move in such a way.

Such retrograde motions, however, are easily understood from the heliocentric perspective. All of the planets revolve in the same direction around the sun. So when Earth is between the sun and Mars (for example), the faster-moving Earth passes the slower Mars, making its motion

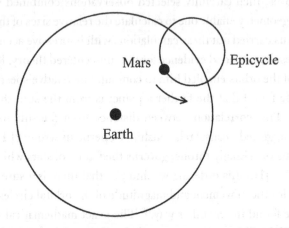

Figure 4. The geocentric theory must use the noncausal device of epicycles to describe retrograde motion.

appear retrograde, or backward, from our vantage point (see Figure 5). The Copernican theory explained the retrograde motions of Jupiter and Saturn in the same way, and made perfectly clear why such apparent motions depend on the planet's position relative to Earth and the sun. Copernicus showed that the most perplexing features of "wandering stars" could be understood as inevitable consequences of observing them from the orbiting Earth. As he put it, "All these things proceed from the same cause, which resides in the movement of the Earth."[3]

Now consider the inner planets, Mercury and Venus. According to the geocentric view, their behavior is very peculiar. Unlike the other planets, they follow the sun in its orbit around Earth, as if attached to the sun by a leash. So Ptolemy asks us to accept—without explanation—that there are two different kinds of planets: those that follow the sun and those that do not. In contrast, the heliocentric theory introduces no such mystery. Since Mercury and Venus orbit closer to the sun than Earth, it is obvious why these planets are always observed in the vicinity of the sun. So, unlike Ptolemy, Copernicus could account for the observations by means of a theory in which all the planets move in essentially the same way.

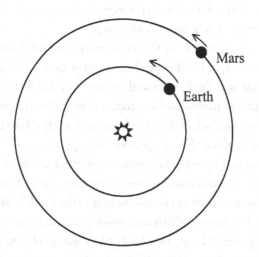

Figure 5. The heliocentric explanation for the retrograde motion of Mars: When the sun and Mars are in opposition, Earth passes the slower Mars.

The heliocentric theory had a crucial implication regarding the distance between Earth and the stars. The angular positions of the "fixed stars" do not change noticeably as Earth moves around the sun. This was surprising; as our location changes, the direction from us to the observed star should change as well. The only possible explanation, according to the heliocentric theory, is that the distance over which Earth moves (i.e., the diameter of Earth's orbit) is negligibly small compared to the distance to the stars. Given the accuracy of the measured angular positions, and Aristarchus' estimate of the Earth–sun distance, this implied that the stars must be at least ten billion miles away. This is two orders of magnitude greater than Ptolemy had thought; thus the mathematics of the heliocentric theory required a much larger universe.

While the new scale of the universe was difficult for some to accept, the major obstacle to accepting the heliocentric theory was the motion of Earth itself. On the basis of the Greek theory of motion, it was thought that such rapid movement of Earth would lead to obvious and catastrophic effects (e.g., incredible winds, people flying off Earth into space, and so on). In the sixteenth century, the idea of our world spinning on its axis and orbiting the sun still evoked the reaction expressed by Ptolemy: "But indeed this sort of suggestion has only to be thought of in order to be seen to be utterly ridiculous."[4]

To gain a hearing for his theory, Copernicus had to offer some answer to this charge. He did not have to provide the full answer (that ambitious task was finally achieved by Newton), but he had to indicate that there is a way to resolve the apparent contradiction between Earth's movement and our lack of direct awareness of it. He did so by citing the relativity of motion. "Every apparent change in place," Copernicus wrote, "occurs on account of the movement either of the thing seen or of the spectator, or on account of the necessarily unequal movements of both. . . . If some movement should belong to the Earth it will appear, in the parts of the universe which are outside, as though the things outside were passing over."[5] Later, he added: "As a matter of fact, when a ship floats on a tranquil sea, all the things outside seem to the voyagers to be moving in a movement which is the image of their own, and they think on the contrary that they themselves and all the things with them are at rest. So it can easily happen in the case of the Earth that the whole [universe of fixed stars] should be believed to be moving in a circle."[6] So, although Copernicus was not a physicist, he did point the way toward the new physics. In the next century, Galileo would seize on and extend this same example of the ship in order to explain the principles of motion underlying heliocentric astronomy.

Lacking a proper foundation in physics, Copernicus retained some of the noncausal features of the geocentric theory. He continued to use epicycles, which were needed not to account for the retrograde motions of planets but to compensate for the erroneous assumption of uniform circular orbits. In addition, the major circles in the Copernican theory were still centered about vacant points, with the sun offset by a distance that was freely chosen to give the best fit to the data. Such features had to be eliminated in order to complete a transformation from the old "astronomy of appearances" to the new celestial physics. At the beginning of the seventeenth century, this was the task undertaken by Johannes Kepler.

Kepler was the greatest theoretical astronomer of his era, and he had the good fortune of inheriting the database of Tycho Brahe, the greatest observational astronomer of the previous generation. The combination was exactly what the new astronomy required: the most complete and accurate measurements in the hands of a brilliant theorist who was committed to understanding the true motions of astronomical bodies. As Kepler himself put it, "Tycho possesses the best observations and consequently, as it were, the material for the erection of a new structure; he has also workers and everything else which one might desire. He lacks only the architect who uses all this according to a plan."[7]

What was Kepler's plan? The goal was to identify the motions of celestial bodies by grasping their physical causes. "My aim in this is to show that the celestial machine is to be likened not to a divine organism but rather to a clockwork. . . . "[8] In a clock, he explained, the regular motions are caused by natural forces acting upon a weight; the solar system, he proposed, can be understood in a similar way. By what means can we discover the causal relationships? In a profound insight, he wrote: "[A]s the eye was created for color, the ear for tone, so was the intellect of humans created for the understanding not just of anything whatsoever but of quantities."[9] If our minds can unlock the secrets of the universe, he thought, the key must be mathematics.

Early in his career, Kepler recognized the powerful evidence in favor of the heliocentric theory: the enormous size of the sun relative to the planets, the relationship between a planet's speed and its distance from the sun, and the theory's explanation of retrograde motion and of the observed differences between inner and outer planets. The meaning of this evidence, he thought, is not merely that the sun is the *central* body in the solar system; the meaning, he reasoned, is that the sun is the *dominant* body in the solar system, i.e., that the sun exerts a physical force on the planets that is the cause of their orbits.

The concept "force" had originally referred only to observable pushes and pulls between bodies in direct contact with each other. But the phenomena of electricity and magnetism compelled scientists to expand the concept. In the case of these phenomena, it was clear that one body can exert a physical force on a distant body by some imperceptible means. In 1600, William Gilbert published his influential book *On Magnets*, which summarized the existing knowledge of electricity and magnetism and announced his discovery that Earth itself is a magnet. Kepler read the book carefully, and took from it the modern concept of "force," which was a prerequisite of celestial physics.

Kepler soon found further evidence for his idea of a solar force. The planetary orbits, he knew, do not all lie in the same plane. They are inclined with respect to the plane of Earth's orbit by varying amounts (up to seven degrees in the case of Mercury). When he carefully determined the inclinations of the orbits, he discovered a crucial fact: *The planes of the orbits intersect at the position of the sun*—and the sun is the only object common to the orbital planes. Thus, by the method of agreement, the sun appeared to be the only possible cause of the orbits. With this discovery, Kepler had begun the process of erecting a new structure from Brahe's data; he had arrived at the physical idea that would serve as the foundation.

At the outset, Kepler's causal approach led to a crucial innovation in the way he analyzed the data. Copernicus had referred planetary positions to the center of Earth's orbit. Since the sun was offset from the center, Copernicus was calculating the positions of planets relative to a vacant point. Kepler objected that such a procedure was physically absurd, and he instead decided to refer all planetary positions directly to the location of the sun. This shift in perspective would prove to be essential to his success.

Given this foundation, Kepler asked: Precisely how do the planets move as a result of the solar force? It was logical that he turned to Mars for the answer. Of all the planets, it was Mars that had given both Ptolemy and Copernicus the most trouble. In both orbital models, there were significant discrepancies between observed and predicted angular positions. Of course, such discrepancies were not the only problem; Kepler also rejected these models because they both used epicycles, requiring that Mars revolve around a vacant point for no physical reason. In Kepler's words, this was a "purely geometric assumption, for which a corresponding body in the heavens does not exist."[10] Since his goal was to develop a celestial physics, the arbitrary device of epicycles could not be tolerated.

So Kepler began his assault on Mars by shunning epicycles and attempting to construct the best possible orbit using the other standard mathematical devices in the astronomer's toolkit. Following a two-thousand-year tradition, he assumed the orbit to be circular. The sun was offset some distance from the center of the circle, and an "equant point" was placed on the other side of the center point. The device of the equant point was first introduced by Ptolemy as a way of "saving the appearances" by departing from the principle of uniform motion. The motion appears uniform only from the equant point; i.e., a line from this point to the planet will sweep out equal angles in equal times. But since the equant point is not at the center of the circle, the planet must actually move slower when it is closer to the equant and move faster when it is farther away (see Figure 6).

On the surface, it seems that Kepler should have rejected equants for

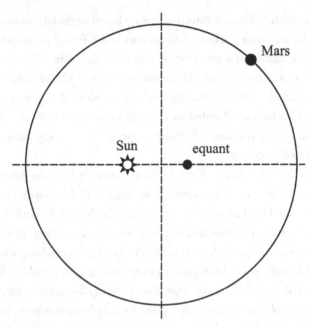

Figure 6. In Kepler's original circular model for the orbit of Mars, the sun is offset from the center and an "equant" point is used to vary the speed.

the same reason he rejected epicycles; it is a vacant point controlling the motion of a physical body. However, he grasped that the equant could be given a physical interpretation. By placing this point in an appropriate location, he could model the way in which a planet's speed varies with its distance from the sun. So Kepler began by using the equant as a convenient mathematical device for modeling a causal relationship between the planet and the sun.

Once the model had been selected, he faced the difficult task of determining the specific numerical parameters that best fit the observed angular positions of Mars. The observational data give the direction of the line from Earth to Mars, but the variations in this direction depend on both the motion of Mars and the motion of Earth. The changing position of Earth is a complicating factor; modeling the orbit of Mars around the sun would be much easier if our observations were made from the sun.

Kepler solved this problem by carefully selecting a small subset of data that eliminated the complicating factor. About every two years, there is a time when Earth is between the sun and Mars and located on the same line. At such times, Mars is said to be in opposition (on the opposite side of Earth from the sun). When in opposition, the direction from Earth to Mars is the same as the direction from the sun to Mars; i.e., the measured angular position is the same as that which would be measured from the sun.

Brahe's database contained ten such Mars oppositions. Kepler needed to determine four parameters in his circular model of the orbit: the angular speed, the ratio of the sun–center distance to the radius, the ratio of the equant–center distance to the radius, and the direction of the line containing the sun, center, and equant. He selected four opposition points in order to calculate the four parameters. Lacking the methods of modern mathematics, Kepler used a tedious procedure of successive approximation. After more than seventy iterations, he finally arrived at values of the parameters that gave the best fit to the four angular positions. He found that the distance from the sun to the center of the circle had to be significantly larger than the distance from the center to the equant.

Kepler then compared the angular positions predicted by his model to the remaining six opposition points that had not been used in arriving at the model. The predictions agreed with these observations to within about two minutes arc, which was approximately the size of the errors in Brahe's measurements. For the moment, it appeared that Kepler had triumphed over Mars.

However, he was not merely trying to save appearances. He was trying to determine the actual orbit—and there is more to an orbit than angular positions. So Kepler asked the next logical question: Did his model also give the correct distances between the sun and Mars? The opposition data did not provide the information necessary to answer this question. Here he needed observations when Mars was not in opposition, so that he could form triangles with lines drawn between the sun, Earth, and Mars. His approach was to compare such triangles. Starting from knowledge of the angles and the relative Earth–sun distances, he could calculate the relative Mars–sun distances; i.e., he could determine how the distance between the sun and Mars varies in the orbit.

It is worth noting how Kepler knew the angles in such triangles. Of course, Brahe's observations provided the direction of the line from Earth to Mars. For the directions of the other two lines, Kepler used available models rather than raw data. He had already shown that his model of Mars' orbit gave directions of the sun–Mars line that were accurate to within about two minutes arc. For the direction of the sun–Earth line, he used a model developed by Brahe that was accurate enough for his purposes. It was not possible to go directly from raw data to the final theory; these intermediate models, which would eventually be replaced by Kepler's final theory, integrated vast amounts of data and thereby served as indispensable stepping-stones.

Although Brahe's sun-Earth model was accurate enough for angular positions, Kepler was suspicious that it did not model the sun–Earth distances correctly. He reasoned that the planetary orbits have the same cause, and therefore the planets should move in essentially the same way. But Brahe had used a simpler model of the sun-Earth system in which there was no equant point. Kepler was convinced that Earth should move slower when farther from the sun and faster when closer (like the other planets). If so, adding an equant would result in a significantly improved model of Earth's orbit. And Earth's orbit was crucial to his battle with Mars; he needed accurate sun–Earth distances in order to calculate sun–Mars distances.

Developing a new model of Earth's orbit presented Kepler with another difficult problem. Astronomers are trapped on Earth; they cannot go to some distant location to observe Earth's motion against the background of fixed stars. However, Kepler ingeniously thought of a way to overcome this travel restriction. He knew that the period of Mars' orbit is 687 days; i.e., every 687 days Mars completes one entire orbit and thus returns to the location from which it started. Kepler therefore selected observations of Mars at 687-day intervals. This is equivalent to holding the position of Mars constant; in this data set, variations in the angular position of Mars are caused solely by changes in Earth's position. For each data point, Kepler considered the triangle formed by lines between the sun, Earth, and Mars. As we have already seen, he knew the directions of all three lines and thus all three angles of the triangle. And, because the position of Mars is always the same, all the triangles have one side in common (the sun–Mars line). From such triangles, Kepler could calculate how the sun–Earth distance varied from point to point.

The results of these calculations showed that Brahe's value for the distance between the sun and the center of Earth's orbit was too large. Kepler achieved an improved fit to the data with a smaller sun–center distance in combination with an equant that was located an equal distance away from the center on the other side. This was a major step on the way to his goal; he finally had a model of Earth's orbit that was accurate enough to use in calculating sun–Mars distances.

This work had another benefit as well. While developing the above model, Kepler discovered that Earth's speed was very nearly inversely proportional to its distance from the sun. This was the type of causal relationship for which he was searching. He immediately hypothesized that the inverse speed/distance relationship was the true law, and his use of the equant point was only a convenient device for approximating it.

But how close was this approximation? Kepler decided to calculate Earth's orbit by direct application of the speed/distance law and compare these results to his equant model. The mathematical process was extremely tedious. Calculus had not yet been discovered, so Kepler could only divide the orbit into tiny segments, make a calculation for each segment, and laboriously sum the results. While performing these seemingly endless calculations, a clever shortcut occurred to him. What he actually needed to know was how far Earth travels in a given time along its path, which is only indirectly related to the speed/distance law. However, he realized that if the speed is inversely proportional to the distance from the sun, then it is approximately true that the line from the sun to Earth will sweep out equal areas in equal times. Mathematically, the "area law" is much easier to apply—and, of course, it also has the form of a causal law in which the sun determines the variations in Earth's position.

In the case of Earth's orbit, Kepler proved that the differences between the equant model, the inverse speed/distance law, and the area law were negligible (about a half minute of arc, at most). The noncausal feature of the equant point could now be eliminated. In choosing between the two causal laws, Kepler provisionally adopted the area law because it simplified calculations. Eventually, observations of Mars would decide the issue.

Before turning back to Mars, it is worth emphasizing two points about Kepler's method.

First, he did not simply use mathematics to fit Brahe's data; he also used mathematics to generate data. Brahe's raw data consist only of angular positions; Kepler used these angles and trigonometry to generate distance ratios and then demanded that his model fit both the angular positions and the distances. Without trigonometry, there would be no distances for his model to fit.

Second, Kepler's procedure is strikingly similar to experiment. While working on the orbit of Mars, he selected a subset of data that eliminated the complicating variable of Earth's position. While working on the orbit of Earth, he selected a subset of data in which the position of Mars is constant. His biographer, Max Caspar, writes: "It is always the observations which chain him, which he forces to answer his questions."[11] He "forced" the observations to answer his questions by controlling specific variables and thereby isolating the variable of interest—which is the essence of experimental method.

Armed with an accurate model of Earth's orbit, Kepler returned to his mission of forcing Mars to answer his questions. He chose three observations of Mars from Brahe's database, and from the sun-Earth-Mars triangles he calculated the sun–Mars distance at each of the three points. He needed only three points to determine a circle, and he was able to calculate the distance of the sun from the center of the circle. This calculation was a pivotal moment in the history of science. It left Kepler facing a contradiction—a contradiction, as it turned out, that could not be resolved without a revolution in astronomy.

The sun–center distance that Kepler calculated was not the same as the corresponding distance he had used in his model that gave accurate angular positions of Mars. When he substituted the correct sun–center distance into his model, the angular positions were in error by up to eight minutes arc. Brahe's data, he knew, are accurate to within about two minutes arc. There was no way around the conclusion: His circular model for the orbit of Mars was simply wrong. It could not be made consistent with both the observed angular positions and the correct distances.

Unlike his predecessors, Kepler could not evade such a problem by merely inserting an arbitrary feature into his mathematical model. One historian has explained this point as follows:

> It was [Kepler's] introduction of physical causality into the formal geometry of the skies which made it impossible for him to ignore the eight minutes arc. So long as cosmology was guided by purely geometrical rules of the game, regardless of physical causes, discrepancies between theory and fact could be overcome by inserting another wheel into the system. In a universe moved by real, physical forces, this was no longer possible.[12]

But what feature of the model was wrong? Kepler was confident that his value for the sun–center distance was correct. Furthermore, from his work on the orbit of Earth, he was confident that variations of speed were at least well approximated by his law of areas. That left only one possible culprit: the shape of the orbit. Kepler concluded that Mars does not move in a circle. Thus the fundamental tenet of a two-thousand-year tradition was overturned by a small discrepancy between measurement and theory in the case of a single planetary orbit.

When he carefully examined these discrepancies, he saw that the errors in his circular model occurred in a definite pattern. In order to describe the pattern, I must introduce some new concepts that Kepler formed as a result of his causal approach to astronomy.

As we have seen, Kepler was the first astronomer to refer all planetary positions directly to the sun. The point of the orbit where the planet is farthest from the sun he called the "aphelion" (in Greek, "apo" means "away from"); the point nearest the sun he called the perihelion ("peri" means "near"). The line connecting the perihelion, the sun, and the aphelion he called the "line of apsides." He then drew a second line, perpendicular to the line of apsides and passing through the point located halfway between the aphelion and the perihelion (i.e., the center). When the planet is in the vicinity of this second line, he referred to it as being in the "quadrants." The areas of the orbit halfway between the apsides and the quadrants (i.e., at forty-five-degree angles from these perpendicular lines) are called the "octants."

When Mars was near the two perpendicular lines (i.e., the apsides and the quadrants), the circular orbit of Mars predicted the correct angular positions. The errors occurred in the octants; the model put Mars about eight minutes arc ahead of its actual position in two of the octants, and about eight minutes arc behind in the other two (see Figure 7).

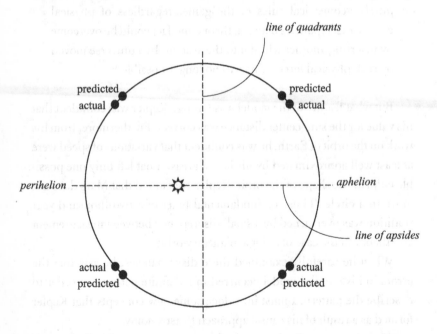

Figure 7. The distribution of errors in Kepler's circular model for the orbit of Mars.

Kepler studied the pattern and grasped the implication: In the circular model, Mars moved too rapidly about the apsides and too slowly about the quadrants. The shape of the orbit needed to be modified in order to correct these speeds; Mars had to be farther from the sun along the line of apsides and closer to the sun in the quadrants. In other words, Mars must move in some oval-shaped orbit, slightly elongated in the apsides and slightly compressed in the quadrants. He confirmed this idea by calculating several Mars–sun distances, which showed that Mars comes inside the circular model near the quadrants.

Giving up circular orbits was not easy, even for an innovative genius such as Kepler. The circle possesses a symmetry that was lacking in the slightly flattened shape demanded by his investigations of Mars. In order to make sense of this result, he returned to his idea of the solar force and searched for a physical cause of the asymmetry. So far, the solar force had served as the guiding idea that made his discoveries possible. At this point, however, he was temporarily led astray by speculations regarding the specific nature of the force.

With hindsight, we can see that Kepler's effort to develop a celestial physics was doomed by a false premise. "[E]very bodily substance," he wrote, ". . . by nature tends to remain at the same place at which it finds itself."[13] He had no grasp of the idea that a force causes a change in motion rather than motion itself; in other words, he had no concept of "inertia." Influenced by ancient Greek physics, he assumed that any motion must be caused by a force in the direction of the body's motion. He combined this assumption with Gilbert's discovery that Earth is a magnet, and thereby arrived at his hypothesis: The sun exerts a magnetic force on the planets that pushes them around in their orbits.

Kepler elaborated this hypothesis in order to account for the oval-shaped orbit of Mars. The solar magnetic force, he proposed, has two components. First, he speculated that the sun is spinning rapidly and this motion somehow creates a magnetic force that sweeps the planets around in circles. Second, the planets themselves are magnets, with the south pole attracted to the sun and the north pole repelled. When the south pole is oriented toward the sun, the planet's orbit is pulled closer;

when the north pole is oriented toward the sun, the planet's orbit is pushed farther away. This attractive/repulsive component of the magnetic force accounts for the noncircular, asymmetric path of the planet.

He convinced himself that such a solar force would result in orbits that are egg-shaped, i.e., narrower in the part of the orbit close to the sun and wider in the part of the orbit farther from the sun. He then spent most of the next year in a futile attempt to fit the egg shape to the observations of Mars. Later, after recognizing his error, he wrote: "What happened to me confirms the old proverb: a bitch in a hurry produces blind pups. . . . The reader must show tolerance to my gullibility."[14]

Of course, what Kepler deserves from us is not "tolerance" but our highest admiration for his relentless pursuit of the truth. Nevertheless, there is some validity to his self-criticism. His hypothesis regarding the specific nature of the solar force was supported only by his attempt to connect it with terrestrial magnetism. But nobody had ever observed a magnet acting in the way that Kepler supposed the sun to act on planets. Despite his use of the word "magnetic," Kepler's solar force was actually sui generis. In the end, he conceded as much when he wrote, "I will be satisfied if this magnetic example demonstrates the general possibility of the proposed mechanism. Concerning its details, however, I have doubts."[15]

Unfortunately, he suffered through a difficult year while pursuing his speculations and the egg they had laid. Despite the fact that he was in the grip of a flawed model, the work had one beneficial effect: He became thoroughly immersed in the observational data and in his calculations of sun–Mars distances. He had gone astray with the egg model, but he never lost sight of the observations—and they inevitably led him back to the truth. The light began to dawn on him when he discovered a peculiar numerical coincidence. The coincidence implied that the distance from the sun to a quadrant point is equal to the major radius of the orbit. After a few minor missteps, Kepler recognized that this equality is a property of an ellipse with the sun at one focus. The hypnotic spell of the egg hypothesis was finally broken, and he commented later: "I felt as if I had been awakened from a sleep. . . ."[16] It was not merely an awakening for Kepler, but for the science of astronomy: One of the out-standing problems of the ages—the orbit of Mars—had been solved.

With knowledge of the precise shape of the orbit, he could resolve an earlier ambiguity. He was able to show that his "area law" gave a better fit to the observed movements of Mars than did the inverse speed/distance law. Furthermore, he grasped the relationship between the two laws: The speed/distance law is correct—and equivalent to the area law—if one uses not the total speed but the component of speed perpendicular to the line from the sun to Mars.

Kepler immediately generalized his results; what was true for Mars was true for all the planets. Thus he arrived at his first two laws of planetary motion: Planets move in elliptical orbits with the sun located at one focus, and the line from the sun to a planet sweeps out equal areas in equal times. With the exception of Earth, he did not perform the same tedious procedure to determine the elliptical parameters of the other planetary orbits. Such an effort would not have provided much further evidence for his laws. Using circles and equants, the other orbits could be modeled nearly within the accuracy limits of Brahe's data. (Mercury would seem to be an exception, since its orbit departs significantly from a circle; however, because of its proximity to the sun, the data were less complete and less accurate.)

It was eminently reasonable that Kepler showed no hesitation in generalizing from the orbit of Mars. At the outset, he had cited strong evidence that the planets were moved by the same cause, and therefore they must move in essentially the same way. Moreover, it was one of the key advantages of the heliocentric theory that the planets did move in the same way; the apparent difference between the movements of "inner" and "outer" planets was eliminated. In the context of Kepler's causal theory, the concept "planet" could and did function as a green light to induction. His investigation was about planetary motion; he had focused on Mars simply because it was best suited to provide the answers to his questions.

Kepler discovered the correct theory of the solar system using only a small subset of Brahe's large database. His conclusions were based primarily on observations of Mars and the sun, and the key steps along the way were often made using only a few carefully selected data points. His calculations were guided at each step by his well-supported hypothesis concerning the causal role of the sun.

The larger context that guided him drew on a vast range of data and many high-level generalizations. In astronomy, it depended on all the knowledge discovered by the Greeks and Copernicus; in mathematics, it depended on the work of Euclid, Apollonius, Archimedes, and Vieta; in physics, we have seen how Kepler made use of the expanded concept of "force" that emerged from studies of electricity and magnetism.

Kepler's first two laws of planetary motion were the jewels contained in his book *New Astronomy Based on Causation,* published in 1609. Nine years later, Kepler discovered his third and final law of planetary motion. In contrast to the first two laws, which specify the nature of an individual orbit, the third law states a mathematical relationship among the orbits, and thus applies to the solar system as a whole.

Although Copernicus had discovered that a planet farther from the sun moves slower, the exact mathematical relationship had remained elusive. Kepler was convinced that since the planetary orbits have the same cause, they should be mathematically the same in some way. Thus he began to search for some function of mean distance and orbital period (which is inversely proportional to average speed) that remained unchanged. In 1618, after much trial and error, he found what he had been seeking. His third and final law states that the cube of the mean distance from the sun divided by the square of the orbital period is a constant for all planets. The discovery of this law was the result of extraordinary persistence—which, in turn, derived from an unwavering conviction that there should be some such relationship between orbits that share the same physical cause.

Kepler's publication of his laws was an historic milestone: They were the first exact mathematical laws describing the motion of bodies (the kinematics of Galileo was not published until the 1630s). In the post-Newtonian era, it is easy to take such laws for granted; however, in the early seventeenth century, the context was quite different. Regarding the state of knowledge when Kepler began his work, one historian comments: "The unutterable patience and toil required to discover the secrets of nature by experiment and observation was still unknown. The concept of laws of nature that establish causal relationships between phenomena and put them in formulas was not yet held. Men had not yet learned the inductive method. . . ."[17]

Kepler did his part to teach men that method by describing with unusual openness both how he made his discoveries and how he made his errors. Unfortunately, anyone familiar with contemporary cosmology has reason to question whether today's researchers have learned the lesson. The purpose of the following sections is to identify some of the main points.

Mathematics and Causality

Prior to the rise of the heliocentric theory, the science of astronomy had renounced causality and thereby detached its mathematics from the physical world. Ptolemaic astronomy was accepted for more than a millennium because man had adopted a very humble attitude toward nature. In the material realm, he had meekly assumed that it was beyond his capacity to grasp necessary connections between the nature of things and their actions. Consequently, astronomers could only hope to invent schemes for "describing the appearances."

Strangely enough, the skeptical "describe the appearances" camp often tries to claim Kepler as one of their own. They insist that the laws of planetary motion are not causal statements, but merely descriptive regularities. After all, they argue, the currently accepted cause of the planetary orbits—the gravitational interaction of masses—was unknown to Kepler. Therefore, they conclude, he discovered no causal connections and his so-called laws are simply empirical descriptions of planetary motion. According to this view, Kepler's generalization from Mars to the other planets was a lucky guess.

As we have seen, such a skeptical view contradicts Kepler's actual discovery process and his conclusions. He thought of his laws in the following way: First, the sun exerts a force on each planet that causes it to move in an elliptical orbit (with the sun located at a focus); second, the solar force causes each planet to move so that the line from the sun to the planet sweeps out equal areas in equal times; third, the solar force diminishes with distance in a way that causes the cube of the mean distance from the sun divided by the square of the orbital period to be constant for all planets. Clearly, these are causal statements—as they must be in order to qualify as laws.

In fact, Kepler *did* know the cause of planetary orbits: He correctly identified the cause as the sun and some property of planets that responds to the sun. This was the causal knowledge necessary to reach and validate his generalizations. Later, Newton discovered that the relevant property is mass, which gives rise to gravitational attraction. This was the more advanced causal knowledge necessary to validate Newton's much wider generalizations, which subsumed Kepler's laws as concretes. Perhaps, in the future, physicists will reach a deeper understanding of the cause in terms of a fully consistent, physical theory of the gravitational field. If so, such knowledge will no doubt play a key role in validating still wider generalizations.

The above causal identifications do not contradict one another. Kepler's statement is correct as far as it goes—but it says less than Newton's, and implies a great deal less. And Newton's statement is correct as far as it goes—but Einstein discovered more about gravitation, and there is still more to be discovered.

The causal knowledge necessary to prove a generalization is delimited by the scope of the generalization. For example, consider Kepler's law of elliptical orbits. If it is a general law, and not simply a description of particulars, we must be able to answer certain questions. Orbits around what? The sun, which is located at a focus of the ellipse. Why the sun? Because it exerts a force on the planet causing the orbit. How do we know this? Here we cite Kepler's evidence for the solar force: the enormous size of the sun, the dependence of planetary speed on distance from the sun, and the fact that the sun is the only body contained in all the orbital planes. This is all that is required. In contrast, consider Newton's law that all bodies attract each other with a force that is proportional to the product of their masses and inversely proportional to the square of the distance between them. The questions that we must answer in order to validate this generalization are too numerous to list here, but they pertain to the concepts of "mass" and "acceleration," the laws of motion, and the integration of terrestrial physics with astronomy (see the next chapter).

It is important to recognize that the causal knowledge necessary to prove a generalization is *not* the same as the causal knowledge from which the generalization can be deduced. It is a common error to substitute the latter for the former in an effort to reduce all logical reasoning to deduction. According to this view, Kepler's laws are mere hypotheses until they are deduced from Newton's laws, which are mere hypotheses until they are deduced from more general laws, and so on. Thus "knowledge" is nothing more than a pyramid scheme of hypotheses, which are ultimately validated only by an intuitive revelation of the so-called first cause. This approach leads to two camps: the skeptics who admit that they lack such intuition, and the rationalists who pretend to have it.

The rationalists typically appeal to the symmetry, elegance, and beauty of their mathematical theory, claiming that such pleasing aesthetic features imply real insight into the world of Forms (Plato) or the mind of the Creator (any religion). Like the skeptics, they introduce a breach between physical causation and mathematics. The skeptics do so because they regard causes as unknowable and mathematical formalism as arbitrary; the rationalists in physics do so because they hold that the fundamental causes are nonphysical and that the laws of nature can be grasped independent of sensory contact with the physical world.

It is often claimed that Plato paved the way for the scientific revolution by emphasizing the value of mathematics. But such a claim ignores the essence of Plato's view. Mathematics is properly valued as a tool for grasping the causal laws of the physical world; Plato, on the other hand, valued mathematics as a means of directing the mind away from the physical world and toward the world of Forms. In his view, mathematical ideas do not derive from the physical world, and they do not apply to it except in an approximate way. Such ideas are innate in us from birth, and their referents exist in an extrasensory, nonphysical dimension. Mathematics is supposed to be a perfect science consisting of *pure* knowledge, unsullied by any dependence on the physical world.

This view was a major obstacle for the scientific revolution to overcome. Progress in science required the anti-Platonic view that the *physical world is perfect*—i.e., that it is fully real and worthy of the most painstaking study, and that mathematics is the language for expressing causal connections in the world. This was the idea that motivated Kepler and Galileo to spend decades searching for the exact mathematical laws governing nature, while refusing to accept any inconsistency between their principles and the sensory data.

Tragically, Kepler was torn by conflicting views regarding the nature of knowledge in general and of mathematics in particular. He opened the door to modern science, but he stepped through only halfway. He was held back by his partial allegiance to a Christianized version of Platonism. When in the grip of this view, he searched for causes in the mind of God rather than in the nature of physical entities, sanctioned wild speculations based on "intuition," and tolerated the resulting breaches between theory and observation. Thus Kepler stood with one foot forward in the Age of Reason and one foot back in the Middle Ages. By doing so, he presents a unique case study. In the previous section we saw the results of his first method; let us now look at his second method and its results.

The Platonic Kepler was guided by his belief that the physical world was created out of the Divine mind, that God's mathematical ideas are innate in us, and that the purpose of studying the physical universe is so the "thought of the Creator be recognized in its nature, and that His inexhaustible wisdom shine forth more brightly."[18] Thus his explanations relied on appeals to the perfection and aesthetic beauty of God's blueprint for the universe. He regarded mathematics as independent of and prior to the physical world. "Mathematical things are the causes of the physical," Kepler wrote, "because God from the beginning of time carried within himself in simple and divine abstraction the mathematical things as prototypes of the materially planned quantities."[19] When Kepler followed this approach, he bypassed physics and went straight to its alleged source: God's love of mathematical regularities.

An example of how Platonism affected Kepler's astronomy can be found in his first book, *The Cosmic Mystery*, published in 1596. Greek mathematicians had discovered that there are five symmetrical, solid geometric figures that can be constructed from identical plane surfaces (an example is the cube, which is formed by six identical squares). These figures, called the five regular solids, were held in high esteem because of the perfection of their symmetry. The planetary orbits, Kepler thought, must have been arranged by God such that the five perfect geometric figures fit between them, which implied there must be six and only six planets.

By judiciously choosing which figure to fit between each pair of adjacent planets, Kepler arrived at a scheme that very roughly approximated the relative sizes of the orbits (the average error was more than 20 percent). Qua Platonist, he was more tolerant of discrepancies with the observations; after all, Plato had emphasized that the physical world is an imperfect realm. So, despite the inaccuracy of the scheme, Kepler ecstatically declared that he had discovered the mathematical basis of God's plan.

Later, Kepler carried this approach further by relating aspects of the planetary orbits to musical tones in an attempt to understand the solar system as a celestial symphony written and conducted by God. The ancient Pythagoreans had discovered the mathematical regularities underlying musical harmonies; Kepler sought to relate these harmonies to the structure of the solar system. For instance, he found that the ratio of the minimum and maximum angular speed of Saturn is approximately 4:5, corresponding to the musical chord known as the major third. Similarly, the ratio of Jupiter's slowest to its fastest angular speed corresponds to a minor third, Mars' represents the quint, and so on. He then compared the extreme angular speeds of different planets and managed to construct the intervals of the complete musical scale. Finally, he declared that when several planets are simultaneously at the extreme points of their respective orbits, this scheme gives rise to a motet with each planet singing its assigned part. He concluded:

> The heavenly motions are nothing but a continuous song for several voices (perceived by the intellect, not the ear). . . . It is, therefore, no longer surprising that man, in imitation of his creator, has at last discovered the art of figured song, which was unknown to the ancients. Man wanted . . . to partake of his joy by making music in the imitation of God.[20]

This musical theory of the cosmos was published in a book titled *The Harmony of the World*. Explaining Kepler's concept of "harmony," one historian writes:

> The feeling of harmony arises when there occurs a matching of the perceived order with the corresponding innate archetype. The archetype itself is part of the mind of God and was impressed on the human soul by the Deity when He created man in his own image. The kinship with Plato's doctrine of the ideal forms is clear.[21]

A particularly striking result of Kepler's contradictory philosophic premises can be seen in his views on the cause of ocean tides. Qua scientist, he started from observational evidence and searched for a physical cause. The correlation between the tides and the orbit of the moon led him to the correct idea that the tides are caused by an attractive force exerted by the moon on Earth's oceans. However, when he considered the same problem from the perspective of his Platonic/Christian mysticism, he searched for a spiritual cause. He speculated that God endowed the planets with souls, and he explained the ocean tides as due to the breathing of the animated Earth body. The two explanations are poles apart—as far apart as the philosophic ideas that led to them. "Two Keplers, so to speak, face each other," writes his biographer, Max Caspar. "Both pursue to its final consequence one thought which they have caught hold of or which, rather, has caught hold of them. With the one Kepler it was the thought of gravitation, with the other that of the Earth soul. Now they collide. What can they tell each other? The contradiction is unresolved."[22] Hence we have the spectacle of a great but conflicted mind that was simultaneously pulled in opposite directions, with one path leading to crucial discoveries and the other to dead ends.

Thus Kepler's legacy involves much more than his three laws of planetary motion. By following two opposite methods and showing us the results, he unwittingly conducted an experiment in philosophy of science. Specifically, he tested the nature of mathematics: Is it the key to grasping causal connections in this world, or the key to a supernatural realm of abstractions?

The results of the experiment could not have been more decisive.

The Power of Mathematics

What knowledge of astronomy is possible without mathematics?

We can look back to the beginning of recorded history for the answer. Ancient Babylonian shepherds knew the constellations of stars and could describe their annual movements, and they could give rough descriptions of the changing positions of the planets, the sun, and the moon. For instance, a well-informed shepherd might say: Mars is now in constellation X, a little above and to the east of star Y; it will continue to move slowly westward for about the next two full moons, and then it will resume its normal eastward course.

Notice that even the ancient shepherd could not escape entirely from mathematics; the above description includes a time measurement in which the movement of Mars is compared quantitatively to the phases of the moon. The shepherd used the sky as his compass and clock, and even his primitive knowledge had to be quantified in order to serve his purposes. However, his use of mathematics was minimal (i.e., simple counting), and the state of his knowledge reflects what is possible without measuring instruments and higher mathematics.

Of course, the shepherd's knowledge does not qualify as science; it consisted of disconnected observations with no understanding of causes. A science is an integrated body of knowledge, and in the physical sciences this integration is made possible by mathematics. In astronomy, the process starts when the observational data are expressed in terms of numbers denoting latitudes and longitudes of celestial bodies (at numerically specified times). These numbers (e.g., Brahe's data) are then integrated by means of a causal theory (e.g., Kepler's theory of the solar system). One scholar has eloquently summarized the essence of what Kepler did with Brahe's measurements: "Kepler brought order out of this chaos. He had hunted out the laws uniting these numbers, so that they no longer stand together unrelated but rather each can be calculated from the other."[23] The chaos was transformed into order by first expressing the observations numerically, then using geometry and algebra to deduce further numerical relationships, and finally arriving at equations that are the laws of planetary motion. The entire process was mathematical from beginning to end.

Only by means of mathematics could Kepler relate the positions and movements of celestial bodies. Let us look again at his laws and examine them from this perspective.

The law of elliptical orbits states a relationship that can be written as follows (see Figure 8):

$$r = a + c \, (\cos \beta)$$

where

r = the planet's distance from the sun,
a = the major radius,

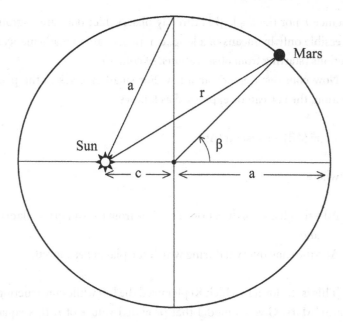

Figure 8. Kepler discovered that the orbit of Mars is described by the equation $r = a + c (\cos \beta)$, which is an ellipse with the sun at a focus.

c = the distance from the sun to the center of the ellipse, and
β = the angle between the line of apsides and the line from the center to the planet.

The equation expresses a numerical relationship between two variables: the distance r and the angle β (the other terms are constants). In the process of reasoning from observations to the law, Kepler first discovered this equation and only later realized that it describes an ellipse with the sun at a focus. At the beginning of the seventeenth century, the algebraic equations describing geometric figures were not yet known. In order to understand the solar system, Kepler found it necessary to pioneer the branch of mathematics that would become known as analytic geometry.

Notice that there is no relationship between these distances and angles that can be observed and described in a qualitative way. Neither the distance r nor the angle β is directly observable; both are cognitively accessible only by means of a long, complex chain of mathematical deductions (starting from observations, of course).

Now consider Kepler's area law. For small changes in the planet's position, the law can be expressed as follows:

$$r^2 (\Delta\theta) = \text{constant} (\Delta t)$$

where

$\Delta\theta$ = the change in direction of the line from the sun to the planet, and

Δt = the time interval during which the planet has moved.

This is the form in which Kepler used the law while constructing the orbit of Mars. Given a model that provided values of r, this equation enabled him to calculate the angular position change during any given time interval (by laboriously summing the changes during small time intervals). And, again, the law relates variables (r and θ) of which we have no awareness except by means of mathematics.

Recall the way in which the above two laws complemented each other in the discovery process. While developing his model of Earth's orbit, Kepler arrived at the area law without knowing whether it was an exact truth or merely a very good approximation. He then used the law to predict angular positions of Mars and compare them to observed angular positions. This revealed errors of eight minutes arc in the circular model of Mars' orbit—which led to the discovery that planetary orbits are ellipses. Finally, after discovering the shape of Mars' orbit, Kepler then proved that the area law is indeed exact. In this way, the laws were discovered together, with each playing a part in validating the other.

Most importantly, the role of mathematics in this discovery process was *fundamental*. Astronomers did not begin by grasping the structure of the solar system in some rough, qualitative way and then use mathematics merely to fill in the quantitative details. Rather, the reverse is true: *It was the quantitative details—such as the small errors of eight minutes arc—that led to a grasp of the basic principles.*

Finally, consider Kepler's third law, which can be expressed as follows:

$$a^3 / T^2 = \text{constant (i.e., the same number for all planets)}$$

Recall that Copernicus had compared the planetary orbits and emphasized that a planet farther from the sun moves slower. However, such a qualitative statement is of little value except insofar as it motivates the search for a mathematical law. As we shall see in the next chapter, Copernicus' statement would have been useless to Newton; on the other hand, Kepler's third law enabled Newton to discover universal gravitation. Once again, we see mathematics as the means of discovering and expressing causal connections—and, ultimately, as the means of integrating such causal laws into a fundamental theory.

Mathematics enabled the founders of modern science to extract the full meaning of their observations, and the results were often very surprising. These results are implicit in the original observations—but without mathematics such implications would remain hidden forever.

Proof of Kepler's Theory

Although Kepler cited very strong evidence in support of his laws of planetary motion, he could not validly claim that his theory of the solar system was proven.

The obstacle to proof was the conflict between Kepler's astronomy and his physics. Recall that he believed motion is caused by a force in the direction of the motion; in particular, he thought that Earth was pushed around in its orbit by the solar force. Since Earth moves very quickly, this force must be quite strong. It is difficult to imagine how we could be pushed in this way without feeling it or observing any effects. Furthermore, Kepler hypothesized that the solar force is magnetic in nature. If this were true, then all nonmagnetic bodies (including ourselves) would be left behind as the magnetic Earth was pushed away. Thus Kepler could not answer the traditional objections to the movement of Earth, and therefore he could not achieve the integration of astronomy and physics that was necessary for proof of his theory.

Galileo's physics, unfortunately, was not published until after Kepler's death. Galileo understood that forces cause *changes in motion*, not motion itself. Therefore Earth, its atmosphere, and its inhabitants can move together at high speed without being subjected to a pushing force and its potentially catastrophic effects. This was one of Galileo's great achievements: He provided the foundation in physics that was necessary to make sense of the heliocentric theory.

In addition, the discoveries Galileo made with the newly invented telescope provided further evidence for the theory. When he directed his telescope at Venus, he observed a full cycle of phases—which implies that Venus orbits the sun (in direct contradiction to Ptolemy's theory). He discovered that Jupiter was a miniature Copernican system, with four smaller moons orbiting the large planet. Also, his analysis of sunspots and of the eclipses of Jupiter's moons provided strong evidence for the movement of Earth. These discoveries were made in the years 1610–13, immediately following Kepler's publication of his first two laws.[24]

Despite Galileo's understanding of motion and his telescopic observations, he also failed to grasp the full proof of the heliocentric theory. He was dismissive of Kepler's mysticism, and he made the tragic mistake of throwing out the baby with the bathwater. He never understood that Kepler's other side—the scientist—had revolutionized astronomy by discovering the causal laws of planetary motion. So Galileo, in his effort to establish the heliocentric theory, was left defending Copernicus—but the Copernican theory retained arbitrary, noncausal features such as epicycles and therefore it could not be proven.

Thus there was a brief period (about three decades) during which Kepler's theory of the solar system had a peculiar status: The pieces of a full proof had been discovered, yet no individual had grasped all the pieces and put them together. This integration was finally achieved in the 1640s and 1650s as scientists accepted the laws of both Galileo and Kepler.

Then the stage was set for Isaac Newton.

4.

Newton's Integration

Galileo and Kepler swept aside the old conceptual debris and laid the foundation for modern science. The unnatural categories of "natural" and "violent" motion, the strange celestial apparatus of circles on eccentric circles driven around by vacant points—it was cleared away to make room for a new structure, built by means of the new experimental and mathematical method. We have seen the first pieces of this new structure: Galileo's kinematics and Kepler's astronomy.

We have also seen the first steps taken toward integrating the sciences of physics and astronomy. Earth was identified as one of the planets, and the telescope revealed that some celestial bodies have Earth-like characteristics: Our moon has mountains and valleys, Jupiter has moons, and the sun rotates. Nevertheless, at this early stage the connection between the terrestrial and celestial realms was tenuous. Although Galileo had used the "relativity of motion" to make sense of the Earth's movement, there was nothing else to connect his laws of terrestrial motion with Kepler's laws of planetary motion.

How does one identify fundamental connections between phenomena that seem so radically different—for instance, between an apple falling or a pendulum bob swinging and a planet orbiting in an ellipse? The key was to discover a mathematical theory relating motions to the forces that cause them. This task was extraordinarily ambitious; in addition to the need for crucial new experiments and more accurate astronomical data, it required the development of new concepts and new mathematical methods. When it was finally completed, the modern science of physics had been created—and celestial bodies took their place among its subjects, ruled by its laws.

The Development of Dynamics

Newton began with a problem that was simple enough to solve, yet complex enough to yield crucial new insights. He began by analyzing the form of motion that the Greeks had regarded as perfect: uniform circular motion. In one sense, it *was* perfect—it was perfectly suited to expose the errors of Newton's predecessors and illuminate the principles of a new dynamics.

As we saw in Chapter 2, Galileo never grasped that bodies move with constant speed *in a straight line* in the absence of all external forces. Lacking the concept "gravity," he suggested that horizontal motion at constant speed ultimately meant motion in a circle around Earth, which he thought could occur in the absence of an external force. In Chapter 3, we saw that Kepler never grasped that any motion could occur in the absence of a force; he assumed that every motion is the result of an external push in the direction of the motion. In Newton's analysis of circular motion, he identified and rejected both of these errors.

Prior to Newton, the case of the moon circling Earth was regarded as entirely different from the case of a hawk circling its prey. Newton, however, ascended to a level of abstraction that treated these two phenomena as the same; his goal was to analyze circular motion as such, and apply what he found to any and all instances of it. His policy here is expressed in the dictum he would later identify as a "rule of reasoning": "[T]o the same natural effects we must, as far as possible, assign the same causes."[1]

A major part of Newton's motivation for studying circular motion was the planetary orbits, which are nearly circular. But he did not begin his analysis by considering the planets; he began with cases in which the cause of the motion is much easier to identify. He considered a weight attached to the end of a rope and swung around in a circle, and a ball rolling around in a circle inside a bowl. In these cases, what is the cause of the circular motion? For the weight, it is the tension in the rope; the man holding the rope must pull inward. At the instant he lets go, the weight will no longer move in a circle, but will fly off horizontally in a straight line (while the force of gravity pulls it to Earth). For the ball in the bowl, the circular motion is caused by the inward push exerted by the surface of the bowl. If the ball escapes the bowl, then it too will initially fly off in a straight line. In both cases the uniform circular motion of the body is sustained by a constant force directed toward the center of the circle.

In a notebook, Newton wrote an early version of what later became his first law of motion: "A quantity will always move on in the same straight line (not changing the determination or celerity of its motion) unless some external cause divert it."[2] The external cause is a force, i.e., some push or pull.

Newton recognized that it was crucial to distinguish between the type of motion that results from a force and the type that can occur in the absence of force. The concepts of motion used by Galileo were inadequate for this purpose. Recall that Galileo's definition of "constant acceleration" applied only to the case of motion in a constant direction. For him, acceleration meant change of speed. In the case of uniform circular motion, the speed of the body is constant and therefore its "Galilean acceleration" is zero. However, there is something essentially the same about the cases of acceleration studied by Galileo and the case of uniform circular motion: In both there is a change in the motion that results from an applied force on the body. An expanded concept of "acceleration" was needed to integrate these instances.

In order to study and understand the effects of forces, motion had to be characterized in terms of both its magnitude and direction. Thus the concept "velocity" was formed, and "acceleration" was then defined as rate of change of velocity. Both velocity and acceleration are vector quantities, i.e., they are integrations of magnitude and direction. The forma-tion of these concepts was a revolutionary step that made possible the science of dynamics.

Armed with these concepts, Newton could ask: What is the accel-eration of a body that moves with constant speed in a circle? From sym-metry, he knew that the acceleration is constant and always directed toward the center of the circle. But what is its magnitude? He considered a short time interval in which the body moves through a small arc on the circle. During this time, the body has deviated from a straight path by a small distance, d. For cases of constant acceleration, Galileo had given the mathematical law relating the distance d to the acceleration and the time interval. Using Galileo's law and classical geometry, Newton was able to derive an equation that expressed the acceleration as a function of the arc chord, the time interval, and the radius of the circle.

In his next step, Newton made use of a new concept—"limit"—that lies at the foundation of calculus, the branch of mathematics he had dis-covered. As the above time interval is made progressively shorter, the chord of the arc becomes ever more nearly equal to the arc itself. In the "limit," i.e., as the time interval approaches zero, the ratio of the chord length to the arc length approaches one. Therefore in this limit the chord can be replaced with the arc. Newton made this substitution and ar-rived at his law of uniform circular motion: The magnitude of the ac-celeration at any point on the circle is equal to the speed of the body squared divided by the radius of the circle.

Newton assumed nothing about the specific nature of the force caus-ing this acceleration. His analysis relied only upon the fact that a force causes a body to deviate from motion in a straight line at constant speed, and hence for the purpose of studying forces we must define acceleration as indicated earlier. Therefore his law is unrestricted by the physical causes operating in any particular case; it is applicable to *any* body mov-ing uniformly in a circle.

It was at this stage that Newton turned his attention to the planets. If the orbits are approximated as circular and if we express the speed as a function of radius and period, then Newton's law implies that a planet's acceleration is proportional to its orbital radius divided by its period squared. He then recalled that, according to Kepler's third law, the period squared is proportional to the radius cubed. By combining these two relationships, he derived an extraordinary result: The sun exerts an attractive force on each of the planets, causing accelerations that are inversely proportional to the square of the planet's distance from the sun.

Next he considered the moon and its approximately circular orbit around Earth. Such motion, he knew, implies that Earth exerts an attractive force on the moon. Since he was always seeking to connect disparate but related facts, Newton thought to ask: Is Earth's attractive force of the same nature as the solar force, i.e., does it cause accelerations that also vary as the inverse square of the distance? If Earth had multiple moons at different distances, then the question could be answered by comparing the different accelerations. But we have only the one moon—so how could Newton determine the variation of acceleration with distance?

The answer lies in the concept of acceleration itself. The concept identifies an essential similarity between uniform circular motion and free fall: A body in circular motion is continuously falling away from a straight path and accelerating toward the center of the circle. Thus the moon falls toward Earth with a constant acceleration, as does a body dropped near the surface of Earth. Galileo had studied terrestrial free fall, and it was this acceleration that Newton could compare to that of the moon. This is an historic example of a concept functioning as a green light to induction. Newton's legendary comparison between the moon and the falling apple was demanded by the (inductively reached) vector concept of acceleration.

The quantities needed to make the comparison were known. The distance of the apple from the center of Earth is one Earth radius and the distance to the moon is sixty Earth radii. If the acceleration varies as the inverse square of the distance, then the apple's acceleration will be greater than the moon's acceleration by the factor $(60)^2$. Using rough data about free fall and the size of Earth, Newton calculated the ratio of accelerations and found approximate agreement with the inverse square law. Thus terrestrial gravity seemed to be the same force that holds the moon in its orbit and that the sun exerts on the planets. Kepler's dream of one integrated science encompassing physics and astronomy was no longer merely a dream; with this calculation, it became a real possibility.

This was the birth of the idea of universal gravitation, but it was far from being the proof of it. At this early stage, Newton had many more questions than answers. For example, what about the fact that the actual orbits are ellipses, not circles? And what is the justification for using one Earth radius as the distance between the apple and Earth? Much of Earth is closer to the apple, and much is farther away; why would Earth attract from its center? Furthermore, if gravity is truly universal and each bit of matter attracts all other matter, the implications and complexities are daunting. For example, what is the effect of the moon's attraction of Earth, or of the sun's attraction of the moon, or of a planet's attraction of other planets? What about strange bodies like comets, which move so differently?

The main difficulty that Newton confronted was not that such questions were as yet unanswered. The difficulty was that they were not yet answerable—not without a much deeper understanding of the relation between force and motion. It is one thing to say that a push or pull is necessary to change a body's velocity; it is quite another feat to identify the exact mathematical law relating the external force to the body's acceleration, and it is still another feat to identify a law that tells us what happens to the body exerting the force. Newton was just beginning to develop the cognitive tools he would need to prove universal gravitation.

We have seen how Newton grasped that a body's velocity remains constant in the absence of an external force, which is his first law of motion. Now let us follow the main steps of reasoning that led to his second and third laws of motion.

The concept "force" originates from sensations of pressure that we experience directly when we hold a weight or when we push or pull a body. Force has magnitude and direction, and scientists learned to measure the magnitude using balances, steelyards, and spring scales. The concept "acceleration," on the other hand, is a more advanced development. It was Galileo who first explained how linear acceleration could be calculated from measured times and distances, and we have now seen the concept expanded from a scalar to a vector quantity. At this stage, when Newton inquires into the mathematical relation of force and acceleration, both quantities are clearly defined and independently measurable.

Furthermore, a key fact had already been discovered. Force is directly proportional to acceleration, and this had been proven by experiments in which the force was varied in a known way and the resulting acceleration was measured. Galileo's investigations of a ball rolling down an inclined plane provided the first such experiments.

Galileo described a procedure for directly measuring the force on the ball.[3] First, he said, attach the ball to a known weight by means of a string and attach a pulley to the top of the inclined plane. Place the ball on the inclined plane with the string over the pulley and the weight hanging vertically. Then adjust the weight until it exactly balances the ball; this weight is the force on the ball in the direction of its constrained motion down the plane. The result of this measurement is what one might expect: The force on the ball is simply the component of its weight in the direction of the incline, i.e., it is the weight of the ball multiplied by the height-to-length ratio of the plane.

Therefore we can quadruple the force on the ball simply by quadrupling the height of the plane (while keeping the length the same). If we do so, we find that the time of descent is half what it was before, which implies that the acceleration has quadrupled—i.e., it has increased by the same factor as the force. Alternatively, by using Galileo's method for measuring the final speed of the ball (see Chapter 2), we can demonstrate by experiment that the initial height is proportional to the square of the final speed. With a little algebra, it can be shown that this relationship also implies that force is directly proportional to acceleration.

The pendulum provides another experiment that leads to the same conclusion. The period of a cycloid pendulum is independent of amplitude, and it can be demonstrated mathematically that this fact also implies a direct proportionality between force and acceleration. Because the inclined plane and pendulum experiments were so well-known,

Newton took this proportionality for granted and never bothered to present its inductive proof in any detail.

Of course, he did not yet have a law of motion in the form of an equation. There was still a concept missing, and one can sense Newton's frustration in some of his early notes. At one point, he wrote: "As the body A is to the body B so must the power or efficacy, vigor, strength, or virtue of the cause which begets the same quantity of velocity. . . ."[4] As he was writing, Newton must have been asking himself: As *precisely what about* the body A is to *precisely what about* the body B? Nobody had yet formed a clear concept of "mass."

The Greeks had proposed that all matter is endowed with either "heaviness" or "lightness." The elements earth and water were claimed to be intrinsically heavy, whereas air and fire are intrinsically light. These properties were regarded as the cause of natural, vertical motion. The invalid Greek concept of "lightness" was a red light that stopped anyone from discovering that all matter has the property "mass." In 1643, Evangelista Torricelli performed a crucial experiment that removed this red light from the path of modern physics.

Torricelli sought to explain a fact that was well-known to mining engineers: A pump cannot lift water more than thirty-four feet above its natural level. The first question Torricelli asked himself was: Why does a pump work at all? In other words, when one end of a tube is inserted into water and the air is pumped out of the tube, why does the water rise into the tube? The commonly accepted answer was that "nature abhors a vacuum," but this answer implies that the absence of matter in the tube is the cause of the water's movement, i.e., "nothingness" is literally pulling the water up the tube. It was obvious to Torricelli that those who tried to explain the effect by reference to nothingness had in fact explained nothing.

Instead, Torricelli identified something that did explain the effect: the weight of the air pressing down on the water surface. When air is removed from the tube, the atmosphere outside pressing on the water surface pushes water up the tube. It is similar to the action of a lever; the weight of the air will raise that same weight of water (per unit surface area). Hence the weight of the entire atmosphere above a particular surface must be equal to the weight of thirty-four feet of water over that surface.

Torricelli's idea implied that air pressure would lift the same weight of any fluid. For example, 2.5 feet of mercury weighs the same as thirty-four feet of water; therefore, when an evacuated tube is placed in a pool of mercury, the mercury should rise 2.5 feet up the tube. Torricelli did the experiment and observed precisely this result. Note that he used the method of agreement here: The same cause (i.e., the same weight of air) leads to the same effect (i.e., raises the same weight of fluid). Later experiments by Blaise Pascal and Robert Boyle used the method of difference to arrive at the same conclusion. These experiments demonstrated that decreasing the amount of air above the fluid surface results in less fluid rising in the tube; i.e., as we remove the cause the effect disappears.

Thus it was proven that even air is heavy. Contrary to the Greeks, there is no such property as absolute "lightness." When something rises in air, it does so because it is less heavy than the air it displaces. In other words, such "natural" rising is explained by Archimedes' principle of buoyancy, a principle that applies to air as well as to water. After the work of Torricelli, scientists accepted the fact that all matter is heavy.

The next step was to clarify the meaning of "heaviness." The Greeks had regarded heaviness as an intrinsic property of a body. However, to weigh a body is to measure the magnitude of its "downward push," and this depends on something other than the body itself. As we have seen, Newton realized that heaviness is a measure of Earth's gravitational attraction, and this force varies with the position of the body relative to Earth. Additional evidence for this conclusion was discovered in the 1670s. Two astronomers, Edmund Halley and Jean Richer, independently discovered that pendulum clocks swing more slowly near the equator than at higher latitudes, and they correctly inferred that pendulum bobs weigh less near the equator. Therefore "heaviness" arises from three factors: the nature of the body, the nature of Earth, and the spatial relationship between the body and Earth.

But what is the property of the body that contributes to its heaviness? Newton identified it as the body's "quantity of matter," or "mass." His reasoning made use of both the method of difference and the method of agreement. First, he considered two solid bodies of the same material, weighed at the same location. Their weights are found to be precisely proportional to their volumes, and the constant of proportionality is an invariant characteristic of each pure, incompressible material. Therefore the weight of a body is proportional to its "quantity of matter"; by doubling the volume we have doubled the amount of matter, and the weight has doubled (method of difference). Second, Newton considered a compressible material such as snow. We can weigh a sample of snow, then compress it to a smaller volume, and then weigh it again. The quantity of matter has remained the same, and we find that the weight is the same (method of agreement).

Newton then asked how a body's mass affects its motion when a force is applied. It is obvious that the mass does affect the motion; in order to cause a particular acceleration, a greater force is required for a greater quantity of matter (e.g., pushing a car requires more effort than pushing a bicycle). But what is the exact relationship? In order to answer the question, he needed an experiment in which the acceleration is held constant while the mass of the body and the applied force are varied. Newton did not have to look far to find such experiments; Galileo had done them when he investigated free fall.

From the top of a tower, Galileo had dropped two lead balls that differed greatly in size and weight. Let us assume that the larger ball had a volume ten times that of the smaller ball; therefore, its quantity of matter, or mass, was ten times greater. The force on each ball is simply its weight; by using a balance or a steelyard, we can determine that the weight of the larger ball is ten times the weight of the smaller ball. So, considering the larger ball relative to the smaller ball, we have increased both the force and the mass by a factor of ten. Yet Galileo demonstrated that the acceleration of free fall remains the same. We know that acceleration is exactly proportional to force, so it must be exactly inversely proportional to mass (so that the factors of ten cancel). This result accords with our common experience; it implies that for a body of greater mass a proportionally greater force is required to achieve a particular acceleration. Newton thus arrived at his second law of motion: The applied force is equal to the product of the body's mass and its acceleration, or $F = mA$.

The scope of this generalization is breathtaking. It may seem astonishing that Newton could arrive at such an all-encompassing, fundamental law from the observations and experiments that have been described. But once one has the idea of grouping together all pushes and pulls under the concept "force," and of grouping together all changes of velocity under the concept "acceleration," and of ascribing to all bodies a property called "mass," and of searching for a mathematical relationship among these measured quantities—then a few well-designed experiments can give rise to a law. At this stage, however, the proof of this universal law is not yet complete. It depends not only on the foregoing, but on all the evidence presented in this section and the next; i.e., the law is part of a theory that must be evaluated as a whole.

We have seen how this law rests on Galileo's principle that all bodies fall with equal acceleration. Because this principle was so crucial to his theory of motion, Newton demanded that it be established by experiments more accurate than those of Galileo. He wished to prove beyond any doubt that a body's inertial mass—the property by which it resists acceleration—is exactly proportional to its weight.

Newton realized that the pendulum provided the means for such an experimental proof. He deduced from $F = mA$ that the inertial mass of a pendulum bob is proportional to its weight multiplied by the period squared (assuming the length of the pendulum is held constant). Thus if the period is always the same for any and all pendulum bobs, then inertial mass must be exactly proportional to weight. By using a small container as a pendulum bob, Newton varied both the mass and material of the bobs; he filled the container with gold, silver, glass, sand, salt, wood, water, and even wheat. All the bobs swung back and forth with the same period, and he performed the experiment with such care that he could easily have detected a difference of one part in a thousand. (The creator of modern physics had a passion for accurate measurement.)

So far, Newton had been focused on the movement of one body subject to an applied force. At this stage, he turned his attention to the force itself and its origin: It is exerted by another body. What happens to this other body?

In order to answer the question, Newton needed to study the interaction of two bodies under conditions where the forces are known and the subsequent motion of both can be accurately measured. He devised the perfect experiment using a double pendulum with colliding bobs. He used pendulums with a length of ten feet, and he carefully measured and compensated for the small effects of air resistance. He varied the mass of the bobs and their initial amplitudes, and then measured their final amplitudes after the collision.

Galileo had proven that a bob's speed at the bottom of the swing is proportional to the chord of the arc through which it has swung. At the moment of collision, therefore, Newton knew the relative speed of both bobs. Furthermore, from his measurements of the final amplitudes, he could compute the relative speed of both bobs immediately after the collision. The results of the experiment showed that the mass of the first bob multiplied by the change of its speed is equal to the mass of the second bob multiplied by the change of *its* speed. Since the force exerted on each bob is equal to the product of its mass and its change of speed, Newton had proven that the bobs exert forces on each other that are equal in magnitude and oppositely directed.

Newton performed this experiment with pendulum bobs made of steel, glass, cork, and even tightly wound wool. In his choice of materials, he deliberately varied the hardness of the bobs and thereby proved that his law applied to both elastic and inelastic collisions. Since all collisions fall into one of these two categories, his generalization followed: Whenever two bodies exert forces on each other by means of direct contact, the forces are equal in magnitude and oppositely directed.

Newton then investigated the case of noncontact forces, i.e., forces that act over distances by imperceptible means. He attached a magnet and some iron to a piece of wood and floated the wood in calm water. The magnet and the iron were separated by a short distance and each exerted a strong attractive force on the other. Yet the vessel did not move—implying that the two forces were equal in magnitude and oppositely directed, thus giving rise to zero net force.

Does the law also apply to bodies that attract each other gravitationally? Newton answered that it does and gave a convincing argument. Since Earth attracts all materials on its surface, it was reasonable to suppose (and it would later be proven) that every part of Earth attracts all other parts. So consider the mutual attraction, say, of Asia and South America. If these two forces were not equal and opposite, there would be a net force on Earth as a whole—and hence Earth would cause itself to accelerate. This self-acceleration would continue indefinitely and lead to disturbances in Earth's orbit. But no such disturbances are observed; on the contrary, Earth's acceleration is determined by its position relative to other bodies (primarily the sun). Therefore the mutual attractive forces exerted by any two parts of Earth must be equal and opposite. (Newton could also have pointed out that unbalanced forces would lead to other effects that are not observed, e.g., asymmetries in Earth's shape and in ocean tides.)

At this point, Newton had shown that his law applies to gravitational forces, magnetic forces, elastic collisions, and inelastic collisions—i.e., he gathered evidence over the range of known forces and found no exceptions. He had thus arrived at his third law of motion: All forces are two-body interactions, and the bodies always exert forces on each other that are equal in magnitude and oppositely directed.

When considering only one body, the concept "velocity" identified that which remained the same in the absence of an external force (this is the first law). In the case of two interacting bodies, Newton identified a total "quantity of motion" that remains the same before and after the interaction. This quantity, which we now call "momentum," is the product of a body's mass and its velocity. Newton's third law implies that the total momentum of two interacting bodies always remains the same, provided there is no external force. Furthermore, this "conservation of momentum" principle applies even to a complex system of many interacting bodies; since it is true for each individual interaction, it is also true of the sum.

After forming the concept of "momentum," Newton could give a more general formulation of his second law. In its final form, which is applicable to a body *or system of bodies*, the law states that the net external force is equal to the rate of change of the total momentum. This form of the law can be applied in a straightforward way to more complex cases (e.g., imagine two bodies that collide and explode into many bodies).

Newton recognized that his three laws of motion are intimately related. We have seen that the third law prohibits the self-acceleration of Earth—but notice that such a phenomenon is also prohibited by the first and second laws, which identify the cause of acceleration as an *external* force. Given the fact that forces are two-body interactions, consistency with the second law demands that these interactions conform to the third law. The laws name related aspects of one integrated theory of motion; indeed, when the second law is given its general formulation, both the first and third laws can be viewed as its corollaries. Hence the laws mutually reinforce one another and therefore the experimental evidence for the third law also counts as evidence for the second law.

I have outlined the main steps by which Newton induced his laws of motion. In their final statement, the laws appear deceptively simple. But we can now appreciate that they are very far from self-evident. In order to reach them, Newton needed complex, high-level concepts that did not exist prior to the seventeenth century, concepts such as "acceleration," "limit," "gravity," "mass," and "momentum." He needed a variety of experiments that studied free fall, inclined-plane motion, pendulums, projectiles, air pressure, double pendulums, and floating magnets. He relied upon the observations that had led to the heliocentric theory of the solar system, upon the experience of pulling inward in order to swing a body in a circle, upon the observations that determined the distance to the moon, upon the instruments invented for measuring force, and even upon chemical knowledge of how to purify materials (since this played a role in forming the concept "mass"). His laws apply to everything that we observe in motion, and he induced them from knowledge ranging across that enormous database.

For the past century, however, some philosophers, physicists, and historians of science have claimed that the laws of motion are not really laws at all; rather, they are merely definitions accepted by convention. This view derives from empiricist philosophy and was famously advocated by Ernst Mach.[5] The empiricists regard the second law as a convenient definition of the concept "force," which allegedly has no meaning except as a name for the product of mass and acceleration; similarly, they argue that the third law amounts to a convenient definition of "mass." Those advocating such views have left themselves the inconvenient task of answering some obvious questions. Why is a particular definition "convenient," whereas any alternative definition would be cognitively disastrous? What about static forces that exist and can be measured in the absence of acceleration? How is it possible that the concept "force" was formed millennia before the concepts "mass" and "acceleration"? No answers have been forthcoming from Mach's disciples.

Newton did not anticipate the skepticism that became rampant in the post-Kantian era. He regarded as obvious the fact that the laws of motion are general truths reached by induction, and therefore he did not go out of his way to emphasize the point. Indeed, he regarded the laws of motion as uncontroversial, which is why his discussion of them in the *Principia* is so concise.

He viewed these laws as the means to his end, not the end itself. The laws enable us to reason from observed motions to the forces that cause them, and then reason from these known forces to all their diverse effects. As Newton put it, "[T]he whole burden of philosophy seems to consist in this—from the phenomena of motions to investigate the forces of nature, and then from these forces to demonstrate the other phenomena."[6] He made his meaning clear by providing a grand-scale example of this program.

The Discovery of Universal Gravitation

The *Principia* presents a long and complex argument for the law of universal gravitation. Today the law itself is familiar to any educated person. Newton's argument and its epistemological implications, however, are less familiar. I will outline the steps of his reasoning in this section, and discuss some of the implications in the next.

Newton began by inferring the nature of the solar force from Kepler's laws of planetary motion. Of course, this had been Kepler's goal—but without an understanding of dynamics and without the method of differential calculus, it had been unattainable. Three-quarters of a century later, Newton had the right tools for the job.

His first step was to prove a result that is initially somewhat surprising: Kepler's area law is true even in the absence of a force. Using trigonometry, Newton showed that a line from any fixed point to a body moving with constant velocity will sweep out equal areas in equal times. So he immediately established a connection between his dynamics and Kepler's planetary theory: Inertial motion conforms to the area law. From this result alone, it was clear that this law has broad application beyond planetary motion.

In his next step, Newton assumed that the body is subject to a series of impact forces that are always directed toward a fixed point. He showed that the area law is true for this case as well. He then let the time interval between these impacts approach zero, and thereby proved that Kepler's law holds for any continuous force that is always directed along the line connecting the body to some fixed point (such forces are called "central forces"). It makes no difference how the force varies with distance, or whether it is attractive or repulsive. So long as the force has no tangential (or sideways) component, the area law is valid.

So the area law tells us the direction of the solar force, but it contains no information about the magnitude. It was Kepler's law of elliptical orbits that enabled Newton to prove that the magnitude of the solar force varies as the inverse square of the distance. Those who study the details of this proof will be impressed by Newton's mathematical genius. For our purposes, however, we can pass over these details and merely identify the essential elements of the proof.

First, the solar force is related to the planet's acceleration by Newton's second law of motion. Second, for any short time interval during which the acceleration may be regarded as constant, Galileo gave the law relating the acceleration to the time interval and to the distance that the body falls (in this case, the planet's "fall" is its movement away from a straight path and toward the sun). Third, Kepler's area law enabled Newton to replace time intervals with areas, thereby transforming a problem of dynamics into a problem of geometry. Finally, certain theorems about ellipses (discovered in antiquity by Apollonius) enabled Newton to relate the small distance the planet "falls" during the interval to other distances defining its location on the ellipse. Therefore he had all the pieces that he needed: He knew the relation between force and acceleration, and he could express the acceleration in terms of the geometric properties of the ellipse. In the end, this mathematical complexity led to a simple result: The sun exerts an attractive force on the planets that varies as the inverse square of the distance.

Just as with the area law, Newton recognized that the law of elliptical orbits is a special case of a more general truth. The geometric properties that Newton had used are not unique to ellipses; they are general properties of conic sections, i.e., they also apply to parabolas and hyperbolas. Therefore the solar force will not necessarily cause a body to move in an elliptical orbit; the path may be a parabola or a hyperbola instead. In general, an inverse square attractive force causes a body to move in a conic section; the particular conic section is determined by the initial position and velocity of the body. If the initial conditions are such that the body is captured by the sun's gravitational field, then the orbit will be an ellipse (or a circle). However, if the body's velocity is too great, then it will pass through our solar system in a parabolic or hyperbolic path. Newton presented the details, showing how to calculate the path of a body from any set of initial conditions.

Finally, Newton considered Kepler's third law. For an elliptical orbit, he showed that this relationship between the orbital period and the major radius follows from the nature of the solar force. In the proof, he used all the facts that had entered into his proof of the inverse square law, plus he used the inverse square law itself and the well-known expression for the area of an ellipse. Here we see yet another example of an astounding connection established by means of mathematics. There is no way to guess that the orbital period is proportional to the three-halves power of the major radius and that it is entirely independent of the minor radius. This fact is implicit in the premises of Newton's argument, but advanced mathematics is required to make the deduction.

This mathematical analysis had another implication: It showed that Kepler's third law is not exact. In his proof, Newton assumed that the sun is not accelerating. However, his third law of motion implies that the planet exerts an equal and opposite force on the sun, causing it to move in a very small orbit of its own around the center of mass of the two bodies. Newton proved that this effect leads to a slight modification of Kepler's third law; the correction, he showed, depends on the ratio of the planet's mass to the sun's mass. In the case of Jupiter, the most massive planet, the magnitude of this correction is about one part in a thousand.

Newton induced the nature of the solar force from Kepler's laws, and, in the process, he gained a much deeper understanding of those laws. He proved that the area law applies to any two bodies that attract or repel each other; that the law of elliptical orbits can be expanded to a law of conic sections describing the movements of any two bodies attracting by an inverse square law; and that Kepler's third law is very nearly true because the mass of the sun is so much greater than the mass of the planets.

In Newton's analysis, we can see three interrelated aspects of the power of mathematics. First, mathematics enables us to discover new facts (such as the law of gravitation) by deriving further implications of that which is already known. Second, it connects known facts (such as the laws of Galileo and Kepler) that would otherwise stand apart with no relation. Third, it gives crucial insight into the domain over which a generalization is valid—by making clear what the generalization depends upon and what it does not depend upon (as we saw in the case of Kepler's laws).

After inferring the sun's inverse square attraction from the observed planetary motions, Newton investigated force laws that can be inferred from other types of motion. For example, he considered the eccentric circles that astronomers had used since antiquity. He proved that the force required to produce such motion is physically absurd; the attractive force exerted by the sun on a planet would have to depend not only on where the planet is, but also on *where it will be at a later time*. So, even in cases where such a model is consistent with available data, it is ruled out because it violates the law of causality.

Interestingly, Newton proved that an attractive force proportional to distance would cause an elliptical orbit. In this case, however, the sun must be at the center rather than at a focus of the ellipse. Furthermore, all the planets would revolve around the sun with the same period, in marked contrast to the observations. Newton then considered the case of an attractive inverse cube solar force and showed that the resulting orbit would be spiral with a constant angle between the radius and the velocity vector.

The most important of these "counterfactual cases" that Newton analyzed was that of an inverse square force with a small inverse cube term added. Here he showed that the resulting orbits could obey Kepler's laws to a very close approximation. However, Newton was still able to identify a difference between these orbits and those actually observed. When a small inverse cube term is added, the major axis of the ellipse does not remain fixed in space; instead, it slowly rotates at a rate that depends on the magnitude of the inverse cube term.

Newton was not merely flexing his mathematical muscles in this calculation. He realized that if the idea of universal gravitation is correct, then the planetary orbits are not exactly elliptical; a planet's motion will be slightly disturbed by bodies other than the sun. Furthermore, he was keenly aware of the fact that we are always reasoning from data of limited accuracy. While he had already shown that an exactly elliptical orbit implies a solar force that is exactly inverse square, it does not necessarily follow that an approximately elliptical orbit implies such a solar force. Newton was cautious about making such inferences, and so he decided to investigate the effects of a deviation from the inverse square law. By proving that even a small deviation would change the planetary orbits in a way that contradicts the observations, he removed any lingering doubts about the nature of the solar force.

At this stage, Newton turned his attention to bodies other than the sun. Galileo had discovered four moons orbiting Jupiter, and later Christian Huygens and Gian Cassini had discovered five moons orbiting Saturn. Because astronomers had made remarkable improvements in the design of telescopes, Newton had accurate data about these lunar orbits. He found that Kepler's laws applied to these moons as well as to the planets. Most impressively, he showed that for both sets of moons the orbital period squared was precisely proportional to the orbital radius cubed. It follows that Jupiter and Saturn attract their moons with the same type of inverse square force that the sun exerts on the planets.

Newton also cited evidence that the planets attract each other. Astronomers had noticed that there are disturbances in the orbit of Saturn when it is in conjunction with Jupiter. Of course, the idea of universal gravitation explains such disturbances. Jupiter is the most massive of the planets, and at its point of closest approach it exerts a significant pull on Saturn. Newton identified a simple way to improve the model of Saturn's orbit: The focus of the ellipse should be placed at the Sun-Jupiter center of mass, rather than at the sun itself. In this way, Newton reduced the maximum errors in Saturn's angular position to only two minutes arc.

Finally, Newton's focus returned to Earth—and to the origin of his great idea. He once again calculated the relative accelerations of the moon and the apple. In the rough calculation he had performed many years earlier, there had been about a 10 percent discrepancy with the inverse square law. He was now prepared to eliminate the assumptions, the approximations, the inaccuracies in the data—and to see whether Earth's attraction really did vary exactly as the inverse square of the distance.

In his original calculation, Newton had used one Earth radius as the distance between the apple and Earth. This is equivalent to assuming that the spherical Earth attracts as if all of its mass is at the center. But why would it attract in this way? Universal gravitation implies that every bit of matter is independently pulling the apple toward it, with a force that is inversely proportional to the square of its distance from the apple. It seems almost miraculous that all of these independent pulls from every part of Earth are exactly the same as the entire mass of Earth pulling from the center. Without a mathematical proof, Newton was not inclined to believe it.

Today, with the full power of integral calculus available, this proof can be performed by any competent student of physics. It was more challenging for Newton, but he succeeded by constructing a very clever geometrical proof that took full advantage of the symmetry of the sphere. The Earth attracts from its center, he showed, if and only if the attractive force varies as the inverse square of the distance and the mass density of Earth depends only on the distance from the center.

Earlier, his use of one Earth radius for the distance to the apple had been a dubious assumption; now, with his mathematical proof, it was demanded by the idea of universal gravitation. The radius of Earth had been measured accurately, and the value Newton used was very close to the one accepted today. For the distance to the moon, Newton carefully reviewed the independent measurements of several researchers and adopted sixty Earth radii as the best available value. So, if Earth's attraction varies in the same way as the attraction of Jupiter and Saturn and the sun, then the moon's acceleration multiplied by $(60)^2$ should equal the apple's acceleration.

The period of the moon's orbit was known very precisely. Since the orbit is nearly circular, Newton could use his law of circular acceleration (as he had years before). However, this time he added a small correction for the attraction of the sun, which slightly decreased (by one part in 179) his estimate of the acceleration caused by Earth. He also estimated the minor effect of the moon's reciprocal pull on the Earth. When he at last arrived at his final answer and multiplied by $(60)^2$, his predicted value for the gravitational acceleration on Earth's surface was 32.2 ft/sec^2.

Years earlier, Huygens had used pendulums to measure this acceleration very accurately. The measured value matched Newton's calculated value: It was 32.2 ft/sec^2. Newton had proven that terrestrial "heaviness"—the ubiquitous phenomenon known to every toddler—is the same force that moves planets and moons.

Note that it would be invalid if Newton had merely said: "The moon falls toward Earth; the apple falls toward Earth; therefore the cause is the same in both cases." Different causes can sometimes lead to qualitatively similar effects (e.g., a magnet with electric charge on its surface will attract both straw and iron filings, but for different reasons). However, when Newton proves that the moon and the apple fall at rates that are precisely in accordance with a force that varies as the inverse square of the distance from Earth's center—then there can be no doubt that the same cause is at work.

Once Newton proved that the attraction between celestial bodies is the familiar force of terrestrial gravity, then everything known about gravity on Earth was applicable to the celestial force. Therefore the experimental proof that terrestrial gravity is proportional to mass also serves as a proof that the attractive force of any celestial body is proportional to its mass. Furthermore, by Newton's third law, the gravitational interaction must depend on the mass of both attracting bodies in the same way. Thus Newton arrived at the complete law of gravitation: The force varies directly as the product of the masses and inversely as the square of the distance between them.

For the purposes of comparing the acceleration of the moon to that of the apple, Newton could approximate the moon's orbit as circular without introducing any significant error. The orbit can be modeled more accurately, of course, as an ellipse. However, the observational data of astronomers proved that the orbit of the moon is quite complex; it does not precisely obey Kepler's laws. The reason for the anomalies in the orbit is the gravitational pull of the sun; the moon–sun distance differs slightly from the Earth–sun distance, and this causes a small relative acceleration between the moon and Earth.

Newton made an enormous effort to explain the lunar anomalies.

Starting from the fact that the sun's gravitational attraction varies as the inverse square of the distance, he showed that the perturbing accelerations caused by the sun vary as the inverse cube. We have already seen that such a force causes the major axis of the orbit to rotate; from the magnitude of the term, Newton was able to explain the three-degree per month rotation in the moon's orbit that had been observed by astronomers. He also explained the variations in the eccentricity of the orbit, the movement of the points at which the moon crosses the plane of the ecliptic, and the annual variations in these anomalies. His analysis provided very impressive evidence for the law of universal gravitation; in addition to explaining Kepler's laws, he could explain the observed deviations from Kepler's laws.

Newton continued to exploit the moon when he turned his attention to the ocean tides. The correlation of the tides with the position of the moon had been noticed by the first Greek explorers who ventured out into the Atlantic Ocean. Prior to the formation of the concept "gravity," however, the idea that the moon could influence our seas was often dismissed as equivalent to a belief in magic. Newton's discoveries brought about a radical change by identifying the physical cause and thereby making it clear that such an influence was a necessary consequence of natural laws.

Ocean tides are caused by the fact that the moon does not attract all parts of Earth equally. The side of Earth nearest the moon is attracted slightly more than Earth's center (pulling it toward the moon), whereas the opposite side of Earth is attracted less than the center (leaving it farther from the moon). This causes the oceans to bulge on both sides, giving rise to high tides. The bulges are fixed with respect to the moon, but the daily rotation of Earth causes the tides to rise and fall at any particular location. If the moon were stationary, the time between high tides would be twelve hours; the moon's movement increases this time interval to 12.5 hours. Newton pointed out that the sun also causes ocean tides, but he showed that the sun's effect is less than one-third that of the moon.

He was able to explain all the main features of the tides. The tides are greatest when the lunar and solar tides coincide, and this happens when the moon is in opposition or conjunction with the sun (i.e., when the moon is full or new). During half-moons, the tides are least because the sun partially cancels the effect of the moon. He explained the observed variations in the tides that are caused by variations in the distance to the sun, in the distance to the moon, and in the inclination of the moon with respect to the equator. Furthermore, he analyzed the reverse tidal effect on the moon caused by the attraction of Earth. This attraction gives rise to bulges of almost a hundred feet on the near and far sides of the moon. Newton pointed out that Earth's pull on these tidal bulges explains why the same side of the moon always faces Earth.

The tides affect the shape of Earth by raising our oceans by a mere ten feet (at most). Newton realized that his dynamics implied another effect on the shape of Earth that is much greater in magnitude. If Earth's matter is (or once was) sufficiently mobile, then the daily rotation of Earth will cause it to bulge at the equator and flatten at the poles. This must be the case, since otherwise matter that is mobile would move to the equator and the Sahara desert would be at the bottom of a very deep ocean. Given the rate at which Earth spins and some assumption about the distribution of mass within Earth, Newton could use his laws of motion and gravitation to calculate the size of the equatorial bulge.

Of course, there was no data available regarding the variation of mass density within Earth. Newton decided to perform the calculation using a constant density, while explicitly noting that ignorance of this factor caused some uncertainty in the result. He estimated that the equatorial radius exceeded the polar radius by seventeen miles, which is reasonably close to the actual difference of thirteen miles. Thus Earth is an oblate spheroid rather than a sphere, and the size of the effect is such that there should be observable consequences.

In fact, scientists had already observed some of the consequences. Recall, for example, that it was discovered in the 1670s that pendulum clocks swung more slowly near the equator than in Paris or London. Newton explained that the pendulum bobs move slower at the equator for two reasons: The gravitational force is weaker because they are farther from Earth's center, and their acceleration is further reduced by the centrifugal effect of Earth's rotation. He proved that the mathematical expression for the weight of a terrestrial body contains a small variable term that is proportional to the square of the sine of the latitude, and his analysis accounted for the observed changes in the clock rates.

Further evidence for Newton's theory came from observations of Jupiter. Astronomers had discovered that Jupiter's equatorial radius is greater than its polar radius by about one part in thirteen. By observing the spots on Jupiter, they knew the rate at which the large planet rotated. Newton calculated its equatorial bulge and his result was close to the measured value. He was demonstrating the explanatory power of his dynamics on an ever-increasing scale.

Newton's calculation of Earth's shape enabled him to clear up another mystery, which had perplexed astronomers for eighteen centuries. In the second century B.C., Hipparchus discovered that the stars move in a peculiar way. In addition to the apparent daily rotation, the center of this celestial rotation (i.e., the location of the "north star") also moves slowly around in a small circle. Given the heliocentric theory, this implies a precession of Earth's spin axis, i.e., the axis sweeps out a cone just as we can observe in the case of a spinning top. Newton's laws of motion and gravitation explained this effect. The moon and sun attract the mass of Earth's equatorial bulge, causing a torque that moves Earth's spin axis in a cone with an angular radius of twenty-three degrees (equal to the angle between the plane of the equator and that of the ecliptic). The torque is small and therefore the precession is very slow. Newton carefully estimated the gravitational pull on the equatorial bulge and calculated the precession rate. He arrived at a value close to the one measured by astronomers, who had determined that Earth's axis completes one revolution in about twenty-six thousand years. With nearly every turn of a page in the *Principia*, another phenomenon was explained.

The *Principia* was a tour-de-force demonstration of the intelligibility of the universe. The grand finale of this demonstration was Newton's analysis of comets, the mysterious and previously unpredictable objects that were widely regarded as signs of God's anger. Newton dispelled such fears by proving that comets are ruled by the force of gravitation, not by a moody God.

Astronomers had collected accurate data on the movements of a comet that had appeared in 1680 (first observed by Gottfried Kirch). Newton analyzed this data with great care and concluded that the comet moved in an extremely elongated ellipse. Its speed was observed to change rapidly, but always in perfect conformity to Kepler's area law. The orbit is inclined at an angle of sixty-one degrees with the plane of Earth's orbit. The comet approaches the sun very closely every 575 years and its maximum distance from the sun is 138 times greater than the mean Earth–sun distance. One can hardly imagine an orbit that differs more dramatically from the planetary orbits, yet Newton proved that the comet is moving in accordance with the same laws. He drew the only possible conclusion: "The theory which justly corresponds with a motion so unequable, and through so great a part of the heavens, which observes the same laws with the theory of the planets, and which accurately agrees with accurate astronomical observations, cannot be otherwise than true."[7]

Another comet was observed in late 1682. Newton's friend Edmund Halley processed the data and calculated the orbit. He showed that the comet approaches inside the orbit of Venus every seventy-five years, its maximum distance from the sun is about thirty-five times greater than the Earth–sun distance, and the orbit is inclined by eighteen degrees with respect to the plane of Earth's orbit. Halley predicted that the comet would appear again in 1758—and it did return almost exactly on schedule, delayed only slightly by the influence of Jupiter.

The law of universal gravitation integrated and explained diverse observations on an unprecedented scale. Even so, there were scientists who found the *Principia* unsatisfying. They raised the same criticism that they had directed earlier at Newton's theory of colors. Again, they complained, Newton had failed to identify the first cause. At bottom, they charged, his explanations were empty because he had not explained the physical means by which bodies attract one another.[8]

This criticism derives from the idea that we must deduce knowledge from "first causes" rather than induce it from experience. Newton's opponents could not grasp that knowledge is gained by starting with observations and proceeding step by step to the discovery of causes, and eventually to the discovery of fundamental causes. They wished to start with the first causes and deduce the entire science of physics from them. Newton knew that this rationalist method led to the indulgence of fantasy, not to scientific knowledge. In responding to his critics, he repeated the point he had made years earlier:

> I have not been able to discover the cause of those properties of gravity from phenomena, and I frame no hypotheses; for whatever is not [inferred] from the phenomena is to be called a hypothesis, and hypotheses . . . have no place in experimental philosophy. In this philosophy particular propositions are inferred from the phenomena and afterward rendered general by induction. Thus it was that . . . the laws of motion and gravitation were discovered. And to us it is enough that gravity really does exist and act according to the laws which we have explained, and abundantly serves to account for all the motions of the celestial bodies and of our sea.[9]

Scientists who follow the rationalist method attempt to bypass the process of discovery. Using nothing more than imagination and deduction, they fabricate whole sciences—discovering no knowledge, while leaving no questions unanswered. Newton's inductive method leads to the opposite result: an enormously expanded context of knowledge, with each discovery giving rise to further questions.

Today, Newton's refusal to speculate about an underlying mechanism of gravitational attraction is sometimes misinterpreted in a way that would have been inconceivable to him. The modern empiricists, in an effort to claim Newton as one of their own, argue that he advocated a noncausal, descriptive approach to physics.[10] But Newton was not a skeptic. In conjunction with the laws of motion, the law of gravitation is the very archetype of a causal law: It states a necessary relationship between a property of an entity (mass) and its action. Throughout the *Principia*, Newton was focused on identifying causal relationships.

The final book of the *Principia* is appropriately titled "The System of the World." Newton had inherited a wealth of knowledge from his predecessors, but it was knowledge that consisted of separate laws belonging to separate sciences. Newton induced the fundamental causal relationships that connected this knowledge into a systematic whole. With this achievement, the science of physics reached maturity.

Here we see the result of the inductive method in its full glory.

Discovery Is Proof

The "problem of induction" is usually posed in a way that seems to preclude a solution. It is described as the problem of justifying an inductive "leap" from a relatively few observations to a universal truth. It is then asked: How can we be certain of a conclusion that transcends the evidence in this way?

This perspective is strangely detached from the actual discovery process that culminated in Newton's laws of motion and gravitation. In the past three chapters, we have followed the reasoning that led to these laws and yet we have not encountered any steps that could reasonably be described as "leaps" beyond the evidence. On the contrary, every new step followed from the evidence, given the prior context of knowledge. So now the question is: How did scientists manage to arrive at universal laws without making any illogical leaps?

A large part of the answer lies in the objectivity of the concepts themselves. When the concept "force" was expanded to include pushes and pulls exerted across a distance by imperceptible means, this was not done arbitrarily; it was necessitated by observations of electric and magnetic phenomena. Similarly, there was nothing arbitrary about the expansion of the concept "acceleration" to include changes in a body's direction as well as its speed; this was necessary in order to distinguish motion caused by a force from motion that can occur in the absence of force. The concepts "force" and "acceleration" then made it possible to identify that both the sun and Earth exerted an attractive force of the same nature, denoted by the concept "gravitation." This concept, in turn, made it possible to identify that weight is a measure of gravitational force, and it became necessary to isolate the property of bodies that causes this force; experiments then determined that a body's weight and inertia are proportional to its "quantity of matter," or "mass."

Likewise, there was nothing arbitrary in the reasoning that identified the causal connections made accessible by these concepts. The variables were systematically isolated and measured in a series of experiments involving free fall, inclined planes, pendulums, and double pendulums. By the time Newton announced his mathematical laws, he had studied mechanical, gravitational, and even magnetic forces; he had studied masses that ranged in magnitude from that of a pebble to that of the sun, and included a wide variety of different materials; he had studied motions that ranged in speed from a bob swinging slowly at the end of a long pendulum to a comet streaking across the night sky, and ranged in shape from linear to circular to parabolic to elliptical. Thus the laws were truly integrations of data, not leaps of faith.

A rigorous process of inductive logic enabled Newton to climb from narrower generalizations to his fundamental laws. For example, he did not leap to the law of universal gravitation and then search for confirming instances. Rather, as we saw, he began by identifying the nature of the solar force on the planets. In the *Principia*, he then showed that a similar force is exerted by Jupiter and Saturn on their respective moons—and he therefore had a law pertaining to both planets and moons. He next showed that a similar force is exerted by Earth on both terrestrial bodies and our moon—and he therefore had a law that applied to all bodies on Earth's surface as well as planets and moons. He then showed that the attractive force is not merely exerted by Earth as a whole, but it is exerted independently by every bit of matter making up Earth (his analysis of Earth's shape and precession, and the ocean tides, provided important evidence for this conclusion). Finally, he showed that the law applied even to comets, the celestial bodies that were legendary for their mysterious behavior and appearance. This was the genesis of Newton's discovery that all bodies have the property "mass" and thus attract in accordance with his law of gravitation.

If, at the end, Newton had been asked, "Now that you have this theory, how are you going to prove it?" he could answer simply by pointing to the discovery process itself. The step-by-step logical sequence by which he arrived at his theory *is* the proof. Each step was the grasp of a causal connection by the mathematical processing of observational data. Since there were no arbitrary leaps, there is no problem of justifying them.

To state this point negatively: In order to ask the above question, one has to drop the relevant context. The question does not arise if one keeps clearly in mind the whole sequence that led from observations to the fundamental laws. If, however, one assumes that the theory was created from the resources of Newton's imagination, then the issue of proof becomes an insolvable problem. The mere process of deducing consequences of a theory that are confirmed by observations never does or can lead to a proof. Such a process is insufficient even when the predictions range over a wide variety of different phenomena. The inevitable counterargument, offered by all those who take concepts and generalizations as given, without inquiring into their source, is: Perhaps someone else, possessing an equally rich imagination, can dream up an entirely different theory that accounts for the same facts. Without grasping the way in which Newton's conceptual framework emerged from and is necessitated by the observations, there is no answer to this objection. Given the inductive proof, however, one can and must answer simply by dismissing this suggestion as an arbitrary fantasy.

Today it is almost universally held that the process of theory creation is nonobjective. According to the most common view, which is institutionalized in the so-called "hypothetico-deductive method," it is only the testing of theories (i.e., comparing predictions to observations) that gives science any claim to objectivity. Unfortunately, say the advocates of this method, such testing cannot result in proof—and it cannot result even in *dis*proof, since any theory can be saved from an inconvenient observation merely by adding more arbitrary hypotheses. So the hypothetico-deductive method leads inevitably to skepticism.

Despite its implicit denial of scientific knowledge, this view of method strikes many scientists as plausible. One reason can be found in the way that science is taught; fundamental truths about nature are handed out like Halloween candy to young students, who are given only random snippets of the evidence from which the theories were induced. The education of a scientist today is focused on developing his proficiency in deducing consequences of the theories. Thus the scientist emerges from his training with memorized floating abstractions and a great deal of expertise in applying them. When he hears a description of the hypothetico-deductive method, he then recognizes it as an accurate description of his own state of mind. In this way, an embarrassing failure of education becomes a standard theory of scientific method.

The difference between a scientist who induces a theory and one who "freely creates" a theory is the difference between a man standing on solid ground and a cartoon character hovering in midair over an abyss. It is little wonder that those who believe theories are "free creations" sense the impending disaster—i.e., they typically believe that all theories are doomed to fall and be replaced by other imaginative constructs. In contrast, the inductive method leads to the opposite conclusion: A theory reached and validated by this method is never overthrown. Thus, for example, Newton's laws have not been contradicted by any discoveries made since the publication of the *Principia*. Rather, all subsequent discoveries in physics have presupposed his theory and built on it. His laws have been the rock-solid foundation for the work of every physicist of the past three centuries, and they continue to be applied today in countless ways.

The widespread confusion regarding this point is caused by treating scientific laws as out-of-context dogmas rather than as integrations of concretes. Newton himself, however, *never* said, "My laws apply without modification not only to all that is currently known in physics and astronomy, but also to every phenomenon that will ever be studied, no matter how far removed it is from any phenomenon studied to date. I give these laws as commandments, to be applied independent of cognitive context." He did not make any such statement because he knew that the process of inductive reasoning that led to his laws established the context within which they are proven. Further evidence is required if the laws are to be extended into previously unstudied realms.

The cases in which Newton's laws are said to fail are all the same: They are cases where his laws have been torn from the context in which they were discovered and applied to a realm far removed from anything ever considered by him. The cases pertain to bodies moving at near light-speed, which is about ten thousand times the speed of Earth in its orbit around the sun; or they pertain to subtle effects of very strong gravitational fields, none of which could be measured until more than a century after Newton; or they pertain to the behavior of subatomic particles, a realm that physicists began to study about two centuries after Newton.

In order to clarify the relation between early theories and the later advancements that they make possible, let us examine one particular piece of evidence that is often said to refute Newton's gravitational theory. The major axis of Mercury's orbit is observed to rotate very slowly. As seen from Earth, the total rotation appears to be about 1.56 degrees per century. Calculations show that almost 90 percent of this apparent rotation is caused by the precession of Earth's spin axis, which is entirely explained by Newton's theory. Of the remaining effect, more than 90 percent is caused by the gravitational pull of other planets, which is also explained by Newton's theory. That leaves less than 1 percent of the total observed effect, which amounts to forty-three arc seconds per century, unexplained by Newton's theory. This residual effect is explained by Einstein's theory, the predictions of which differ slightly from Newton's in the strong gravitational field near the sun.

Einstein did not refute the laws of Newton, just as Newton did not refute the laws of Kepler. In both cases, the truth of the earlier theory was presupposed and then a more general theory was developed that applied within an expanded context of knowledge. And, in both cases, the expanded context of knowledge included small discrepancies between new data and the old theory, which were then explained by the new theory. This is often how science progresses.

There is only one aspect of Newton's theory that was rejected rather than absorbed into Einstein's theory (and, in this case, one can only wish that Einstein had been consistent in his rejection). Newton treated the concepts "space" and "time" as existents independent of bodies, rather than as relationships among bodies. Thus he viewed space as an infinite cosmic backdrop that exists independent of the bodies placed in it, and he claimed that this backdrop has real physical effects on the bodies that accelerate with respect to it.

Newton offered scientific arguments to support his view of space and time, but these arguments are non sequiturs.[11] "Absolute" space and time played no role in the reasoning that proved his theory (thus I had no need to mention these ideas while presenting his discovery process). In fact, "absolute" space and time were intimately connected to Newton's religious views, and therefore they are an arbitrary element in his theory. He occasionally made concessions to religion and thereby departed from his explicitly stated scientific method. This is the most egregious example of such a departure.

In Newton's theory, the frame of absolute space is identified with a coordinate system in which the fixed stars do not rotate. This frame is defined objectively, on the basis of observation. Therefore Newton could have replaced his discussion of absolute space (and time) with the following statement: "The laws of motion and gravitation presented in this book are valid in the frame of the fixed stars, or in any frame that can be approximated as unaccelerated with respect to the fixed stars. Whether it is possible to develop a theory that is free from this restriction, I leave to the consideration of the reader." Such a statement would have made clear the objective status of his theory, and it would have eliminated the impossible task of trying to establish the existence of space as a supernatural pseudo-entity.

No later discoveries in physics were required in order to identify and reject Newton's error. Several of Newton's contemporaries pointed out that there was no justification for reifying space and time.[12] The correct relational view dates back to Aristotle, who treated space as a sum of places and explained that the concept "place" refers to a relationship among bodies. Thus the ideas of absolute space and time were identified as arbitrary two thousand years earlier; the discoveries of Einstein are not needed in order to understand this issue.

Later discoveries add to the cognitive whole but they never refute it. Indeed, there is a symbiotic relationship here; the earlier knowledge makes it possible to discover the later knowledge, and the later knowledge often makes it possible for us to see profound new implications in the early knowledge.

Consider, for example, the relationship between Newton's dynamics and Galileo's kinematics. It has always perplexed historians of science that Newton credited Galileo with the second law of motion (F = mA). Since Galileo did not know this law, why did Newton say that he learned it from him? The answer provides insight into the way Newton took full advantage of his predecessor's achievements. This law was out of Galileo's reach because he did not have the prerequisite concepts. In Newton's context, which included the vector concept "acceleration" and the concepts "gravity" and "mass," Galileo's experiments do imply that F = mA. In effect, Newton could read his second law of motion between the lines of Galileo's text, even though this message was invisible to the author himself.

We have encountered other similar examples. Torricelli's discovery that air has weight led scientists to a more general formulation of Archimedes' principle of buoyancy. In the light of Newton's dynamics, Kepler's area law of planetary motion was generalized to the conservation of angular momentum principle, which applies to all bodies. The acquisition of knowledge is not merely a step-by-step climb up the hierarchy, with one's eyes always forward on the next step. Such a metaphor misses the fact that a thinker's focus must regularly return to earlier knowledge in order to integrate it with new discoveries. A crucial aspect of cognitive integration is the task of revisiting old knowledge and extracting from it the new implications that can be seen only in the light of more recent advances.

The scientific revolution of the seventeenth century achieved the ambitious goal that was first pursued in ancient Greece. The Greeks attempted to identify basic principles that could integrate their knowledge of the universe into one intelligible whole. However, they lacked the necessary experimental and mathematical methods. In their impatience, they bypassed the slow, painstaking process of discovery; instead, they attempted a giant leap from observations to the fundamental principles—and they fell short. Eventually a loss of confidence led to the pragmatic acceptance of Ptolemy's senseless theory, with its hodgepodge of arbitrary elements.

At the outset of the scientific revolution, Copernicus commented on the lack of integration in astronomy. Regarding his predecessors, he wrote: "[T]hey are in exactly the same fix as someone taking from different places hands, feet, head, and other limbs—shaped very beautifully but not with reference to one body and without correspondence to one another—so that such parts make up a monster rather than a man."[13] We saw that Copernicus took the first steps toward transforming this monster into a man. The task was completed by Newton, who made physics and astronomy into one body of knowledge with all parts fitted together in a perfect whole.

We have seen the inexorable logic of the progression from Copernicus to Galileo and Kepler and finally to Newton. Under Newton's powerful influence, the inductive method rose to prominence and its nemesis—the arbitrary—fell into disrepute. The method that scientists learned from the *Principia* and *Optics* provided a green light to a new era, an era in which many long-held secrets of nature were finally illuminated and new sciences were born (e.g., electricity, chemistry, and geology). Because such illumination was so characteristic of the century that followed Newton, historians have given this era an appropriate name: the Enlightenment.

5.

The Atomic Theory

Scientists need objective standards for evaluating theories. Nowhere is this need more apparent than in the strange history of the atomic theory of matter. Prior to the nineteenth century, there was little evidence for the theory—yet many natural philosophers believed that matter was made of atoms, and some even wasted their time constructing imaginative stories about the nature of the fundamental particles. Then, during the nineteenth century, a bizarre reversal occurred: As strong evidence for the theory accumulated rapidly, many scientists rejected the idea of atoms and even crusaded against it.

Both of these errors—the dogmatic belief that was unsupported by evidence, followed by the dogmatic skepticism that ignored abundant evidence—were based on false theories of knowledge. The atomists of ancient Greece were rationalists, i.e., they believed that knowledge can be acquired by reason alone, independent of sensory data. The nineteenth-century skeptics were modern empiricists, i.e., they believed that knowledge is merely a description of sensory data and therefore references to nonobservable entities are meaningless. But scientific knowledge is not the floating abstractions of rationalists or the perceptual-level descriptions of empiricists; it is the grasp of causal relationships identified by means of the inductive method. In this chapter, we will see how the atomic nature of matter was identified as the fundamental cause that explains a wide range of narrower laws.

If we follow the idea of atoms from ancient Greece to the nineteenth century, one remarkable fact stands out: So long as the atomic theory was not induced from scientific data, it was useless. For more than two millennia, scientists were unable to make any predictions or to devise any experiments based on the theory. It explained nothing and integrated nothing. Because the Greek idea of atoms did not derive from observed facts, it remained isolated from the real knowledge of those who investigated nature. If one tries to think about the implications of an arbitrary idea, one simply draws a blank; implications depend upon connections to the rest of one's knowledge. In terms of Rand's analogy, the word "atom" was just a label on an empty file folder.

Everyone, including scientists, must start with the evidence available to the senses, and there is no *direct* perceptual evidence for the existence of atoms. On the perceptual level, matter appears to be continuous. At the early stages of science, questions about the ultimate, irreducible properties of matter—including the question of whether it is discrete on some imperceptible scale—*do not legitimately arise.* The questions that do arise from observations are very challenging. For example: How do bodies move? What forces can they exert on each other? How do they change when heated or cooled? Why do objects appear colored, and how is colored light related to ordinary white light? When different materials react, what transformations can they undergo, and under what circumstances?

By 1800, after centuries of investigating such questions, scientists finally had the advanced knowledge that made the question of atoms meaningful and the answer possible. When the idea of atoms arose from observed facts, scientists had a context in which they could think about it, and therefore they could derive implications, make predictions, and design experiments. The result was a sudden flurry of scientific activity that quickly revealed an enormous depth and range of evidence in favor of the atomic composition of matter.

Chemical Elements and Atoms

There was no science of chemistry prior to the Enlightenment. There was practical knowledge about the extraction of metals, the synthesis of glass, and the dyeing of clothes. There were also premature attempts to reduce the bewildering variety of known materials to a few basic elements. The Greeks had supposed that all terrestrial matter was made of four elements: earth, water, air, and fire. Later, some alchemists tried to reduce "earth" to salt, mercury, and sulfur. But these early attempts were empty speculation, not scientific theory; such ideas were unsupported by the observations and incapable of explaining them.

The situation changed dramatically in the second half of the twentieth century, when the method that had led to such spectacular success in physics was applied to chemistry. The father of modern chemistry, Antoine Lavoisier, wrote in a letter to Benjamin Franklin that his aim was "to follow as much as possible the torch of observation and experiment." He added: "This course, which has not yet been followed in chemistry, led me to plan my book according to an absolutely new scheme, and chemistry has been brought much closer to experimental physics."[1]

The first step in the science of chemistry was to make a clear distinction between pure substances and mixtures. Unlike mixtures, pure substances have well-defined and invariant properties. Under the same conditions, every sample of a pure substance will melt (or boil) at precisely the same temperature. Every such sample has the same hardness and the same mass density, and the same amount of heat will always cause the same rise in temperature (for a unit mass). Furthermore, when a portion of a substance undergoes a chemical reaction, the properties of the remaining part do not change. Thus the concept "substance" relied on the prior conceptualization of various physical and chemical properties, and the knowledge of how to measure those properties. The concept "mixture" could then be defined as a material composed of two or more substances.

The next key step was the division of substances into elements and compounds. This was made possible by the discovery that mass is conserved in chemical reactions, i.e., the weights of the reactants are always equal to the weights of the products. It was found that some substances can be decomposed into two or more other substances with the same total weight; on the other hand, other substances resisted all such attempts at chemical decomposition. Those that cannot be decomposed are elements; those that can be decomposed are compounds, i.e., they are substances made of two or more elements. Armed with the principle of mass conservation and the method of quantitative analysis, chemistry was finally freed from arbitrary conjecture; the weight scale gave an objective verdict.

The "elements" of the Greeks could not withstand this new quantitative method. In 1774, air was discovered to be a mixture of nitrogen and oxygen. At about the same time, Lavoisier proved that combustion was the result of combining substances with oxygen, not the release of elementary "fire." A few years later, water was shown to be a compound of two elements, hydrogen and oxygen. The remaining Greek element, earth, was shown to consist of many different substances. In total, chemists of the eighteenth century identified more than twenty elements.

Much of the confusion that had plagued early chemistry was built into its terminology. The same name was often used for different substances (e.g., all gases were referred to as various modifications of "air"). Conversely, different names were sometimes used to refer to the same substance, depending on how it was synthesized (e.g., the element antimony had at least four names). In other cases, compounds were named after their discoverer or the place where they were found; such names gave no clue to the composition of the substance. The situation was made worse by the legacy of the alchemists, who had viewed themselves as a secret cult and therefore used terminology that was intentionally obscure (e.g., "green lion," "star regulus of Mars").

Lavoisier took the lead in bringing order to this chaos. He recognized that true generalizations can be reached and expressed only by means of an objective language. He originated many of the modern names for elements, and his names for compounds identified their con-

THE LOGICAL LEAP · 155

stituent elements. Substances were placed into wider groups (e.g., acids, alkaloids, salts) according to their essential properties. He understood that concepts are not arbitrary conventions; they are integrations of similar particulars, and the groupings must be based on the facts. A word that refers haphazardly to a collection of dissimilar things can give rise only to error and confusion. On the other hand, Lavoisier noted, "A well-composed language . . . will not allow the teachers of chemistry to deviate from the course of nature; either they must reject the nomenclature or they must irresistibly follow the course marked out by it. The logic of the sciences is thus essentially dependent on their language."[2] He presented his new language—the chemical language we still use today—in a landmark book, *Elements of Chemistry*, published in 1789.

With the foundation provided by a quantitative method and an objective language, the chemists who followed Lavoisier made rapid progress in understanding how elements combine to form compounds. The next crucial discovery was made by Joseph Louis Proust, who devoted many years to studying various compounds of metals (e.g., carbonates, oxides, sulfides). In 1799, he announced *the law of constant composition*, which states that *different samples of a compound always contain the same elements in the same proportions by mass*. For example, he showed that copper carbonate always contains copper, oxygen, and carbon in the same mass ratio (roughly five to four to one), regardless of how the sample was prepared in the laboratory or how it was isolated from nature.

Initially, the evidence supporting Proust's law was strong but not conclusive. Another French chemist, Claude Louis Bertholett, claimed to find counterexamples. He pointed out that lead can react with a variable amount of oxygen, resulting in a material that changes color in a continuous manner. A similar example is provided by mercury dissolved in nitric acid, which also reacts with a variable amount of oxygen. However, Proust carefully analyzed these cases and showed that the products were mixtures, not compounds; lead forms three different oxides and the mercury was reacting to form two distinct salts. By about 1805, after numerous alleged counterexamples had been identified as mixtures of two or more compounds, chemists accepted the law of constant composition.

Chemists of this period discovered that several other metals, like lead, combine with oxygen to form more than one compound. There are two oxides of tin, two of copper, and three of iron. Furthermore, this phenomenon was not limited to metal oxides; chemists identified two different gases made of carbon and oxygen, and another two gases made of carbon and hydrogen. When they carefully measured the weights of the combining elements in such cases, a crucial pattern emerged.

In 1803, John Dalton analyzed three gases composed of nitrogen and oxygen. The first is a colorless gas that has a pleasant odor and the capacity to cause hysterical laughter when inhaled; the second is colorless, nearly odorless, and has a significantly lower mass density; the third has the highest mass density of the three and a deep brown color at high temperatures. Quantitative analysis showed that the three gases are also distinguished by the relative weights of the two combining elements. If we consider samples of each gas that contain 1.75 grams of nitrogen, then we find that the laughing gas contains one gram of oxygen, the second gas contains two grams, and the third gas contains four grams. Dalton found a similar result when he analyzed two different gases that are both composed of carbon and hydrogen; for samples containing the same weight of carbon, the weight of hydrogen contained in one of the gases is precisely twice that of the other. On the basis of such data, Dalton arrived at a new law: *When two elements combine to form more than one compound, the weights of one element that combine with identical weights of the other are in simple multiple proportions.*

As was the case with the law of constant composition, chemists did not immediately accept the law of multiple proportions when Dalton published his book *A New System of Chemical Philosophy* in 1808. There were three problems. First, more accurate data was needed to verify the integer mass ratios. Second, more instances of the law were needed, spanning the range from light gases to heavy metal compounds (Dalton had studied only a few gases). Third, apparent violations of the law needed to be resolved by showing that such cases always involve mixtures, not compounds. Thanks in large part to the outstanding work of a Swedish chemist, Jons Jacob Berzelius, all three problems were solved in less than a decade. By 1816, Berzelius had proven the law of multiple proportions beyond any reasonable doubt.

This law gave the first clear evidence for the atomic theory of matter. It implies that when elements combine into compounds, they do so in discrete units of mass. A compound may contain one unit of an element, or two, or three, but never 2.63 such units. This is precisely what one would expect if each chemical element is composed of atoms with identical masses. The discrete nature of matter had finally revealed itself in observations.

The concept "atom" that emerged from observations differed from the old idea based on deductions from floating abstractions. In ancient Greece, the "atom" had been defined as the ultimate, immutable, irreducible unit of matter. However, Lavoisier pointed out that the Greek idea was vacuous because nothing was known about such ultimate particles. In contrast, the new scientific concept that took shape in the early nineteenth century was that of the *chemical atom*. Scientists came to understand that an atom had to be redefined as *the smallest particle of an element that can enter into a chemical combination*. The question of whether it is possible to break these chemical atoms into smaller constituents by nonchemical means had to be put aside and left open. With this understanding, the concept "atom" was given real content for the first time.

At about the same time that Dalton's book was published, the French chemist Joseph Louis Gay-Lussac discovered another law manifesting the discrete nature of chemical elements. Gay-Lussac found that the *volumes* of gases involved in a reaction can always be expressed as a ratio of small whole numbers. At a temperature above the boiling point of water, for example, one liter of oxygen will combine with two liters of hydrogen to give exactly two liters of steam. He cited several other instances of the law. For example: One liter of nitrogen will combine with three liters of hydrogen to give exactly two liters of ammonia gas, or the one liter of nitrogen can react with one liter of oxygen to produce two liters of nitric oxide.

Although Gay-Lussac described his law of combining gas volumes as "very favorable to the [atomic] theory," he did not make the implications explicit.[3] That task was left to an Italian scientist named Amedeo Avogadro.

A substance, according to the atomic theory, is composed of molecules, i.e., particles that consist of one or more atoms. Considered at the microscopic level, a chemical reaction occurs when a small number of molecules (usually two) come together, the atoms rearrange, and the product is a small number of different molecules. Thus if we compare the number of molecules of each reactant and product, they must exist in ratios of small whole numbers. But this is precisely what Gay-Lussac found for the volumes of gases involved in a reaction. Therefore, Avogadro reasoned, there must be a direct relationship between volume and number of molecules. In 1811, he proposed his hypothesis: *Equal volumes of gases (at the same temperature and pressure) contain the same number of molecules.* (Here the term "hypothesis" refers not to an arbitrary proposition but to one induced from evidence that is not yet conclusive.)

Avogadro's hypothesis has extraordinary implications. It relates volume ratios—a measurable, macroscopic quantity—to the number of molecules involved in each individual, microscopic chemical reaction. Thus the fact that two liters of hydrogen react with one liter of oxygen to produce two liters of steam implies, according to Avogadro, that two hydrogen molecules react with one oxygen molecule to produce two water molecules. In many cases, his hypothesis enabled him to determine the number of atoms in each molecule. By comparing the various known reactions, he concluded that the common gases are diatomic; i.e., a hydrogen molecule consists of two hydrogen atoms bound together, and the same is true for oxygen and nitrogen. From the volume ratios and his hypothesis, Avogadro concluded that a water molecule is composed of two hydrogen atoms combined with an oxygen atom, and an ammonia molecule is three hydrogen atoms combined with a nitrogen atom. The measurement of macroscopic variables such as mass and volume was unveiling the hidden world of atoms and molecules.

Scientists soon discovered another macroscopic variable that shed light on the microscopic realm. The "specific heat" of a substance is defined as the amount of heat required to raise the temperature of one gram of the substance by one degree. It was known that the specific heats of different elements vary over a wide range. When scientists compared equal weights of copper and lead, for example, they found that in order to cause the same rise in temperature, the copper requires more than three times as much heat as the lead.

In 1819, two French physicists, Pierre Dulong and Alexis Petit, measured the specific heats of many pure metals and discovered a remarkable relationship. Rather than comparing equal weights of the different elements, they decided to compare samples with equal numbers of atoms. So they multiplied the measured specific heats by the relative atomic weights that had been determined by chemists. This simple calculation gives the specific heat for a particular number of atoms, rather than the specific heat for a unit mass.

When Dulong and Petit performed their careful measurements of specific heat and multiplied by the atomic weights, they arrived at very nearly the *same number* for all of the metallic elements they tested. In other words, they found that equal numbers of atoms absorb equal amounts of heat. Thus the wide variations in the specific heats of metals can be explained simply by differences in the number of atoms. This is impressive evidence for the atomic composition of matter.

The Dulong-Petit law was shown to be approximately true for the vast majority of solid elements. However, one major exception was discovered: Carbon has a specific heat that is far lower than the value predicted by the law. But since carbon was known to have other unusual properties, it was reasonable for scientists to accept the causal relationship between heat capacity and number of atoms, and to regard carbon as a special case in which additional, unknown causal factors played a major role.

One of the unusual properties of carbon had been demonstrated a few years earlier by Humphry Davy, an English chemist. The common form of pure carbon is the black, chalky substance we call graphite. However, carbon also exists in another solid form. In 1814, Davy used an enormous magnifying glass to burn a diamond in the presence of oxygen, and the product was carbon dioxide gas. He had proven that graphite and diamond—materials with radically different properties—are composed of the same element. This is a rare phenomenon, but not unique; chemists also knew that tin exists as both a gray powder and a white, malleable metal. Different forms of the same element are called "allotropes."

In the next decade, chemists discovered a similar phenomenon among compounds. In 1823, the German chemist Justus von Liebig carried out a quantitative analysis of silver fulminate; at about the same time, his colleague Friedrich Wohler analyzed silver cyanate. These compounds have very different chemical properties; for example, the fulminate reacts explosively, whereas the cyanate does not. Yet when the two chemists compared notes, they found that both compounds are made of silver, oxygen, carbon, and nitrogen in identical proportions. Soon thereafter, Wohler proved that ammonium cyanate and urea—which, again, have very different properties—are composed of identical proportions of hydrogen, nitrogen, carbon, and oxygen. Several other such cases were discovered in the 1820s. Different chemical compounds made of the same elements in identical proportions were named "isomers," a term that derives from the Greek words meaning "equal parts."

The existence of allotropes and isomers was recognized to be problematic for any continuum theory of matter. Such a theory would seem to imply that the same elements mixed together in the same proportions should always result in the same material. However, according to the atomic theory, the chemical properties of a molecule are determined by the elements *and their arrangement*; i.e., it is not merely the proportions of elements that are relevant, but also which atoms are attached to which other atoms and in what spatial configuration. Thus when Berzelius discussed isomers, he stated the implication clearly: "It would seem as if the simple atoms of which substances are composed may be united with each other in different ways."[4] As we shall see, isomers were destined to play an important role in the determination of many molecular structures and in the proof of the atomic theory.

About a decade after the discovery of isomers, yet another field provided evidence for the atomic composition of matter. Since 1800, when Alessandro Volta announced his invention of the electric battery, scientists had investigated the relation between chemical reactions and electricity. A battery is simply a chemical reaction occurring between electrodes, one that generates an electric current in any conductor that connects the electrodes. Such a chemical reaction occurs spontaneously and causes the current. Scientists quickly discovered that they could reverse this process: Under specific conditions, an electric current can be used to charge electrodes and stimulate a chemical reaction in the solution between them. This reverse process is called electrolysis.

Recall that Dulong and Petit had discovered that heat capacity is proportional not to the mass but to the number of molecules contained in the sample. In the early 1830s, Michael Faraday found that a similar relationship exists between electricity and number of molecules. Consider, for example, an electrolytic solution of hydrochloric acid. Faraday discovered that a specific amount of electricity passing through the solution will generate one gram of hydrogen gas at the negative electrode and thirty-six grams of chlorine gas at the positive electrode. It was known that hydrochloric acid contains hydrogen and chlorine in the mass ratio of one to thirty-six. Faraday concluded that the molecules of hydrochloric acid are broken into positively charged hydrogen "ions" (attracted to the negative electrode) and negatively charged chlorine "ions" (attracted to the positive electrode), with each atom carrying an equal magnitude of electric charge through the solution.

Faraday reached this view after conducting experiments with many different electrolytic solutions. In each case, he used the relative atomic weights to show that the quantity of electricity is always proportional to the number of molecules reacting at each electrode. "[T]here is an immensity of facts," he wrote, "which justify us in believing that the atoms of matter are in some way endowed or associated with electrical powers. . . ."[5] And, he added, the results of his electrolysis experiments seem to imply that "the atoms of bodies . . . have equal quantities of electricity naturally associated with them."[6]

Actually, some of the elements in Faraday's experiments were singly ionized, carrying one unit of electric charge, while others were doubly ionized, carrying two units of electric charge. Faraday overlooked this fact because in the cases of doubly ionized elements he used atomic weights that were half of the correct value, and this error caused him to underestimate the electric charge per atom by a factor of two. In conjunction with the correct atomic weights, his experiments would have led him to the crucial discovery that the electric charges of ions vary in discrete units.

At this stage, there was still a great deal of controversy and confusion about the relative weights of atoms. In an invalid argument based mainly on "simplicity," Dalton had concluded that a molecule of water contains one hydrogen atom and one oxygen atom. If hydrogen is assigned a weight of one unit, this incorrect molecular formula implies that the weight of oxygen is eight rather than sixteen. Since the weights of many other elements were measured relative to oxygen, this erroneous factor of two propagated through the table of atomic weights like an infectious disease.

The cure for this disease is Avogadro's hypothesis. As we have already seen, Avogadro's idea led to the correct molecular formula for water and thus to the correct atomic weight for oxygen. Unfortunately, there were two false premises that prevented many scientists from grasping this crucial truth.

The first false premise was a hasty generalization regarding the nature of chemical bonding. Because compounds can be decomposed into positively and negatively charged ions by electrolysis, many scientists concluded that chemical bonding can be explained simply as an electrical attraction. For example, a molecule of hydrochloric acid was assumed to be held together by the attractive force between the electropositive hydrogen and the electronegative chlorine. All chemical bonding, according to this idea, must occur between atoms with different "electrical affinities," so that an attractive force can arise between the positive and negative atoms.

Avogadro's hypothesis, however, implies that the molecules of many gaseous elements are diatomic. For instance, Avogadro claimed that two atoms of hydrogen—both electropositive—bind together, and two atoms of chlorine—both electronegative—bind together. But since like charges repel, the existence of such diatomic molecules seemed impossible according to the electrical theory of chemical bonding. As a result, many chemists—including leaders in the field such as Berzelius and Davy—rejected Avogadro's hypothesis.

The second false premise concerned the physical nature of gases. Many scientists, including Dalton, thought that the pressure and elasticity of gases implied the existence of a repulsive force between the identical atoms of the gas. Dalton proved that in the case of gaseous mixtures each elemental gas behaved independently, i.e., the total pressure was simply the sum of the individual pressures. Thus he concluded that there was no repulsive force between unlike gas atoms. However, because he thought there was such a force between identical atoms, he could not accept Avogadro's hypothesis and its implication of diatomic molecules. How could two atoms that strongly repelled each other come together and bond?

Without Avogadro's hypothesis, there was no explanation for the law of combining gas volumes and no way to arrive at unambiguous atomic weights. The wrong atomic weights led to a myriad of problems, from incorrect molecular formulas to clashes with the Dulong-Petit law of heat capacities. Thus the explanatory power and integrating function of the atomic theory seemed to be severely undercut. It took decades to solve this problem, despite the fact that the pieces of the solution were available the whole time. The reason is that chemists alone could not validate the pieces, put them together, and reach a fundamental theory of matter. As it turned out, they needed help from those who studied the fundamental science of matter—i.e., they needed help from the physicists.

The Kinetic Theory of Gases

It was the study of heat and gases that led physicists to the atomic theory, and eventually brought the sciences of physics and chemistry together into a unified whole.

In the eighteenth century, heat was widely believed to be a fluid (called "caloric") that flowed from hot to cold bodies. At the end of the century, however, two experiments provided strong evidence that heat was not a substance, but rather some internal motion of the matter comprising the bodies.

In 1798, Count Rumford (aka Benjamin Thompson) was supervising the manufacture of cannons at the military arsenal in Munich. He was surprised by the enormous amount of heat generated in the process of boring the cannons, and he decided to investigate the phenomenon. He placed a brass gun barrel in a wooden box containing cold water and bored it with a blunt steel drill. After about two and one-half hours, the water began to boil. The apparently inexhaustible supply of heat led Rumford to reject the caloric theory. As he put it, "Anything which any insulated body, or system of bodies, can continue to furnish without limitation, cannot possibly be a material substance."[7] In the experiment, what was being supplied to the system of bodies was motion; thus Rumford concluded that heat must be a form of internal motion.

In the following year, Humphry Davy was led to the same conclusion by means of an experiment in which the heated bodies were more carefully insulated. In an evacuated glass container that was kept at a temperature below the freezing point of water, he contrived a means of vigorously rubbing together two blocks of ice. The ice melted, despite the fact that there was no possible source of "fluid heat." Davy stated his conclusion emphatically: "It has then been experimentally demonstrated that caloric, or the matter of heat, does not exist." Agreeing with Rumford, he added: "Heat . . . may be defined as a peculiar motion, probably a vibration, of the corpuscles of bodies. . . ."[8]

Although these experiments pointed the way toward a new understanding of heat, there were two reasons why they did not influence physics significantly in the early nineteenth century. First, many physicists were reluctant to give up the concept "caloric" because it seemed to explain the similarities between heat conduction and fluid flow. Second, the merely qualitative idea that heat was some unspecified form of internal motion had little explanatory power. Until the quantitative relationship between heat and motion was identified, the idea lay dormant; it could not be integrated with mechanics, and its implications could not be investigated and exploited. When the idea was finally given mathematical form, it quickly led to crucial discoveries.

The quantitative relationship was established in a brilliant series of experiments conducted by James Joule in the mid-1840s. Joule designed an apparatus in which falling weights were used to turn paddle wheels in a container of water. In this arrangement, the external motion of the weights is converted into heat, raising the temperature of the water. He showed that the rise in temperature is proportional to the product of the weights and the distance through which they fall.

The paddle wheels were driven by two thirty-pound lead weights falling repeatedly through a distance of about five feet. The temperature of the water was measured by thermometers that were accurate to within one-hundredth of a degree Fahrenheit, and Joule was extraordinarily careful to account for possible sources of error in the experiment (e.g., the heat absorbed by the container, and the loss of motion when the weights impacted the floor). He concluded that a 772-pound weight falling through a distance of one foot is capable of raising the temperature of one pound of water by one degree Fahrenheit, a result that is impressively close to the correct value of 778 pounds. In addition, he performed similar experiments using sperm oil and mercury instead of water, and showed that the conversion factor between external motion and heat is always the same.

Joule's quantitative analysis could be integrated with Newtonian mechanics to provide insight into the specific function of motion that is related to a rise in temperature. In free fall, the product of the body's weight and the distance fallen is equal to half the body's mass multiplied by the square of its speed. Physicists refer to this function of motion as the body's "kinetic energy." Joule proved that when the temperature of a material is raised by the conversion of motion into heat, it is the amount of external kinetic energy expended that is proportional to the rise in temperature. Thus if temperature can be interpreted as a measure of the internal kinetic energy of molecules, then this process is simply one of converting external to internal kinetic energy.

J. J. Waterston, another English physicist, was familiar with Joule's work and took the next crucial step. Waterston turned his attention to the absorption of heat by gases, rather than by liquids or solids. It was known that gas volumes are enormous compared to the corresponding liquid volumes; for example, at standard atmospheric pressure and boiling temperature, steam occupies a volume about 1,500 times that of the same mass of liquid water. According to the atomic theory, this means that the distance between gas molecules is very large compared to their size. Thus, in opposition to Dalton, Waterston argued that any forces between the molecules must be negligibly small in the gaseous state. If so, each molecule will move with constant velocity until it collides with another gas molecule or with the walls of the container.

Waterston could also make a reasonable hypothesis about the nature of such collisions. It was known that when heat is transferred from hot bodies to cold bodies, the total amount of heat is conserved. It was also known that kinetic energy is conserved in the case of *elastic* collisions. So, if heat is a measure of the internal kinetic energy of molecules, then molecular collisions must be elastic in nature. Thus Waterston arrived at his simple model of gases: The molecules move freely except at impact, when they change their motion in such a way that both momentum and kinetic energy are conserved.[9]

On the basis of this model, Waterston was able to derive a law relating the pressure, volume, and energy of a gas. He showed that the product of pressure and volume is proportional to the number of molecules and the average kinetic energy of the molecules. This result integrated perfectly with what was already known about heat and gases. If temperature is equated with the average kinetic energy of molecules, then Waterston's law says that the product of pressure and volume is proportional to temperature—which is precisely the gas law that had been proven experimentally by Jacques Charles almost sixty years earlier. Furthermore, Waterston's law implies that at constant temperature the pressure of a gas is proportional to its mass density—a relationship that had also been proven experimentally decades earlier. Finally, the law implies that equal volumes of gases must contain equal numbers of molecules, provided that the pressure and temperature are the same— i.e., *Avogadro's hypothesis follows necessarily from this molecular model of gases and Newton's laws.* The explanatory power of Waterston's analysis was astonishing. We can understand why he wrote, "It seems almost impossible now to escape from the inference that heat is essentially molecular [kinetic energy]."[10]

The atomic law of gases had an implication, however, that initially struck many physicists as problematic. The law relates the average speed of gas molecules to the pressure and mass density of the gas, both of which can be measured. Thus the speed of the molecules could be calculated, and the result was surprisingly high. For example, at standard temperature and pressure, the law implies that air molecules move at an average speed of nearly five hundred meters per second. However, it was known that when a gas with a strong odor is generated at one corner of a laboratory, a couple of minutes may pass before it is detected at the far side of the room. If gas molecules travel so quickly, what is the reason for the time delay?

The answer was first given in an 1858 paper by Rudolf Clausius, a German physicist. Clausius suggested that molecules travel only a very short distance before impacting other molecules. While traversing a room, the progress of a molecule is greatly slowed by billions of collisions and subsequent changes of direction. Thus he introduced the idea of the "mean free path" of a molecule, i.e., the average distance that a molecule travels before suffering a collision. He estimated that this distance, although perhaps a thousand times greater than the diameter of the molecule, was still very small compared to macroscopic dimensions.

The idea of "mean free path" was seized on by the greatest theoretical physicist of the nineteenth century, James Clerk Maxwell, and it played a key role in his development of the atomic theory of gases. Maxwell was able to derive equations relating the mean free path to rates of gaseous diffusion and heat conduction. He showed that the diffusion rate is proportional to the product of the average speed of the molecules and their mean free path, and the rate of heat conduction is proportional to the product of speed, mean free path, and heat capacity. These equations were soon verified by experiment, and Maxwell declared with satisfaction: "The numerical results . . . agree in a very remarkable manner with the formula derived from the kinetic theory."[11]

Although this explanation for rates of diffusion and heat conduction was very impressive, the single most remarkable prediction of Maxwell's theory concerned the viscosity of gases. Viscosity is a measure of the internal resistance to flow; to cite a familiar example comparing liquids, honey has a much higher viscosity than water. Maxwell showed that the viscosity of a gas is proportional to the product of the mass density, the mean free path, and the average speed of the molecules. Considered in isolation, this relationship may not seem surprising. However, the mean free path is inversely proportional to the number of molecules per unit volume in the gas, i.e., to the density—and therefore, combining these relationships, gaseous viscosity is independent of density. The atomic theory predicts that the viscosity will remain the same even when most of the gas molecules are removed.

At first glance, this result seems to violate common sense. In a letter to a colleague, Maxwell commented: "This is certainly very unexpected, that the friction should be as great in a rare as in a dense gas."[12] Initially he was not inclined to believe that experiments would confirm the law. His prediction provided a crucial test of the atomic theory—but when he searched the literature in 1860, he found that no adequate experiment had been done.

Maxwell decided to perform the experiment himself. He devised a torsion pendulum in which the back-and-forth rotation of glass discs was resisted by air friction. In this case, the damping rate of the oscillating discs is proportional to the viscosity of the air. The apparatus was enclosed in a glass container, and a pump was used to vary the air pressure in the container (which was measured by a mercury barometer). It was a dramatic triumph for the atomic theory when Maxwell observed that the damping rate of the oscillations remained constant as the air pressure was varied from one-half inch to thirty inches of mercury.[13] In 1866, he published these results.

Although the law seems paradoxical, Maxwell grasped why the atomic theory implies that gaseous viscosity must be independent of density. The air very close to the glass disc tends to move with the disc, causing little frictional resistance; the air farther away, on the other hand, shares this motion to a lesser degree. When most of the air is removed, the number of collisions between air molecules and the disc is decreased—but since the colliding molecules are coming from farther away, the momentum transferred per collision is proportionally increased. Therefore, the resisting force remains constant. A generation later, one physicist commented: "[I]n the whole range of science there is no more beautiful or telling discovery than that gaseous viscosity is the same at all densities."[14]

The theory of gases had yet another interesting implication. It was shown that the diameter of molecules can be expressed in terms of two quantities: the mean free path in the gaseous state, and the "condensation coefficient," which is the ratio of liquid to gas volume at the boiling point. The mean free path could be determined from the results of experiments measuring gaseous viscosity, diffusion, or heat conduction. The condensation coefficients for several gases had also been measured. In 1865, the German physicist Joseph Loschmidt put this data together and came to the conclusion that molecules are about one nanometer in diameter. Shortly thereafter, Maxwell improved the calculation and arrived at a somewhat smaller and more accurate estimate of molecular diameters.

In 1870, Lord Kelvin (aka William Thomson) extended the analysis by showing that sizes of molecules could be estimated by several methods. To the above result, he added estimates based on the dispersion of light, contact electricity in metals, and capillary action in thin films such as soap bubbles.[15] The results of the four independent methods were in agreement, and Kelvin noted that it was very impressive that such a vast range of data should all point to the same conclusion.

Physicists had done their part. And while they had been developing the atomic theory of gases, the chemists had not been idle. The middle decades of the nineteenth century were a period of extraordinary progress in chemistry, and the progress was dependent upon thinking in terms of atoms.

The Unification of Chemistry

Earlier, we left chemists facing a problem. They had discovered strong evidence in favor of the atomic theory, but false ideas concerning the nature of gases and chemical bonding had led many to deny the possibility of diatomic gas molecules—which led them to reject Avogadro's hypothesis—which left them unable to arrive at the correct atomic weights—which led to a hornet's nest of problems, including contradictions with the Dulong-Petit law of heat capacities. The fact that elemental gas molecules often consist of more than one atom had to be accepted before chemistry could free itself from the contradictions.

An important clue to resolving this problem came from the same type of experiments that had been used to justify the oversimplified ionic theory of bonding. When powerful batteries were employed in electrolysis experiments, some chemists noted an "odor of electricity" at the positive electrode. It was the same odor that had been noticed previously in experiments that involved electrical discharges in air. Chemists realized that some new gas, which they named "ozone," was being produced in such experiments.

The first breakthrough regarding the identity of this gas was made in 1845 by Jean de Marignac, a chemistry professor in Geneva. Marignac showed that ozone could be produced by an electrical discharge through ordinary oxygen gas, and he concluded that ozone must be an allotrope of oxygen. The existence of two very different oxygen gases seemed impossible to explain unless oxygen atoms could combine with other oxygen atoms. Here was an experimental result that directly contradicted the argument against diatomic gas molecules. Berzelius himself, one of the leading proponents of the ionic theory of bonding, recognized the importance of this discovery. It was no longer reasonable to deny that gas molecules could be combinations of identical atoms.

Thus the discovery of ozone, in combination with Waterston's derivation of the gas law, should have led to the acceptance of Avogadro's hypothesis in the 1840s. However, for reasons that will be explained in the next chapter, there was a strong bias against the atomic theory, and consequently Waterston's paper was never published. As a result, the widespread confusion about atomic weights persisted for longer than necessary. It was a German physicist, August Kroenig, who eventually repeated Waterston's derivation and had it published in 1856.

Unlike Waterston, Kroenig did not explicitly point out that the atomic theory of gases provided a fundamental validation of Avogadro's hypothesis. Nevertheless, at least one chemist grasped the implication. In 1858, Stanislao Cannizzaro presented the solution to the problem of atomic weights in a landmark paper titled "Sketch of a Course of Chemical Philosophy." The paper is a model of clear thinking about an issue that had been mired in obscurity and contradictions for decades.

Cannizzaro showed how to integrate all the relevant data to arrive at one uniquely determined set of atomic weights. Avogadro's hypothesis formed the centerpiece of his argument. Many of the most common elements—for example, hydrogen, carbon, nitrogen, oxygen, sulfur, chlorine—combine in various ways to form gases. The vapor densities of the gases had been measured. Furthermore, in the compound gases, the percentage weight of each element was known. The product of the vapor density and the percentage weight gives the mass density of each element in the gas. Since the number of molecules is always the same for equal volumes (by Avogadro's hypothesis), these mass densities are proportional to the number of atoms of the element that are contained in the gas molecule. Thus the atomic composition of gas molecules can be determined, and then the relative atomic weights of the elements can be deduced. Cannizzaro showed that if hydrogen (the lightest element) is assigned an atomic weight of 1, then the weight of carbon is 12, nitrogen is 14, oxygen is 16, and sulfur is 32.

Once the atomic weights of these elements were known, the weights of most other elements could be determined relative to them. In cases where ambiguities persisted, Cannizzaro often resolved them by using the Dulong-Petit law of heat capacities. Typically, the candidate atomic weights differed by a factor of two, with one value conforming to the Dulong-Petit law and the other value contradicting it.

In 1860, Cannizzaro seized the opportunity to present his paper at a major conference held in Karlsruhe, Germany. This famous meeting became a turning point for nineteenth-century chemistry; within a few years, most chemists accepted the correct atomic weights. One professor of chemistry, Lothar Meyer, expressed his reaction to Cannizzaro's paper in the following words: "It was as though scales fell from my eyes, doubt vanished, and was replaced by a feeling of peaceful certainty."[16]

After their greatest obstacle had been removed, chemists made rapid progress over the next decade. With the correct atomic weights, they could determine the correct molecular formulas. A pattern emerged that led to the new concept "valence," which refers to the capacity of an atom to combine with other atoms. For example, a carbon atom can combine with up to four other atoms, a nitrogen atom with three, an oxygen atom with two, and a hydrogen atom with one. Figuratively, valence can be thought of as the number of "hooks" an atom has for attaching to other atoms.

The concept "valence" was first introduced by the English chemist Edward Frankland, who had arrived at the idea while studying the various ways that carbon combines with metals.[17] Frankland was one of the first chemists to make use of ball-and-wire models of molecular structure; in such models the valence of an atom corresponds to the number of wires attached to the ball. In 1861, he wrote: "The behavior of the organo-metallic bodies teaches a doctrine which affects chemical compounds in general, and which may be called the doctrine of atomic saturation; each element is capable of combining with a certain number of atoms; and this number can never be exceeded. . . ."[18] He first identified this "law of valency" in the 1850s, but in many cases the valences he initially assigned to atoms were wrong. In 1866, after the errors had been corrected, Frankland expressed his gratitude to Cannizzaro: "I do not forget how much this law in its present development owes to the labors of Cannizzaro. Indeed until the latter had placed the atomic weights of metallic elements upon their present consistent basis, the satisfactory development of the doctrine was impossible."[19]

In 1869, an English journal published a review article about the atomic theory that referred to valence as "the new idea that is revolutionizing chemistry."[20] This was no exaggeration. Earlier that year, the Russian chemist Dmitry Mendeleyev had proposed a systematic classification of the chemical elements, based on the properties of atomic weight and valence, "which unified and rationalized the whole effort of chemical investigation."[21]

Several chemists had previously noted that there are natural groups of chemical elements possessing similar properties. Six such groups (known at the time) are: (1) lithium, sodium, and potassium; (2) calcium, strontium, and barium; (3) fluorine, chlorine, bromine, and iodine; (4) oxygen, sulfur, selenium, and tellurium; (5) nitrogen, phosphorus, arsenic, and antinomy; and (6) carbon, silicon, and tin. In each group, the elements have the same valence and similar electrical affinities.

Mendeleyev constructed a table of all the known elements in order of increasing atomic weight and he noticed that the similar elements recur at definite intervals. Thus he announced his "periodic law": The properties of elements are periodic functions of their atomic weights. In the modern version of his table, which is presented in every introductory course in chemistry, the elements appear in order of ascending atomic weight in the horizontal rows, with the vertical columns containing elements of the same valence.

Mendeleyev pointed out that "vacant places occur for elements which perhaps shall be discovered in the course of time." By grasping how other properties of an element are related to its atomic weight and valence, he realized that "it is possible to foretell the properties of an element still unknown." For example, there was a gap under aluminum that

was filled when gallium was discovered in 1875, and another gap under silicon that was filled when germanium was discovered in 1886.
Mendeleyev predicted the properties of both these elements—and his
predictions were remarkably accurate. With the construction of the
periodic table, the chemical elements no longer stood apart in isolation;
the atomic theory had made it possible to connect them together into an
intelligible whole.[22]

The correct atomic weights and valences also led to breakthroughs in
the new frontier of chemical investigation: the determination of molecular structure. In 1861, the Russian chemist Alexander Butlerov described
the ambitious goal of this new research program: "Only one rational formula is possible for each compound, and when the general laws governing the dependence of chemical properties on chemical structure have
been derived, this formula will represent all these properties."[23] It was
not enough, Butlerov realized, to know the number of atoms and their
identities; in order to understand the properties of a compound, the spatial arrangement of the atoms within the molecule must be determined.
Among the first major triumphs of this program was the discovery of the
molecular structure of benzene.

The existence of benzene had been known for decades. In 1825, the
Portable Gas Company in London asked Michael Faraday to analyze a
mysterious liquid by-product of the process that generated natural gas
for illumination. By distillation, he obtained the first sample of pure benzene, a compound that was destined to be very useful in both chemical
theory and industrial practice. Faraday's attempt at analysis, however,
was not entirely successful. Without Avogadro's hypothesis and with the
assumption that the atomic weight of carbon is six rather than twelve, he
arrived at the incorrect molecular formula of C_2H.

After Cannizzaro's work, the molecular formula for benzene was correctly identified as C_6H_6, but its structure was still a mystery. It was a
very stable compound that could be converted into many derivatives
without decomposing. This was surprising, given that the ratio of hydrogen to carbon was so low. In contrast, the compound acetylene (C_2H_2)
has the same low hydrogen-carbon ratio and is highly reactive.

The study of benzene derivatives, i.e., compounds in which one or more of the hydrogen atoms are replaced by a different atom (or group of atoms), revealed another interesting property. It was found, for example, that only one chlorobenzene compound is formed when a chlorine atom is substituted for any of the hydrogen atoms. Thus the hydrogen atoms must occupy indistinguishable positions in the structure, implying that the benzene molecule is highly symmetrical.

The molecular structure of benzene that explains both its stability and its symmetry was first proposed in 1861 by Loschmidt. The six carbon atoms form a symmetric hexagonal ring, with one hydrogen atom attached to each carbon. The tetravalent nature of carbon implies that the ring must be held together by alternating single and double bonds; in this way, each carbon atom uses three of its bonds on adjacent carbon atoms and the fourth on the hydrogen atom.

Unfortunately, Loschmidt's book was given only a small printing by an obscure publisher and, consequently, few chemists read it. Most chemists learned about this proposed structure of benzene from the famous German chemist August Kekule, who published it in 1865. Kekule went much further than Loschmidt by conducting a lengthy study of many isomers of benzene derivatives. For example, he showed that dichlorobenzene, trichlorobenzene, and tetrachlorobenzene each exist in three different isomeric forms—exactly as predicted by the hexagonal ring structure. By 1872, Kekule reported that "no example of isomerism among benzene derivatives had come to light which could not be completely explained by the difference in relative positions of the atoms substituted for hydrogen."[24] It was a landmark achievement: Chemists now had the knowledge and experimental techniques required to infer the spatial distribution of atoms in molecules. The molecules themselves could not be seen—but they could no longer hide, either.

The case of benzene was simplified by the fact that the molecule has a planar structure. In most molecules, the atoms are distributed in three dimensions. The study of three-dimensional molecular structures is called stereochemistry, and its origins can be traced back to the first great discovery of Louis Pasteur.

In 1846, Pasteur began a study of sodium ammonium tartrate, a crystalline substance that was known to be optically active (i.e., it rotates the plane of polarized light). When he viewed the small crystals with a magnifying glass, he noticed that they were subtly asymmetric; there was a small facet on one side that did not appear on the other side. He thought that this asymmetry might be the cause of the optical activity. So he decided to examine the crystals of sodium ammonium racemate, an optically *in*active isomer of the tartrate. If the crystals of the racemate were symmetric, he would have strong evidence that the asymmetry in the tartrate causes the rotation of the light.

Instead, Pasteur discovered that the racemic crystals came in two varieties, both asymmetric and each the mirror image of the other. Using tweezers, he painstakingly separated the two types of crystals. One of the crystals was identical to the tartrate, and it rotated the plane of polarized light in the same direction. The mirror-image crystal rotated the light by the same amount but in the opposite direction. The racemate is optically inactive because the effect of one crystal is canceled by the effect of its mirror image.

Why is this relevant to molecular structure? Because these isomeric compounds rotate the plane of polarized light even when they are dissolved in solution. The asymmetry that causes the rotation persists after the crystal is broken apart into its component molecules. Pasteur concluded that the asymmetry is a property of the molecules themselves. In 1860, he wrote: "Are the atoms . . . grouped on the spiral of a right handed helix, or are they situated at the apices of a regular tetrahedron, or are they disposed according to some other asymmetric arrangement? We do not know. But of this there is no doubt, that the atoms possess an asymmetric arrangement like that of an object and its mirror image."[25]

The answer to Pasteur's question was provided by Jacobus van 't Hoff in 1874. Van 't Hoff realized that the mirror-image structures, and the resulting optical activity, could be explained if the four bonds of a carbon atom pointed to the vertices of a tetrahedron (a triangular pyramid). In this arrangement, whenever four different atoms (or groups of atoms) are attached to the carbon in the center of the tetrahedron, it will be possible to create two isomers that are mirror images. The tetrahedral structure of carbon bonds explained Pasteur's results and the other known instances of optical activity in organic compounds (e.g., lactic acid or glyceraldehyde).

Furthermore, Van 't Hoff's symmetrical 3-D arrangement of carbon bonds provided the solution to another problem. The assumption of a planar structure with the four carbon bonds arranged in a square had led to the prediction of nonexistent isomers. For example, consider the compound methyl dichloride, which has the formula CH_2Cl_2. The planar structure predicts two isomers; the chlorine atoms can be on one side of the square or diagonally opposite each other. In the tetrahedral structure, however, all arrangements are identical—which was consistent with the laboratory analysis that could isolate only one methyl dichloride.

Two decades earlier, the goal of understanding the properties of compounds in terms of the spatial arrangement of atoms in the molecules had seemed unattainable. It had now been attained. The atomic theory had integrated the science of chemistry and demonstrated its explanatory power in dramatic fashion. In regard to Van 't Hoff's contribution, one historian writes, "By 1874 most chemists had already accepted the structure theory, and now here was definitive proof. To all intents and purposes the great debate about whether atoms and molecules truly existed, the roots of which could be traced back to Dalton, and before him to the ancients, was resolved."[26]

This is true; by the mid-1870s, the evidence for the atomic theory was overwhelming. Reasonable doubts were no longer possible.

The Method of Proof

Nineteenth-century scientists discovered the fundamental nature of matter in the same way that seventeenth-century scientists discovered the fundamental laws of motion. Throughout this chapter, we have seen the same method at work—i.e., objective concepts functioning as green lights to induction, the role of experiment and mathematics in identifying causal laws, and the grand-scale integration culminating in proof. Let us now analyze the steps that led to this magnificent achievement.

Lavoisier understood that language is more than a necessary precondition for expressing our thoughts about the world; our concepts entail a commitment to generalize about their referents, and thus they both direct and make possible our search for laws. As he put it, if chemists accepted his proposed language, "they must irresistibly follow the course marked out by it."

Lavoisier's language guided chemists down the path that eventually led to the atomic theory. His system mandated that certain questions be answered in order to properly conceptualize a material: Is it a substance or a mixture? If it is a substance, can it be decomposed into different elements? In cases where different substances are made of the same elements, how are the substances distinguished? These are the questions that put chemists on a course to discover the laws of constant composition and multiple proportions, and eventually to identify the relative weights of atoms and the molecular formulas of compounds.

As was the case in physics, the path to modern chemistry first needed to be cleared by the elimination of invalid concepts. For example, Lavoisier led the battle against the concept "phlogiston," which referred to the alleged element associated with fire. It was thought that a burning candle releases phlogiston into the surrounding air. If the candle is placed in a closed container, the flame is extinguished when the air becomes saturated and can absorb no more phlogiston. The remaining gas that would not support combustion—which was pure nitrogen—was identified as normal air plus phlogiston. When the part of air that did support combustion—i.e., oxygen—was isolated, it was identified as normal air minus phlogiston. A similar error was made when water was first decomposed into hydrogen and oxygen. Hydrogen was identified as water plus phlogiston, and the oxygen was identified as water minus phlogiston.

By quantitative analysis, however, it was discovered that a substance undergoing combustion gains weight while the surrounding air loses weight. Those who followed the course marked out by the concept "phlogiston" were then compelled to ascribe to this element a negative mass. If chemists had continued down this path and conceded the possibility of elements with negative mass, they would have given up the principle that enabled them to distinguish elements from compounds—and progress in chemistry would have come to an abrupt halt. Fortunately, most chemists dismissed the idea of "negative mass" as arbitrary. They followed Lavoisier when he rejected phlogiston and identified combustion as the process of a substance combining with oxygen.

Lavoisier's chemical language provided part of the foundation, but we have seen that the atomic theory required the formation of many other concepts. Nearly every law that contributed to the proof of the theory made use of a crucial new concept. There is Avogadro's hypothesis and the concept "molecule," the Dulong-Petit law and the concepts "specific heat" and "atomic weight," Faraday's law of electrolysis and the concept "ion," Waterston's gas law and the concept "energy" (integrating motion and heat), Maxwell's laws of gaseous transport processes and the concept "mean free path," and Mendeleyev's periodic law and the concept "valence." In each case, the facts gave rise to the need for a new concept, and then that concept made it possible to grasp a causal relationship that had been inaccessible without it.

Given a valid conceptual framework, the causal relationships were discovered by means of experiment. In some cases, they were induced directly from the experimental data (e.g., Charles' law of gases, the law of constant composition, the law of multiple proportions, and the law of combining gas volumes). These laws were reached and validated independent of the atomic theory. In other cases, as illustrated by the kinetic theory of gases, laws were mathematically deduced from premises about atoms that were themselves based on experimental data; these laws were then confirmed by further experiments.

All of the experiments discussed in this chapter contributed to the proof of the atomic theory. Nevertheless, some of them stand out as crucial. The best example is Maxwell's experiment showing that gaseous viscosity is independent of density. The atomic theory offered a simple explanation for this surprising result, an explanation relying on the fact that gases consist of widely separated particles moving freely between collisions. In contrast, a continuum theory of matter would seem to imply that a denser medium should offer greater resistance to motion through it. Thus this experiment isolated a case in which the atomic theory made a prediction that differentiated it from any continuum theory.

A "crucial" experiment or observation confirms a prediction of one theory while contradicting the alternative theories. A good example from astronomy is provided by Galileo's telescopic observations of Venus, which showed a full range of phases as the planet moved around the sun. These observations were predicted by the heliocentric theory and they flatly contradicted Ptolemy's theory. Another example can be found in optics: Newton's recombination of the color spectrum to produce white light was predicted by his theory, and it contradicted the alternative theories proposed by Descartes and Hooke.

Many philosophers of science deny that any particular experiment can be regarded as "crucial." This rejection of crucial experiments can be traced back to Pierre Duhem and Willard Quine, and it is commonly referred to as the Duhem-Quine thesis. They argued that no single experiment can play a decisive role in validating or refuting a broad theory. In a trivial sense, this is true: An experiment—*considered in isolation*—cannot perform such a function. However, the results of a single experiment—when its implications are not evaded by arbitrary hypotheses and *when it is judged within the total context of knowledge*—can and regularly do play such a decisive role. The evaluation of the new data as crucial is dependent on the context.

Experiment provides entrance into mathematics by means of numerical measurement. At the beginning of an investigation, nonquantitative experiments may be performed in order to determine whether an effect occurs under specific circumstances. Such experiments characterize the early history of chemistry, electricity, and heat. As the investigation advances, however, the experiments must involve making numerical measurements. The discoveries described in this chapter were entirely dependent on measurements made with precision mass balances, thermometers, barometers, ammeters, apparatus for determining vapor densities, and so on. The causal laws integrated by the atomic theory are equations that express relations among the numerical data.

In regard to chemistry, we can pose the same question that we asked earlier about astronomy: What progress was possible without mathematics? We find a similar answer. Just as an ancient shepherd could use his observations of the sky as a rough clock and compass, an early chemist could use his knowledge of reactions for the practical purpose of purifying metals or synthesizing dyes. In both astronomy and chemistry, however, this premathematical stage consisted of a very long list of separate items of knowledge—with no way to grasp the causal relationships that connect them. Both of these fields became sciences only when numerical measurements were unified by laws expressed in mathematical form.

The same point is seen in the study of heat. The qualitative experiments of Rumford and Davy provided strong evidence that heat was a form of internal motion, yet the idea led nowhere for the next forty-five years. In contrast, when Joule measured the quantitative relationship between heat and motion, he opened the floodgates to further discoveries. Temperature was identified with the average kinetic energy of molecules, and within twenty years the kinetic theory of gases had explained an enormous range of data.

In physical science, qualitative truths are mere starting points; they can suggest a course of investigation, but that investigation is successful only when it arrives at a causal relationship among quantities. Then the power of mathematics is unleashed; connections can be identified between facts that had previously seemed entirely unrelated (e.g., elastic collisions in mechanics and heat flow between bodies, or the heat capacity of an element and the mass of its atoms, or the volumes of reacting gases and the composition of molecules, or heat conduction in gases and the size of molecules). Mathematics is the scientist's means of integrating his knowledge.

Let us now consider the final payoff of the inductive method: the proof of a physical theory. A theory is an integrated set of principles on which an entire subject is based; as such, it subsumes and explains the particular facts and narrower laws. Because of the abstract nature of a theory, it can be difficult for a scientist to decide when the evidence has culminated in proof. Yet this question is of great practical importance. If a scientist's standard of proof is too low, he may easily accept a false theory and pursue research that leads nowhere (the theories based on phlogiston and caloric are good examples). But the failure to accept a proven theory in the name of allegedly "higher standards" is equally disastrous; since further progress in the field is dependent on the theory, the scientist's research will stagnate—and if he persists in pursuing such a course, he will find himself actively engaged in a war against the facts (as illustrated by many opponents of the atomic theory).

We have seen the evidence for atoms accumulate over a period of seven decades. Of course, this progress did not stop in the mid-1870s; every decade thereafter, more discoveries added to the explanatory power of the theory. But these later discoveries did not contribute to the proof, which was already complete. Let us now review the evidence and identify the criteria of proof.

In the first third of the nineteenth century, four laws were discovered that supported the atomic nature of chemical elements: (1) elements combine in discrete units of mass to form compounds; (2) gaseous reactions involve integer units of volume; (3) a solid element has a heat capacity that is proportional to the number of discrete mass units; (4) the amount of electricity generated by a chemical reaction is proportional to the number of discrete mass units that react at the electrodes. Furthermore, the discovery of allotropes and isomers provided additional evidence for the atomic theory, which had the potential to explain them as different spatial arrangements of the same atoms.

These laws subsume a large amount of data, ranging across the fields of chemical reactions, heat, and electricity. By attributing to atoms or molecules the appropriate masses, gaseous volumes, quantities of heat, and electric charges, the atomic theory could offer explanations of all four laws. Why is this not enough to prove the theory?

The problem was that scientists had no *independent* reasons for assigning to atoms and molecules the properties that were required to explain these laws. Consider Avogadro's hypothesis, which was introduced to explain the law of combining volumes. Initially the hypothesis could not be connected to other knowledge about gases and, as we have seen, it clashed with widely held (but false) views about chemical bonding and the cause of gaseous pressure. A similar point applies to the atomic explanation offered by Dulong and Petit for their law of heat capacities. They could give no reason why each atom should absorb the same amount of heat, and they were unable to connect their hypothesis to other knowledge about heat and temperature. Thus, at this stage, the ideas of Avogadro and Dulong-Petit were promising but doubtful—which also meant that atomic weights and molecular formulas remained clouded in ambiguity.

We have seen how these doubts were eventually overcome by discoveries concerning the nature of heat and gases. Experiments studying the conversion of motion into heat provided strong evidence that temperature is a measure of internal kinetic energy. This idea integrated with the Dulong-Petit law; it was reasonable to expect atoms in thermal equilibrium to have the same average kinetic energy. Furthermore, when the idea was combined with a simple molecular model of gases, it could be used to derive the basic law relating the pressure, volume, and temperature of a gas. Avogadro's hypothesis emerged from this analysis as a consequence—thus connecting the hypothesis to Charles' law of gases and to Newton's laws of motion.

This was nearly enough to transform Avogadro's idea from a hypothesis into a law. However, reasonable doubts could still be raised about the simple "billiard-ball" model of gas molecules that had been assumed in the derivation of Charles' law. The theory was not entirely convincing until it could explain other known properties of gases. Thus Maxwell's work was crucial; when he developed and extended the model to explain gaseous transport processes (i.e., diffusion, heat conduction, and viscosity), then the range of data integrated by the kinetic theory of gases left no legitimate grounds for lingering skepticism.

Given the strength of this evidence, chemists were compelled to accept Avogadro's idea along with its full implications. Was the atomic theory then proven? Not quite, for one reason. Chemistry had been in chaos for decades, and it took some time for chemists to use their new knowledge about atoms to integrate and explain the facts of their science. Once they had identified the correct atomic weights and valences, the development of the periodic table and the triumph of molecular structure theory completed the proof.

At this stage, the evidence for the atomic theory satisfied three criteria that are essential to the proof of any broad theory.

First, every concept and every generalization contained within the theory must be derived from observations by a valid method. A proven theory can have no concepts such as "phlogiston" or "absolute space," and no causal relationships that do not follow from the observational data. It is often claimed that a good theory correctly predicts some observations and contradicts none. This commonly stated criterion is necessary, of course, but very far from sufficient; it can be satisfied by theories that are false or even arbitrary. We have seen that the atomic theory has a different relationship to the data: Every law subsumed by the theory was rigorously induced from the results of experiments.

Second, a proven theory must form an integrated whole. It cannot be a conglomeration of independent parts that are freely adjusted to fit the data (as was the case with Ptolemaic astronomy). Rather, the various parts of the theory are interconnected and mutually reinforcing, so that the denial of any part leads to contradictions throughout the whole. A theory must have this characteristic in order to be necessitated by the evidence. Otherwise one could not reach a conclusive evaluation about the relationship between the evidence and the theory; at best, one could evaluate only the relationship between the evidence and *parts* of the theory. On the other hand, when a theory is an integrated whole, then the evidence for any part is evidence for the whole.

By the mid-1870s, the atomic theory satisfied this criterion. Properties of atoms that had been hypothesized to explain one set of experimental facts were found to be indispensable in the explanation of other facts and laws. For instance, Avogadro's hypothesis began as an explanation for a law governing the chemical reactions of gases—and then it became an essential part of a theory that derived the physical properties of gases from Newtonian mechanics. One cannot deny Avogadro's hypothesis without contradicting the explanation for a half-dozen laws and severing the connection between atoms and the laws of motion. Similarly, the atomic hypothesis of Dulong and Petit does not merely explain the heat capacities of solids; it became part of a theory relating heat to atomic motion in all materials. These ideas then led inexorably to a specific set of atomic weights and valences, which were shown to explain the relationships among the elements, the results of electrolysis experiments, and the properties of chemical compounds.

In order to further concretize this point, let us consider the consequences of making one small change to the theory. For instance, imagine that scientists refused to correct Faraday's proposed molecular formula for benzene, C_2H. Vapor density measurements of benzene gas would then contradict Avogadro's hypothesis, which would have to be rejected along with the kinetic theory of gases that entails it. Furthermore, since this incorrect formula implies the wrong valence for carbon, chemists would also be compelled to reject Mendeleyev's periodic law and the theory of molecular structures in organic chemistry. The fallout from this one change would leave the entire atomic theory in ruins. When a theory is a whole, the parts cannot be freely adjusted; they are constrained by their relations to the rest of the theory and the facts on which it is based.

The third criterion pertains to the range of data integrated by the theory. The scope of a proven theory must be determined by the data from which it is induced; i.e., the theory must be no broader or narrower than required to integrate the data. This criterion is not independent of the first two; it simply makes explicit a crucial implication. If the theory is too broad, then it is not necessitated by the evidence and therefore it violates the first criterion (in such a case, the theory may be a legitimate hypothesis, but it cannot be regarded as proven). If the theory is too narrow, it will not achieve the integration described by the second criterion.

For instance, when Kepler integrated Brahe's observations of the planets, he arrived at laws that were restricted to *planetary* motion. In order for Newton to reach universal laws, he had to include data on the movements of terrestrial bodies, moons, oceans, and comets. Similarly, in the early nineteenth century, when the atomic theory was supported only by data from chemistry, conclusions could be reached only about the discrete nature of chemical reactions. At this stage it was a hypothesis that the theory could be generalized to a fundamental theory of matter.

In order to reach this generalization, scientists needed a range of data that compelled them to regard atoms as basic units of *matter*, not merely as the units of *chemical reactions*. The breakthrough occurred when physicists explained the nature of heat and gases in terms of atoms of a certain size moving in accordance with Newton's laws. The laws of motion apply to matter qua matter, not to chemical elements qua chemical elements. When these physical properties of materials could be explained by atoms in motion, the atomic theory became a fundamental theory of matter that brought together into a whole the laws governing chemical reactions, motion, heat, electric current, and the various properties of gases.

The three criteria describe the relationship between a proven theory and the evidence supporting it. When every aspect of the theory is induced from the data (not invented from imagination), and the theory forms a cognitive whole (not an independent collection of laws), and the scope of the theory is objectively derived from the range of data—then the theory truly is an integration (criterion 2) of the data (criterion 1), no more and no less (criterion 3).

A valid concept must satisfy similar criteria; it is derived from observations (not a product of fantasy), it is an integration of similar concretes (not a mere collection), and its definition must not be too broad or too narrow. There are many differences, of course, between a concept and a scientific theory. Yet the criteria of validation are similar, because these are broad principles that identify how a conceptual faculty properly forms a cognitive whole.

These criteria cannot be quantified. It would be ridiculous to claim, for example, that 514 pieces of evidence are required in order to prove a fundamental theory. Yet the criteria identify within narrow limits when the evidence culminates in proof. The atomic theory was obviously *not* proven prior to Maxwell's climactic work on the kinetic theory of gases, published in 1866, whereas the necessary integration of physical and chemical data had clearly been achieved by the time Mendeleyev's prediction of gallium was confirmed in 1875. There may be room for rational debate about whether the atomic theory is properly evaluated as proven in 1870. But little is at stake in such a debate.

The claim that the atomic theory was proven by 1875 does not mean that it left no unanswered questions. On the contrary, the theory gave rise to an entire realm of very important unanswered questions. For example, measurements of heat capacity seemed to imply that diatomic molecules move rapidly and rotate at normal temperatures, but they do not vibrate as expected: Why not? There were many questions about the nature of chemical bonds, for example: Why do some atoms seem to have a variable valence, and how do these atoms differ from those with a constant valence? There were questions about the interaction of atoms and light, for example: Why does each kind of atom emit and absorb light at specific characteristic wavelengths? Furthermore, there was evidence supporting the view that atoms contain electrically charged particles: If so, how could the charge be distributed in a way that is consistent with the stability of atoms? Such questions, however, did not cast doubt on the atomic theory; rather, they presupposed it. The questions pertained to the new frontier that the theory made possible: the investigation of atomic structure. The answers were discovered in the early decades of the twentieth century.

The submicroscopic world of atoms is accessible only by a very long and complex chain of reasoning. For over two millennia, the idea of atoms was nothing more than a hope—a hope that someday, somehow, man's mind would be able to reach far beyond what is given by his senses and grasp the fundamental nature of matter. This could not be done by means of a reckless leap into a cognitive void; scientists had to discover the method of proceeding step by step from observations to knowledge of atoms, while staying on solid ground. No shortcut of this process is possible *or desirable*; every step of the journey is its own reward, contributing a valuable piece of the knowledge that is condensed and integrated by the final theory.

The nature of the inductive method is now clear.

6.

Causes of Error

In contrast to perception, thinking is a fallible process. This fact gives rise to our need for the method of logic.

Logic, when properly applied, enables us to arrive at true conclusions. But it comes with no guarantee that we will apply the method correctly. The laws of deduction were identified by Aristotle more than two millennia ago, yet people still commit deductive fallacies. If one remains attentive to the evidence, however, further use of logic leads to the correction of these errors. The same is true of false generalizations reached by induction. In this chapter we will see that even the best thinkers can commit errors in applying the inductive method. But such errors wither and die in the light shed by continued application of the proper method.

During the past century, however, many philosophers have rejected the validity of induction and argued that every generalization is an error. For example, Karl Popper claimed that all the laws of Kepler, Galileo, and Newton have been "falsified."[1] By demanding that a true generalization must apply with unlimited precision to an unlimited domain, Popper upheld a mystical view of "truth" that is forever outside the reach of man and accessible only to an omniscient god. In the end, he was left with two types of generalizations: those that *have been* proven false and those that *will be* proven false. He was then accused by later philosophers of being too optimistic; they insisted that nothing can be proven, not even a generalization's falsehood.

Such skeptics commit—on a grand scale—the fallacy of dropping context. The meaning of our generalizations is determined by the context that gives rise to them; to claim that a generalization is true *is* to claim that it applies within a specific context. The data subsumed by that context are necessarily limited in both range and precision.

Galileo, for example, committed no error when he identified the parabolic nature of trajectories. Obviously, he was not referring to a six-thousand-mile path of an intercontinental ballistic missile (to which his law does not apply). He was referring to terrestrial bodies that could be observed and studied in his era—all of which remained close to the surface of the earth, traveled perhaps a few hundred feet, and moved in accordance with his law. Similarly, when Newton spoke of bodies and their motion, he was not referring to the movement of an electron in an atom or of a proton in a modern accelerator. He was referring to observable, macroscopic bodies, ranging from pebbles to stars. The available context of knowledge determines the referents of the concepts that are causally related in a generalization.

The context also includes the accuracy of the data integrated by a law. In order to understand the variations revealed by new data of much greater accuracy, it is often necessary to identify additional causal factors. Kepler's laws of planetary motion illustrate this point. The laws are true—i.e., they correctly identify causal relationships that explain and integrate the data available to Kepler. By Newton's era, however, the measurement errors in astronomical data had been reduced by more than a factor of ten, and today they have been reduced by another factor of ten. In order to explain the more accurate data, one must grasp not only that the sun exerts a force on the planets, but also that the planets exert forces on each other and on the sun. The truths discovered by Kepler were essential to these later discoveries; they made it possible to identify deviations of the new data from the original laws, which in turn made it possible to identify the additional causal factors and develop a more general theory.

In cases where the data are insufficient to support a conclusion, it is important to look closely at the exact nature of the scientist's claim. He does not commit an error simply by proposing a *hypothesis* that is later proven wrong, provided that he correctly identified the hypothetical status of the idea. If he can cite some supporting evidence, and he has not overlooked any data that contradict it, and he rejects the idea when counterevidence is discovered, then his thinking is flawlessly logical. An example is provided by the work of Albert Ladenburg, a nineteenth-century German chemist, who proposed a triangular prism structure of the benzene molecule.[2] Ladenburg's hypothesis was consistent with the data available in the 1860s, but it was rejected a few years later when it clashed with Van 't Hoff's discovery of the symmetrical arrangement of carbon bonds. In such cases, the scientist's thinking is guided by the evidence at every step, and he deserves nothing but praise from the epistemologist.

Errors can be divided into two broad categories based on their causes. First, I will discuss errors that are caused by a misapplication of the inductive method. Then I will turn to consider the far more disastrous errors that result from abandoning the inductive method.

Misapplying the Inductive Method

A true generalization states a causal relationship that has been induced from observational data and integrated within the whole of one's knowledge (which, in terms of essentials, spans the range subsumed by the generalization). A scientist makes an error when he asserts a generalization without achieving such an integration. In such cases, the supporting evidence is insufficient and often the scientist has overlooked counterevidence.

I make no attempt here to give an exhaustive list of the essential inductive fallacies. Rather, I have chosen five interesting cases in which scientists have investigated a complex phenomenon and reached false generalizations by deviating from the proper method. In each case I examine the context of knowledge available to the scientist and seek to identify the factors that cast doubt on his conclusion.

Plant Growth

In the early seventeenth century, the Dutch chemist J. B. van Helmont investigated the cause of plant growth. Most people of the time thought that plants absorb material from the soil and convert it to wood and foliage, but this was merely a plausible assumption. Van Helmont attempted to reach a definitive answer to the question by performing a quantitative experiment.

He filled a large planter with two hundred pounds of dry soil. He then planted a willow sapling, which weighed five pounds, and covered the soil to prevent any accumulation of dust from the air. For five years he added only distilled water or rainwater to the planter. When he finally removed the willow tree, he found that it weighed 169 pounds, but the soil had lost only a few ounces in weight. Van Helmont concluded: "Therefore 164 pounds of wood, bark, and root have arisen from water alone."[3] In general, he concluded that plant growth is a process in which water is transformed into the substances making up plants.

The experiment used the method of difference: Van Helmont focused on the fact that he had added one factor—water—and the result was the growth of the willow tree. He certainly did prove that very little of the tree's additional weight came from the soil. We now know, however, that only about half of fresh willow wood is water. Van Helmont's error was to reject the possibility that plants absorb material from the air. Much later, in the 1770s, experiments performed by Joseph Priestley and Jan Ingenhousz proved that plants in sunlight absorb carbon dioxide and release oxygen.[4] A large portion of their weight is carbon, which they obtain from the air.

Ironically, it was Van Helmont who originated the concept "gas" and identified the gas we now call carbon dioxide as a product of burning charcoal or wood. So why did he dismiss the possibility that a gas in the air could be an essential cause of plant growth?

Some of Van Helmont's experiments led him to conclude that gases "can neither be retained in vessels nor reduced to a visible form."[5] When he mixed nitric acid and sal ammoniac in a closed glass vessel, for example, he found that gases were produced that burst the vessel. When he compressed air in an "air-gun" and then released it, he found that the air explosively expanded with a force sufficient to propel a ball through a board. To him, this "wild" and "untamable" nature of gases seemed to prohibit the possibility that they could be absorbed to become part of a plant.

Of course, everyone knew that land animals must breathe air in order to live. The nature of respiration, however, was not yet understood. Van Helmont thought that the air "intermingled" with the blood in our lungs and played an essential role in heating it, but he did not grasp that part of the air (oxygen) is absorbed and another gas (carbon dioxide) is exhaled. Similarly, when he studied combustion, he did not grasp that it involves the consumption of air. He observed that a candle burning in a closed vessel causes a decrease in the air volume, but he thought that the flame was consuming something that existed in the spaces between particles of air. So his hypothetical ideas about respiration and combustion were made to be consistent with his claim that gases could not be converted into liquid or solid substances.

Other phenomena appeared to contradict Van Helmont's view of gases as "wild" and "untamable." Steam obviously condenses into water, and he knew of gaseous acids that dissolved in water. In these cases, however, he attempted to protect his view by introducing a distinction between "condensable vapors" and true "gases." But the protection offered by this false distinction was illusory. In regard to plant growth, it simply modified the question, which became: How did he know that a plant does not absorb "condensable vapors" that exist in the air? The fact remains that Van Helmont offered no convincing argument to eliminate the air as a causal factor in plant growth. His conclusion about the nature of gases was not an integration of all available data, but rather a leap from a few facts to a broad generalization.

There were wider issues that guided Van Helmont's thinking. Like many natural philosophers before him, he was struck by the ubiquitous role of water in nature. Water exists as a vapor, liquid, and solid; it fills great oceans, falls from the sky, forms rivers, and shapes our world; it reacts with and/or dissolves many substances; and it is essential to all life. Following a long tradition that began with Thales, Van Helmont identified water as the fundamental element that can be modified in countless ways. He even connected his views on the nature of water and gas to his metaphysical views on the relation of matter and spirit.[6] These beliefs made up part of the background that predisposed him to accept water as the sole source of plant growth.

Notice the complexity of the context that is relevant to interpreting an apparently simple experiment. The elasticity of gases, the nature of respiration and combustion, the similarities and differences between gases and their proper conceptualization, the prominent role of water in natural processes, the relation between the matter and the "essence" of a body—all these considerations influenced Van Helmont in arriving at his conclusion. Such is the nature of inductive reasoning; the results of a particular experiment are interpreted by means of one's entire conceptual framework. This is why induction is difficult, and why it is valid when properly performed. Van Helmont was led astray on the issue of plant growth by the errors in his conceptual framework, which contained numerous elements that did not follow from observed facts, i.e., that were not reached by a proper application of the inductive method.

Acidity

A scientist with a valid conceptual framework can still commit an error. A good example is provided by Lavoisier's analysis of the cause of acidity.

Acids are compounds that are corrosive, have a sour taste, turn blue litmus red, and react with bases to form neutral substances. Lavoisier hypothesized that these properties derive from some one element that all acids have in common. Thus his approach was to use the method of agreement; he studied the known acids and sought to identify their common element.

He discovered that some substances are transformed into acids when they are burned in the presence of water vapor. Combustion of phosphorus, sulfur, and carbon led to phosphoric acid, sulfuric acid, and carbonic acid. Thus it appeared that the element that is absorbed in combustion—i.e., oxygen—might also be the cause of acidity.

Lavoisier's investigation of nitric acid seemed to provide further support for this idea. In 1776 he combined nitric acid with mercury to form a white salt (mercuric nitrate), which decomposed to form red mercury oxide and nitric oxide gas. On further heating, the red oxide was decomposed into metallic mercury and oxygen gas. He collected the gases in bell jars over water. When he combined the nitric oxide and the oxygen in the presence of water, he came full circle and regenerated the original nitric acid. But Lavoisier misinterpreted this result; he overlooked the crucial presence of water and assumed that the acid was a product of the two gases. Later, in 1783, he discovered that water is a compound of hydrogen and oxygen. By overlooking the role of water in his synthesis of acids, he was neglecting the presence of hydrogen—which left oxygen as the only candidate for the common element in acids.

Lavoisier continued to accumulate evidence that seemed to support his idea that oxygen is essential to acidity. He investigated two organic acids (acetic and oxalic) and proved that both contain oxygen. Furthermore, he showed that sulfur forms two acids, and that the one with the higher oxygen content is the stronger acid (today we express this result by saying that H_2SO_4 is more acidic than H_2SO_3).

Lavoisier's oxygen theory of acidity faced one major obstacle. There was a well-known and very strong acid, referred to as "muriatic" acid, that had not been shown to contain oxygen. Muriatic acid decomposed into hydrogen gas and another green gas. Lavoisier referred to the green gas as "oxymuriatic" acid, thereby making explicit his assumption that it was the part of muriatic acid in which oxygen would eventually be found. But the years went by and nobody managed to extract oxygen from "oxymuriatic" gas. Finally, in 1810, after the most effective methods of extracting oxygen had been tried in vain, Humphry Davy declared that the green gas is an element and recommended that it be called "chlorine." So hydrochloric acid provided the counterexample that refuted Lavoisier's oxygen theory.

In form, Lavoisier's error is like the old joke about the man who vowed to stop getting drunk at parties. The man remembered that at one party he had been drinking bourbon and soda; at another, scotch and soda; at yet another, brandy and soda. Obviously soda was the common factor and the cause of his intoxication. So he resolved to drink his whiskey straight.

This type of error is relatively easy to correct. When the man gets drunk on straight bourbon at the next party, he will realize that the soda was irrelevant. Then he will look for a factor common to bourbon, scotch, and brandy. Similarly, when it was discovered that all of Lavoisier's oxygen-containing acids also have hydrogen, and that muriatic acid contains hydrogen but no oxygen, then hydrogen was recognized as the only element common to all known acids. Later, the hydrogen theory of acidity was proved when it was discovered that bases neutralize acids by absorbing a hydrogen ion from them (which typically combines with a hydroxyl ion to form water).

Lavoisier's theory of acidity illustrates the precarious nature of a generalization that is derived from an observed regularity rather than a causal connection. Lavoisier had no evidence that bases act on the oxygen when they neutralize an acid. In the absence of such knowledge, he did not have sufficient grounds to assert that oxygen would necessarily be found in all acids. Thus we can characterize his error as the fallacy of substituting an observed regularity for a cause.

Electric Current

There was a great deal of interest in electricity during the Enlightenment. It was discovered that some materials conduct electricity and others do not; that electric charge exists in two varieties, called positive and negative; that charge can be stored in "Leyden jars," which can then be discharged through a conductor; that lightning is an atmospheric discharge; and that opposite charges attract and like charges repel with a force that varies as the inverse square of the distance. But even after decades of intensive study, the only known way to generate electricity was by rubbing together dissimilar materials, and the only known movement of electricity was the momentary discharge that occurred during a time interval too short to measure. Near the end of the eighteenth century, however, the science of electricity took a giant leap forward with a breakthrough discovery made by Luigi Galvani.

Galvani was a professor of anatomy at the University of Bologna who became interested in the effects of electricity on animals. It had been discovered previously that electrical discharges through animals could cause muscular contractions, and Galvani investigated this phenomenon using dissected frogs and discharges from a static electricity generator. His breakthrough came, however, when he was not using the generator at all. In one experiment, he found that when a frog was held by means of a bronze hook through its spinal cord and its feet were placed on a silver box, connecting the hook and box caused muscular contractions that made the dead frog appear to jump and dance. Galvani realized that electricity was moving through the frog's leg muscles, but its source was a mystery.

This discovery had crucial implications for both physics and biology. From the perspective of the physicist, Galvani had discovered a new way to generate a flow of electricity. From the perspective of the biologist, he had apparently discovered the physical mechanism controlling the movement of our bodies: The contraction of our muscles is somehow caused by electricity that can flow through our nerves.

Since Galvani was a biologist, it is not surprising that his primary focus was on the frog rather than on the bronze hook or the silver box. He developed a theory in which the source of the electricity is in the animal, while the metals played the passive role of mere conductors that allowed the electricity to flow. His theory claimed that muscles store electricity in much the same way as Leyden jars, and that when a conducting circuit is completed, the resulting discharge causes the contraction.

Galvani noted that strong muscular contractions were observed only when two different metals were used (e.g., bronze and silver). When he placed the frog on an iron surface and used an iron hook, the effect did not occur. But he failed to appreciate the significance of this fact, and his theory offers no explanation for it. If the metals act simply as conductors, then he should have observed the muscle contractions in the experiment that used only iron. Initially Galvani did not seem to recognize that the requirement of two different metals posed a severe problem for his theory.

It was Alessandro Volta, a physics professor at the University of Pavia, who seized on the fact that was overlooked by Galvani's theory. Volta became convinced that the source of electricity was the different properties of the two metals, and it was the frog that played the passive role of merely providing a conducting fluid between the metals. In a series of experiments, he proved that the further apart the two metals stood in the following series—zinc, tin, lead, iron, copper, platinum, gold, silver—the greater the electrical current.

In an attempt to prove that the frog had no part in producing the electricity, Volta performed an experiment in which the frog (and any other conducting fluid) was entirely eliminated. He attached a copper disc and a zinc disc to insulating handles, and then pressed the discs together. When they were separated, he used a delicate electroscope to demonstrate that both discs had acquired an electric charge (the zinc was positive and the copper negative). So a transfer of electric charge is caused by the mere contact of two different metals. This, Volta claimed, was what had occurred in Galvani's experiments: The contact of the two metals had caused a flow of electricity that in turn had caused the muscle contractions of the frog.

Galvani was unconvinced, and he responded by performing an experiment in which the metals were entirely eliminated. When he held a dissected frog by one foot and swung it vigorously so that the sciatic nerve touched the muscle of the other leg, he observed contractions of the muscle. Here was a case in which the contact between nerve and muscle caused a flow of electricity and muscle contractions, without any metals present. Galvani regarded this experiment as a decisive refutation of Volta's theory.

Volta and Galvani had each committed a similar error. In their efforts to localize the cause in either the metals or the frog, they changed the experimental conditions in a way that introduced causal factors not present in the original experiment. In the case of the frog dancing on the silver box, contact between dissimilar metals cannot be the cause because no such contact is necessary; the effect occurs when the experimenter grips the bronze hook with one hand while touching the silver box with the other hand (in other words, the experimenter himself can be the conducting path between the two metals). Likewise, Galvani was misled by his experiment in which the metals were eliminated; his vigorous swinging of the frog had caused muscle injury, which had stimulated the nerve and caused contractions. But the original experiment had involved no such injury; it had been a simple hop-step, not a swing dance.

Although Volta's "contact theory" was untenable, his investigations did refute Galvani's idea that the phenomenon was caused by a special capacity of animals to store and discharge electricity. While keeping other relevant conditions the same, Volta showed that the animal could be replaced by a salt or acid solution between the two metals, and the effect—a flow of electricity—still occurred. This discovery led to his invention of the electric battery. In March 1800, he wrote a paper in which he described how to generate a continuous electrical current with zinc and silver discs separated by cardboard soaked in salt water.

When Volta announced his invention, the cause of the electrical current was still unknown. But it did not remain a mystery for long. A month after receiving Volta's paper, Anthony Carlisle and William Nicholson constructed a battery and observed evidence of chemical reactions occurring at the metallic surfaces. They used their battery to perform the first electrolysis experiment, decomposing water into hydrogen and oxygen gas. This landmark experiment inspired Humphry Davy to investigate the phenomenon. Only seven months later, Davy wrote:

[The battery] acts only when the conducting substance between the plates is capable of oxidizing the zinc; and that, in proportion as a greater quantity of oxygen enters into combination with the zinc in a given time, so in proportion is the power of the [battery]. It seems therefore reasonable to conclude, although with our present quantity of facts we are unable to explain the exact mode of operation, that the oxidation of the zinc in the battery, and the chemical changes connected with it, are somehow the cause of the electrical effects it produces.[7]

It took decades to identify the "exact mode of operation"—i.e., the dissociation of molecules into electrically charged ions and the reaction of those ions at the electrodes—but the essential cause was understood in 1800: The electrical current is generated by a chemical reaction involving the metals and the fluid connecting them.

So Galvani had been right to claim that the frog in his experiments played an indispensable role in causing the electric current: The frog's fluids provided the salt solution essential to the reaction. But Volta had been right to claim that the metals have a crucial role in generating the electricity, not merely carrying it. Both erred only in denying the claim of the other. The cause could not be found in one of the factors, but only in the chemical interaction of the two.

The main lesson illustrated by these errors is the importance of *proper experimental controls*. Galvani and Volta each thought they had performed crucial experiments that refuted the claim of the other, but the experiments were flawed. When Galvani eliminated the metals and still observed an effect, and when Volta eliminated everything but the metals and still saw an effect, both changed the conditions of the original "dancing frog" experiment in a way that left the interpretation of their results ambiguous.

On a broader level, we can see the potential danger of being prejudiced by one's specialized background. As a biologist, Galvani seemed predisposed to find the cause in the animal; as a physicist, Volta seemed predisposed to find the cause in the physical properties of the metals. It was Davy, a chemist, who correctly identified the cause as a complex interaction involving both factors.

Age of Earth

Let us examine another famous controversy involving a clash between different sciences. During the last four decades of the nineteenth century, the British physicist Lord Kelvin engaged in a spirited debate with geologists. In order to explain a fast-growing body of evidence, the geologists were proposing an ever-longer history of Earth. They had discovered that the natural processes shaping our world occur very slowly, and therefore their science had a basic requirement: *time*. But they found themselves in conflict with one of the most prominent physicists of the era. Kelvin would not give them the time they needed; he became convinced that the fundamental laws of physics implied a very restrictive upper limit on the age of Earth.

For most of human history, people attempted to understand the world around them as the result of sudden, global, cataclysmic events in the past (usually of supernatural origin). In the late eighteenth century, however, James Hutton identified the principle that gave rise to modern geology: "The present," he wrote, "is the key to the past. . . . No powers are to be employed that are not natural to the globe, no action to be admitted to except those of which we know the principle, and no extraordinary events to be alleged in order to explain a common appearance."[8] Hutton and the geologists who followed his lead explained the features of Earth by means of natural forces we observe today: wind, rain, chemical reactions, ocean and river currents, expansion and contraction caused by temperature changes, the uplift of land areas caused by sinking ocean sediment, the slow movements of glaciers, and the cumulative effects of local volcanoes and earthquakes.

Of course, it takes a great deal of time for water erosion to carve out a valley and for mechanical pressures to lift a mountain range. Determining how much time was a central issue for nineteenth-century geology. By estimating rates of erosion and sediment deposit, geologists began to construct the timeline for the formation of the various strata they observed in the Earth's crust. They conducted detailed studies of the world's great river basins, measuring and analyzing the sedimentary contents being washed out to sea. By the 1870s they had reached agreement about the average rate of continental erosion. They also collected data from around the globe on the rates of processes that result in the renewal of landmasses. The data led to a consensus among geologists that the Earth's crust we observe today could not have formed in less than one hundred million years.

To his credit, Kelvin was the first to recognize a potential conflict between the laws of physics and the new geology. Geologists were claiming that the temperature and other physical conditions on Earth had remained roughly constant over the past hundred million years. The sun and Earth, however, have a limited amount of energy, which they are expending at a prodigious rate. This energy dissipation must eventually cause a decrease of temperature that will leave Earth barren and lifeless. For Kelvin, the question was: Do the laws of physics sanction or veto the timeline proposed by geologists?

To answer the question, Kelvin began by considering the possible sources of solar and terrestrial energy. He quickly convinced himself that the energy released in exothermic chemical reactions was far too little to play any significant role. Furthermore, since the sun and Earth are electrically neutral, the energy could not be electromagnetic in origin. That seemed to leave only one possibility: The primary source of energy in the solar system is gravitational in nature.

The solar system, Kelvin argued, must have begun as a large gaseous nebula. As the matter condensed, gravitational potential energy was converted into kinetic energy—i.e., heat. Thus Earth was originally an extremely hot molten ball, which has been cooling ever since. "We may follow in imagination," he wrote, "the whole process of shrinking from gaseous nebula to liquid lava and metals, and the solidification of liquid from the central regions outward."[9]

In the 1860s, Kelvin performed his first analysis of the rate at which Earth is losing heat. He acknowledged that the parameters required for the calculation were not precisely known, but he argued that enough was known to make a reasonable estimate. For the temperature of Earth's core, he used the melting point of surface rocks; for the thermal conductivity of Earth, he used the measured value for surface rocks; for the temperature gradient at Earth's surface, he used a measurement of about one degree Fahrenheit per fifty feet. With these parameters, he arrived at a rate of heat loss that implied the Earth's crust had formed less than one hundred million years ago. Contrary to the geologists, the conditions observed today could have existed for only a small fraction of that time. Kelvin stated his conclusion unequivocally: "It is quite certain that a great mistake has been made—that British popular geology at present is in direct opposition to the principles of natural philosophy."[10]

In the decades that followed, Kelvin extended and refined his calculations in ways that escalated the conflict. His estimates of Earth's age steadily decreased, and even more importantly, he arrived at a very restrictive upper limit on the age of the sun. Even when he assumed that the sun's energy was partly replenished by falling meteors, the energy lost in radiation was of such magnitude that he was compelled to conclude: "It would, I think, be exceedingly rash to assume as probable anything more than twenty million years of the sun's light in the past history of the earth, or to reckon on more than five or six million years of sunlight to come."[11]

Kelvin was a brilliant mathematical physicist, and his calculations were essentially correct. Putting aside quibbles, we must grant that his conclusion follows from his premises. The entire analysis, however, rested on the generalization that the energy of stars and their satellite planets derives from the gravitational potential energy of the primeval gaseous nebula (supplemented by falling meteors). If this were true, solar systems would become cold and dark within a relatively short time (tens of millions of years). So, in evaluating Kelvin's view, the key question is: How strong was the argument for this basic premise?

The form of the argument was a process of elimination. Only three possible sources of the internal energy of the sun and Earth were known at the time: chemical, electromagnetic, and gravitational. Kelvin cited good reasons for dismissing the first two, which left gravitational energy as the only viable candidate. This type of argument can be valid, but it carries a heavy burden of proof. One must be able to argue that all the possibilities have been identified; there can be no reason to suspect the existence of any further sources of energy.

The evidence cited by geologists, however, cast doubt on Kelvin's argument. Geologists had not concocted an arbitrary theory; their conclusions integrated an impressive range of observations, including careful studies of strata in the Earth's crust and measured rates of erosion and deposit. Here Kelvin's error was to adopt an attitude that can be described as "elitist"; he seemed to think that evidence from physics trumps evidence from geology. But facts are facts, and all demand equal respect. Physics is the fundamental science, which means that it integrates the widest range of facts. But this does not imply that the facts of geology are subservient to the facts of physics. In this case, the facts of geology provided some (indirect) evidence for the existence of an undiscovered source of energy omitted from Kelvin's analysis.

There was another reason for doubting that gravitation provided the only possible source of energy. As we saw in the last chapter, the atomic theory opened a new frontier in physical science. A large body of data—dealing with such topics as chemical bonding, electrical affinities, ionization, and light emission—provided evidence that atoms have a complex structure. Yet little was known about this structure. What is the nature of the parts composing atoms, how is this subatomic matter distributed within the atom, and what forces hold it together? In the late nineteenth century, various discoveries had raised these fundamental questions but had not yet shed light on the answers. In this context, Kelvin could not reasonably rule out the possibility that the internal energy of atoms provides a major source of heat.

The nineteenth-century American geologist Thomas Chamberlin made precisely this point. He wrote:

> Is our present knowledge relative to the behavior of matter under such extraordinary conditions as obtain in the interior of the sun sufficiently exhaustive to warrant the assertion that no unrecog-

nized sources of heat reside there? What the internal constitution of the atoms may be is yet an open question. It is not improbable that they are complex organizations and seats of enormous energies. Certainly no careful chemist would affirm either that the atoms are really elementary or that there may not be locked up in them energies of the first order of magnitude. . . . Nor would they probably be prepared to affirm or deny that the extraordinary conditions which reside at the center of the sun may not set free a portion of this energy.[12]

In the early twentieth century, physicists proved that the possibility suggested by Chamberlin was a reality. Marie and Pierre Curie discovered that an extraordinary amount of energy is released in the decay of radioactive atoms. This major source of terrestrial heat had been omitted from Kelvin's analysis. Furthermore, Ernest Rutherford—the discoverer of the atomic nucleus—wrote in 1913: "At the enormous temperature of the sun, it appears possible that a process of transmutation may take place in ordinary elements analogous to that observed in the well-known radio-elements." Therefore, he concluded, "The time that the sun may continue to emit heat at the present rate may be much longer than the value computed from ordinary dynamical data."[13] The specific source of the seemingly inexhaustible supply of solar heat was identified in the 1930s when physicists discovered nuclear fusion.

In addition to providing the energy missing from Kelvin's analysis, the emerging field of nuclear physics also provided an accurate means of calculating the age of Earth. Radioactive elements decay at invariable rates into known products. Therefore the age of a rock can be determined from the relative abundance of its radioactive element and its decay products. In 1904, Rutherford analyzed a piece of uranium ore and calculated its age to be seven hundred million years.[14] The next year, the British physicist Robert Strutt measured the helium content of a radium bromide salt and estimated its age to be two billion years.[15] Suddenly the situation was reversed: Physicists were insisting that Earth is much older than the geologists had dared to suggest.

206 • David Harriman

Kelvin assumed that the basic laws of physics were already known in the late nineteenth century. He was reluctant to concede the possibility that investigations on the frontiers of physics—including investigations of atomic structure—could lead to the discovery of new types of forces and energy. In 1894, this attitude was expressed by the American physicist Albert Michelson:

> [I]t seems probable that most of the grand underlying principles have been firmly established and that further advances are to be sought chiefly in the rigorous application of these principles to all the phenomena which come under our notice. . . . An eminent physicist [Lord Kelvin] has remarked that the future truths of physical science are to be looked for in the sixth place of decimals.[16]

Thus Kelvin's basic error can be described as the fallacy of "cognitive fixation." It is instructive to contrast his attitude with that of Isaac Newton, the foremost champion of the inductive method. Newton always regarded his laws of motion and gravitation as a foundation to build upon, never as the completed edifice of physics. He was keenly aware of the vast range of phenomena that remained unexplained. He began his career with many questions—and throughout his life, despite the fact that he discovered so many answers, his list of questions only grew. When Newton surveyed the frontiers of physical science, he saw many areas of investigation—for example, electricity, magnetism, light, heat, chemistry—from which he expected new principles to emerge. Kelvin, on the other hand, had a more "deductive" frame of mind; in his view, the primary task of the physicist is to find further applications of the known principles. This attitude led him to conclude that the energy of a solar system must be gravitational in origin, and thus it led to his losing battle with modern geology.

Cold Fusion

It is possible to commit the opposite kind of error, which can be called the fallacy of "cognitive promiscuity." A scientist commits this error when he chooses to embrace a new idea despite weak evidence and a context that makes the idea implausible. A clear example of this fallacy was provided by the recent proponents of "cold" nuclear fusion.

In 1989, Stanley Pons and Martin Fleischmann announced that they had achieved a sustained deuterium fusion reaction in a room-temperature electrolysis experiment. The experiment consisted of passing an electric current between a palladium and a platinum electrode submerged in a bath of heavy water containing some lithium. The two chemists reported that the heat generated in such experiments was far greater than could be explained by any chemical reaction. In one case, they claimed, the palladium electrode melted and burned a hole through the laboratory floor. They concluded that deuterium from the heavy water was being absorbed within the lattice of palladium atoms, where the deuterium nuclei were squeezed together with sufficient pressure to cause fusion.

To put it mildly, this was a radical idea. Physicists had been studying deuterium fusion since the 1930s and the process was well understood. The reaction occurs only when the nuclei are extremely close together, and this requires enormous energy in order to overcome the electrical repulsion between the protons. Such reactions occur within the sun because the core temperature is over ten million degrees and thus the required energy is available. But how could the deuterium nuclei approach each other so closely in a room-temperature electrolysis experiment?

Pons and Fleischmann offered no answer to this basic question. As experimentalists, their goal was to demonstrate that the effect occurred. They were content to let the theorists wrestle with the problematic question of how it could possibly occur. It was a difficult assignment for the theorists, since cold fusion seemed to contradict everything known about nuclear physics.

For experimental evidence, Pons and Fleischmann relied primarily on their observations of excess heat. Scientific theory, however, cannot be turned upside down every time there is an unexplained explosion in a chemistry lab. The evidence required to support a claim of deuterium fusion is clear: One must detect the products of the reaction. These

208 • David Harriman

products include helium, neutrons, and gamma rays with a specific energy. The helium should have been embedded in the palladium electrode, and a lethal quantity of neutrons and gammas should have been flying through the laboratory. All efforts to detect these products failed, and no researchers suffered any ill effects from radiation.

The cold fusion episode quickly became a media circus in which politics and dreams of Nobel Prizes took precedence over scientific facts. Pons and Fleischmann had shouted "Fire!" and caused a lot of needless excitement. Initially many scientists took the claims seriously. Laboratories across the country performed their own cold fusion experiments in an attempt to reproduce the results. These scientists thought it best to adopt an "open-minded" attitude. As one researcher put it, "[Pons and Fleischmann] said this could be some hitherto unknown nuclear process. Who knows? If it is an unknown process, maybe it doesn't produce neutrons. You can always rationalize anything. . . . One way or the other there has to be a definitive proof, and we wanted to be the ones to definitively prove it."[17]

But it is not true that one can "rationalize anything"—not if "rationalize" means giving a rational argument. The term "open-minded" is an invalid "package deal"; it is used to equate the thinker with the skeptic, and thereby to give sanction to the latter. But the thinker who actively integrates evidence to arrive at new ideas has nothing in common with the skeptic, who feels free to assert possibilities without the required evidence. As we have seen previously, a mind that is open to any "possibility," regardless of its relation to the total context of knowledge, is a mind detached from reality and therefore closed to knowledge.

Pons and Fleischmann suggested the existence of a new source of energy that had not yet been identified by physicists, just as geologists did in the late nineteenth century. But Pons and Fleischmann were unwarranted in doing so, whereas the geologists had been warranted. The difference in the two cases lies in the context of knowledge. In the late nineteenth century, physicists were just beginning to explore the structure of the atom and the hidden energy it contains; they could not rule out the possibility that such energy might play a major role in heating the sun and Earth. In contrast, Pons and Fleischmann trespassed into an area of physics that was already thoroughly investigated. Their inference from "excess heat" to a new type of deuterium fusion—a type that was allegedly overlooked by an army of nuclear physicists who had studied this reaction for fifty years—was not justified by the context of knowledge.

The idea of cold fusion persisted for longer than necessary. It was initially given more credence than it deserved, but scientists soon applied the proper standards of experimental evidence. After a few months, the idea was discredited and discarded.

Induction as Self-Corrective

In each of the above cases, we saw a departure from proper method. Van Helmont committed a type of error that was common in the pre-Newton era: Lacking proper standards of proof, he leapt from a few facts to conclusions about the basic nature of water and gases. Lavoisier generalized about acids on the basis of an observed regularity, without sufficient evidence of a causal connection. In their investigations of electric current, Galvani and Volta both eliminated an essential part of the cause by reasoning from ambiguous experiments that lacked proper controls. Kelvin assumed that the basic principles of physics were already known, and thus he disregarded evidence that supported the possibility of a nongravitational source of solar and terrestrial heat. Finally, the advocates of cold fusion neglected a large context of knowledge that made their idea highly implausible. A false generalization is always the result of a failure to identify and/or to properly apply the principles of inductive logic.

Of course, a scientist's context of knowledge can be limited in a way that makes it easy to overlook a relevant factor. In Chapter 2, I cited the example of Galileo's failure to distinguish between sliding and rolling balls in his inclined-plane experiments. The importance of this distinction was much more obvious after the development of Newtonian mechanics. Today, any student of physics can grasp that the speed of the rolling ball is reduced because some of the gravitational potential energy is converted into rotational motion. Galileo did not have the benefit of the concepts "energy" and "gravity." Even in his less advanced context, however, he could have recognized the difference in the two cases. Rolling is caused by friction, and Galileo certainly knew that friction impedes motion. Furthermore, he had the means to measure the final speed of the ball and thereby to discover that it was less than predicted by his law (which applies only to the case of frictionless sliding). So the error was detectable, and it did result from a failure to integrate his law with the total of his knowledge.

When the relevant context of knowledge is in a primitive state, an error may remain undetected for a long time. For example, Van Helmont investigated plant growth before chemistry had developed into a science. Thus it is not surprising that the causal factor he overlooked (carbon dioxide in the air) was not identified until 150 years later. On the other hand, when the relevant context of knowledge is in an advanced state, errors are usually short-lived (as we saw in the case of cold fusion).

The inductive method is self-corrective. This feature of the method follows from the demand that every idea must be induced from observational evidence and integrated without contradiction into the whole of available knowledge. A false idea cannot live up to this standard. Further investigations will bring to light facts that undercut rather than support it; the idea will lead to predictions of events that are not observed, or it will contradict events that are or have been observed, or it will contradict other ideas for which there is strong evidence. A proper method keeps one in cognitive contact with reality, and therefore any clash between a false idea and reality is eventually revealed.

Thus misapplications of the inductive method pose no significant threat to the progress of science. They provide only routine setbacks that are overcome in the normal course of further research.

THE LOGICAL LEAP • 211

Abandoning the Inductive Method

The only way that progress can be derailed is by the rejection of the inductive method.

Scientists cannot pursue knowledge without a view of what it is and how it is acquired. They need a theory of knowledge, which they get from philosophers (the category "philosopher" includes those rare geniuses, such as Galileo and Newton, who were innovative in epistemology as well as physics). This theory of knowledge then affects every aspect of a scientist's approach to his research, from the questions he asks to the answers he finds acceptable.

A proper epistemology teaches a scientist (or anyone else) how to exercise the full power of his mind, i.e., how to reach the widest abstractions while never losing sight of the concretes. It tells him how to integrate sensory data in a step-by-step hierarchy that culminates in the grasp of fundamental truths pertaining to the whole cosmos.

From the outset, however, modern philosophy has defaulted on this task. Rather than explaining how to reach abstractions that integrate perceived concretes, philosophers have offered only a choice between empty abstractions or disintegrated concretes. They divided into two camps: those who turned inward to invent elaborate conceptual schemes that were detached from concretes (the rationalists), and those who stared outward at perceived concretes while shunning higher-level concepts (the empiricists). The rationalists posed as champions of the mind, but they abandoned physical reality; the empiricists posed as champions of physical fact, but they abandoned the mind.[18]

A physicist who accepts the rationalist epistemology will seek an abstract, fundamental theory that is allegedly validated by characteristics such as "simplicity," "clarity," "beauty," or "internal coherence" (*not* by its relation to observational evidence). A physicist who accepts the empiricist epistemology will seek narrower laws that merely describe regularities in the observational data, while rejecting the need for an integrating theory. Thus we have the false alternative of the theorist who disdains data versus the data collector who disdains theory. Neither approach can lead to a proven theory, which is the proper goal of science.

Rationalism

The physics of René Descartes provides an excellent illustration of the rationalist method. Descartes is known primarily as the father of modern philosophy, but his longest work—*Principles of Philosophy*—is a treatise that deals mainly with physical science. When Descartes published his physics (1644), the scientific revolution had already claimed many victories: the works of Gilbert, Kepler, Bacon, Harvey, and Galileo were being read throughout much of Europe. Rather than joining this revolution, however, Descartes rejected the very method that had made possible the discoveries of his predecessors.

According to Descartes, knowledge does not begin with sense perception; rather, it begins with "clear and distinct" ideas that are "naturally implanted" in our minds. The truth of these ideas is ensured by their intrinsic clarity and by the moral perfection of God, who would not deceive us by implanting false ideas. In effect, Descartes assumed that we possess an inner eye for perceiving abstract truths, and all the rest of knowledge is ultimately based on this introspective awareness. He wrote:

> I call "clear" that perception which is present and manifest to an attentive mind: just as we say that we clearly see those things which are present to our intent eye and act upon it sufficiently strongly and manifestly. On the other hand, I call "distinct" that perception which, while clear, is so separated and delineated from all others that it contains absolutely nothing except what is clear.[19]

This was Descartes' version of the mystical intuition that all rationalists must rely upon. After rejecting the only objective criterion for evaluating truth or falsehood—observational evidence—the rationalist is left with the mystic's subjective criterion: *feeling*. Despite posturing as a staunch advocate of reason, he accepts the ideas he feels are true, i.e., those ideas he wants to believe. He declares that these ideas have the special intrinsic qualities that make their truth manifest. In science, Descartes found himself struck by a series of "clear and distinct" ideas that led him to construct the first "theory of everything."

Descartes began his physics with the intuition that extension is the only fundamental, irreducible property of matter. Following a tradition that dates back to Plato, he attempted to reduce the physical world to combinations of a few basic geometric forms. Rationalists typically have great admiration for geometry, which they regard as an ideal science because it allegedly consists of truths deduced from self-evident axioms. Furthermore, they usually feel alienated from the physical world, which often refuses to conform to their ideas. So the dream of replacing obstinate physical bodies with ideal geometric forms is very appealing to the rationalist.

All matter, Descartes claimed, is composed of three types of elementary particles, which are distinguished only by their sizes, shapes, and movements. He wrote:

> [S]ome people may be led to ask how I know what these particles are like. . . . I took the simplest and best known principles, knowledge of which is naturally implanted in our minds; and working from these I considered, in general terms, firstly, what are the principal differences which can exist between the sizes, shapes and positions of bodies which are imperceptible by the senses merely because of their small size, and, secondly, what observable effects would result from their various interactions.[20]

In other words, he made no observations, did no experiments, and engaged in no reasoning from effects to underlying causes. Instead he looked inward and offered a "clear and distinct" make-believe world that was more imaginative than any fairy tale.

Descartes had no trouble arriving at the laws of motion governing his elementary shapes. Starting from the immutability of God, he deduced that the total "quantity of motion" is always conserved. This may sound like an anticipation of Newton's conservation of momentum principle, but it is not. Descartes defined "quantity of motion" as the product of volume and speed, which is quite different from Newton's product of mass and velocity. When Descartes used his principle to analyze and predict the results of elastic collisions, he arrived at the correct result only in the special case of two bodies with equal volumes, equal mass densities, and equal but oppositely directed speeds. In every other case, his theory gives the wrong answer. "Experience," he conceded, "often seems to contradict the rules I have just explained."[21] He assumed, however, that the apparent contradictions could be attributed to the effects of the medium or the inelastic nature of the collisions. His method freed him from worrying about the observations. He ended the discussion of his laws of motion with the comment: "These matters do not need proof since they are self-evident. The demonstrations are so certain that even if our experience seemed to show us the opposite, we should still be obliged to have more faith in our reason than in our senses."[22]

By this rationalist method, "knowledge" came so easily that Descartes could not stop himself. He explained the nature of planets, moons, and comets and the cause of their movements. He described the formation of the solar system, the nature of sunspots, and the cause of new stars (i.e., supernovas). The part of the book dealing with astronomy ends with this statement: "I think I have here given a satisfactory explanation of absolutely every phenomenon that we observe in the heavens above us."[23] Just one generation after Kepler inaugurated the science of physical astronomy, Descartes claimed to have completed it.

The last part of Descartes' book deals with earthly phenomena. He offered explanations of ocean tides, earthquakes, volcanoes, lightning, the formation of mountains, magnetism, static electricity, chemical interactions, and the nature of fire. At the end of this section, he again cast aside modesty and wrote: "There is nothing visible or perceptible in this world that I have not explained."[24] As one historian of science has noted:

"Descartes left nothing untouched. . . . The *Principles* was a triumph of fantastic imagination which happens, unfortunately, never once to have hit upon a correct explanation."[25] Of course, there is a reason why he never "hit upon" the truth: As we have seen, science is not a guessing game. Descartes' generalizations did not correspond to reality because he did not derive them inductively from observations of reality.

In contrast to induction, the method of rationalism is not self-corrective. If a theory is validated by intrinsic qualities such as clarity or mathematical beauty, then it cannot be overthrown by observational evidence. The theory is merely an integration of floating abstractions, detached from perceptual data and therefore invulnerable to such data. When he wishes, the rationalist is always free to further decorate his theory with "beautiful"— i.e., arbitrary—features in order to deduce any particular facts.

Cartesian physics was overthrown only when Newton rejected rationalism and demonstrated the power of the inductive method, which then gained widespread acceptance during the Enlightenment. Unfortunately, the commitment to this method did not last.

Empiricism

Two very influential philosophers of the eighteenth century—David Hume and Immanuel Kant—developed theories of knowledge that undercut every essential aspect of the inductive method.[26]

As a result, the nineteenth century became a battlefield, with scientists caught in the cross fire between the approach exemplified by Newton and Lavoisier, and a radical new approach to science that emerged from post-Kantian empiricist philosophy. This new view, named "positivism" by the French philosopher Auguste Comte, redefined the basic goal of science. Scientists were no longer to be concerned with discovering the true nature of entities that exist independently in a real, physical world; any attempt to grasp the nature of external entities was dismissed as "speculative metaphysics." We have no direct awareness of such entities, the positivists claimed, but only of subjective "appearances." Thus the proper goal of science must be limited to merely describing regularities in the behavior of these appearances.

Newton's followers had taken for granted that a scientist's task is to identify the underlying cause of events we observe, i.e., to identify the nature of a thing that necessitates its actions. The positivists, however, claimed that any such cause is unknowable. There must be strict limits, they insisted, on the questions that scientists are allowed to ask. It makes no sense to investigate aspects of the appearances that do not appear, for the simple reason that there are no such aspects. A real thing may have many properties that cannot be seen, but a subjective appearance has no such hidden properties—by definition, it is what appears to our senses. If reason is restricted to an inner "world of appearances," then Kant had stated the inevitable conclusion:

> Natural science will never reveal to us the internal constitution of things, which, though not appearance, yet can serve as the ultimate ground for explaining appearances. Nor does science need this for its physical explanations. . . . For these explanations must only be grounded upon that which as an object of sense can belong to experience. . . . [27]

This prohibition against investigating the "internal constitution of things" gained widespread influence during the same period in which scientists were discovering abundant evidence in favor of the atomic composition of matter. The result was one of the most bizarre episodes in the history of science, during which many chemists and physicists rejected and even crusaded against an extraordinarily successful theory.

Initially, the rise of positivism had the effect of slowing progress toward proving the atomic theory. Dalton's theory was, in effect, censored by the authors of chemistry textbooks; they presented his law of multiple proportions as merely an empirical regularity, ignoring the atomic explanation for it.[28] Similarly, there was a great deal of resistance among chemists to the acceptance of Avogadro's hypothesis, which was regarded by positivists as "metaphysics" rather than proper science. And when Waterston applied Newtonian dynamics to molecules in order to explain

Charles' law of gases, the editors of the *Philosophical Transactions of the Royal Society* refused to publish his paper, rejecting it as "nothing but nonsense, unfit even for reading before the Society."[29]

As the evidence for atoms accumulated, the positivist opposition to the theory intensified. In 1867, shortly after Maxwell published his triumphant work on the atomic theory of gases, there was a meeting of the Chemical Society in London. The major event at this meeting was a paper titled "Ideal Chemistry" by Benjamin Brodie, who offered a new approach that entirely rejected atoms. One historian summarizes Brodie's philosophic view as follows: "The true object of science is not to explain, but to describe. We cannot ask what water is, only what it does, or what it becomes. We have no means of grasping the underlying reality of things, and so should content ourselves with the accurate description of what things do. . . ."[30]

How does a chemist avoid making statements about the "underlying reality" and restrict himself to merely describing observable changes? This was the question that Brodie addressed in his presentation. The key to the answer, he claimed, was a new system of classification. Brodie proposed a system that treated chemical changes, rather than chemical substances, as primaries (thereby attempting to evade the question of *what* is changing). The changes are described by chemical equations that name the amounts of reactants and the amounts of products. For example, two liters of steam can change into one liter of hydrogen and one liter of hydrogen peroxide. Or, for instance, two liters of hydrogen chloride gas can change into one liter of hydrogen and one liter of chlorine.

In Brodie's theory, substances are not classified in terms of their essential nature, but instead by the number and type of operations required to make them. He implemented this idea by grouping together chemicals that appear in similar places in similar equations. In the two examples above, both hydrogen peroxide and chlorine appear as products along with hydrogen in equations that have the same coefficients. Therefore, according to Brodie, these two substances should be grouped together and designated by similar combinations of symbols. Thus chlorine is represented by symbols that make it appear to be a compound rather than an element.

The theory provoked some criticism at the meeting. With a touch of sarcasm, Maxwell said that he was surprised to learn that hydrogen and mercury were operations rather than substances. Furthermore, some chemists complained that Brodie's system was based on starting points that were chosen arbitrarily, and different choices would have resulted in a different classification scheme. Nevertheless, the reaction to the theory was surprisingly positive. One author notes that "in spite of some criticisms, the tone of all the speakers was respectful, and at times flattering."[31] After the meeting, the journal *Chemical News* devoted almost a whole issue to Brodie's theory, calling it "The Chemistry of the Future." The theory was also praised in the *North British Review*, which claimed that the idea of atoms remained as doubtful as it had been two millennia earlier.[32]

Since Brodie was rebelling against the very idea of causal explanation, his views are more accurately described as an "anti-theory" rather than a theory. He received a respectful hearing only because there were widespread feelings of distrust and hostility toward atoms. The source of these feelings was positivism.

The hostility became evident at the meeting when Brodie ridiculed the use of atomic models of molecular structure. He read to the audience the following advertisement from a scientific journal: "The fundamental facts of chemical combination may be advantageously symbolized by balls and wires, and those practical students who require tangible demonstration of such facts will learn with pleasure that a set of models for the construction of glyptic formula may now be obtained for a comparatively small sum."[33] This is a perfectly reasonable ad for molecular model kits, which help chemists and students to understand the spatial arrangement of atoms in a molecule. When Brodie read the ad, however, he had to wait for the derisive laughter to subside before continuing. He took for granted that such models were ridiculous, and much of his audience agreed. Brodie then remarked that the ad was clear evidence that chemistry had gotten "upon a wrong track," a track that was "altogether off the rules of philosophy."[34]

The chemist who had introduced these ball-and-wire molecular models, Edward Frankland, was at the meeting. Recall that Frankland had pioneered the idea of atomic valence, which corresponds to the number of wires that an atom has for attaching to other atoms. In his textbook *Lecture Notes for Chemistry Students*, he made extensive use of these models in order to explain the nature of compounds in terms of their molecular structure. This was a crucial advance, and the models had already proven to be enormously useful, particularly in organic chemistry.

Yet it was Brodie who received widespread support while he attacked and ridiculed, and it was Frankland who backpedaled while feeling embarrassed and isolated. In his response, Frankland feebly tried to defend his models by saying, "I certainly do not imagine that any evil is likely to arise from such symbolic representations. . . ."[35] He then emphasized that he never intended the models as accurate depictions of anything real. He conceded the entire issue with the following confession: "I cannot do better than state, simply and at once, that I neither believe in atoms themselves, nor do I believe in the existence of centers of force."[36] When asked why chemists should use the atomic theory, Frankland claimed that the theory serves "as a kind of ladder to assist the chemist in progressing from one position to another in his science."[37] He never explained how a false theory can function as an indispensable means for advancing a science.

Many scientists felt compelled to adopt this contradictory position. One of the chemists at the meeting, William Odling, had made important discoveries about the molecular structure of certain acids and salts; however, he laughed at what he called "Frankland's marvelous picture book."[38] At the meeting, Odling remarked: "[T]here are some who, like myself, do not believe in atoms, and who keep the idea of atoms in the background as much as possible."[39] He did not reject atoms in practice; he realized that without the atomic theory he would not be able to do his research. But he kept atoms in the "background" and refused to acknowledge their reality. Thus he committed an epistemological crime that can only be described as "theory-stealing," i.e., appropriating a theory to which one has no right.

In France, the controversy over atoms erupted in 1877 at a meeting of the Paris Academy of Sciences, where Marcellin Berthelot engaged in a heated debate with Adolphe Wurtz. Both were prominent chemists; Wurtz was one of the few vocal advocates of the atomic theory in France, and Berthelot was a passionate opponent of the theory. After Wurtz cited the abundant evidence for atoms and presented his arguments, Berthelot responded with his famous rhetorical question: "Who has ever seen a gaseous molecule or an atom?"[40] He then declared: "The only thing [the atomic theory] has done has been to intermix the meshes of its hypotheses with our demonstrated laws, and this to the great detriment of the teaching of positive science."[41]

A century earlier, France had been the world leader in chemistry. During the nineteenth century, however, most chemists at French universities stopped their research at the level of empirical laws and refused to advance to a causal theory. The positivist attitude at the root of this stagnation was expressed by Berthelot during a conversation with another chemist in the mid-1880s. While explaining why he crusaded against the atomic theory, Berthelot declared: "I do not want chemistry to degenerate into a religion; I do not want the chemist to believe in the existence of atoms as the Christian believes in the presence of Christ in the communion wafer."[42] His colleague told him not to worry; after all, he reassured Berthelot, atoms are only a mental aid and few believe in their actual existence.

By the 1880s, the evidence for the atomic composition of matter exceeded any reasonable standard of proof. Rejecting atoms was akin to rejecting the heliocentric theory of the solar system. The atomic theory had integrated and explained the fields of chemistry, crystallography, electrolysis, gas theory, and thermodynamics. But there was only one form of evidence that Berthelot would accept: The atomists must present him with an atom that he could hold in his hand and look at. In the absence of such an "appearance," he insisted that accepting the existence of atoms was merely an act of faith. Thus he accepted the false alternative between empiricism and rationalism, and he chose acts of blank staring over acts of blind faith.

In physics, the most famous and influential of the late-nineteenth-century positivists was Ernst Mach. As a teenager, Mach had read Kant and arrived at the view that reality was nothing but a "manifold of sensations." He adopted a perspective in which the entire world of physical entities faded away, leaving only a kaleidoscopic succession of unrelated appearances. After discarding the idea of causality as "formally obscure," he argued that the goal of science was merely to identify mathematical equations that describe patterns in the observed phenomena. Obviously, the atomic theory was incompatible with such a view. "What we represent to ourselves behind the appearances exist only in our understanding," he wrote. "[Such representations] have only the value of aids to our memory whose form, because it is arbitrary and irrelevant, varies easily with the standpoint of our culture."[43]

According to Mach, a scientific theory is merely an arbitrary mnemonic. It serves the same function as the alphabet song, which helps a child remember letters by connecting them with a tune. Of course, successful researchers do not regard theories in this way—they do not use them to remember past experiences, but to explain those past occurrences and to predict never-before-seen phenomena. They also use them to fly astronauts to the moon, to design nuclear power plants, to revolutionize our lives with high-speed computers, or to save our lives with new drugs and medical diagnostic equipment. Theories have such power when they correctly identify fundamental causal relationships.

Mach's basic premises led him to make claims that can only be described as bizarre. When discussing the composition of water, for example, he wrote: "We say that water consists of oxygen and hydrogen, but this oxygen and hydrogen are merely thoughts or names which, at the sight of water, we keep ready to describe phenomena which are not present but which will appear again whenever we decompose water."[44] So oxygen and hydrogen do not refer to the elements composing water; rather, they refer only to the gas bubbles that we see during an electrolysis experiment. (Later positivists would take the next step and claim that the name "Aristotle" does not refer to the Greek philosopher, but only to our perceptual experiences when we read about the name in a book.)

At the turn of the twentieth century, influential scientists across Europe still denied the reality of atoms. In addition to Mach, there was Karl Pearson in England, Henri Poincaré and Pierre Duhem in France, Wilhelm Ostwald and Georg Helm in Germany, and their many followers. They were like members of a "flat-Earth society," except they held prominent university positions and published papers in prestigious journals.

Finally, discoveries made in the first decade of the twentieth century convinced some positivists (but not Mach) to concede the heuristic value of the atomic theory. For example, Ostwald made this concession when Einstein identified collisions with molecules as the cause of the observed "Brownian" motion of very small (but perceptible) particles. The successful integration of entire sciences had left Ostwald unimpressed; he reconsidered his opposition to the atomic theory only after watching tiny particles bounce around. This is typical of the "conversion" that took place among positivists. Since their epistemology restricted them to abstractions near the perceptual level, only this type of more direct observational evidence could have any impact on them.

Although atoms were accepted with a pragmatic shrug, the philosophy that had opposed them survived. It continued to exert a strong influence on the next frontier of research: subatomic physics. In the 1920s, the founders of quantum theory explicitly rejected causality and restricted themselves to developing a mathematical formalism that describes and predicts observable events.[45] Thus the legacy of positivism remains with us to the present day. More than a century has passed since the discovery of the electron and the atomic nucleus—yet physicists still have no causal theory of subatomic processes, and the prohibition against developing such a theory is rarely challenged.

The empiricist method leads to stagnation.

Rationalists and empiricists have bickered for centuries, but they are in agreement in rejecting the view that scientific theory is the hard-won reward of a step-by-step process of abstracting from sensory data. The rationalist claims to reach knowledge in another way: He looks passively at the content of his mind and declares that the constructs of his imagination are validated by their "beauty" or "clarity." The empiricist, on the other hand, denounces as unscientific the very goal of discovering a causal theory and demands that researchers settle for describing "appearances."

They both deny that abstract knowledge can be discovered by means of a rigorous application of inductive logic.

7.

The Role of Mathematics and Philosophy

Throughout this book, we have seen that the physical sciences are dependent on two other sciences: mathematics and philosophy.

The fundamental role of mathematics is widely recognized, yet the reason has remained mysterious. Mathematics is the language of physical science—but why? Although the question has been asked for centuries, no rational answer has been offered.

Historically, the most popular answer has been that God is a mathematician and He chose to create the universe accordingly. But the efficacy of mathematics is not explained by the arbitrary claim that "God did it"; nothing is made intelligible by referring to the wishes of an unintelligible, supernatural entity who acts by unintelligible means. Since the seventeenth century, scientists have rejected superstitions about phenomena such as comets, plagues, and volcanoes and replaced them with natural explanations. It is time that we did the same for the role of mathematics.

Philosophy provides the basic view of existence and of knowledge that is necessary to pursue the specialized sciences. Today, however, physicists are reluctant to concede their dependence on philosophy, a field that has collapsed into skepticism and lost the capacity to answer (or even to ask) any interesting questions. Physicists are right when they dismiss the mainstream of contemporary philosophy as irrelevant to their work. But they are wrong to judge a field by its irrational practitioners, and they are naïve to think that they can escape from the foundational issues of philosophy. We have seen that the different approaches to physics taken by Descartes, Newton, and Mach had their roots in different systems of philosophy. The philosophic ideas of scientists are sometimes left implicit and unstated, but their influence is always real and powerful.

Recognizing the dependence of physics on philosophy entails a responsibility for the physicist: He must arrive at his philosophic conclusions by using the same logical rigor that he demands in reaching his scientific conclusions. This implies an obligation on philosophy, which can command such respect only if it lives up to the high standards that it prescribes for the specialized sciences. The generalizations of philosophy must themselves be induced from observational data by the very method that a rational philosophy defines.

Let us begin by demystifying the relationship between mathematics and physics. Then, in the following section, we will examine whether the fundamental science that identifies the principles of a proper inductive method can actually follow that method. Finally, we will look at how the collapse of philosophy has affected contemporary physics.

Physics as Inherently Mathematical

A proper theory of concepts is a prerequisite for understanding why mathematics is the language of physical science.

The pseudo-explanation offered by religion is based on a Platonic view of mathematical concepts. According to Plato, the source of mathematics is an extrasensory realm of ideas that existed prior to and caused the physical world. Recall that when Kepler was in the grip of this view, he bypassed the search for physical causes and instead trusted his intuitions regarding God's design. This rationalistic approach detaches mathematics from the world, and, as a result, its proponents find themselves unable to use mathematics to understand the world.

Those who have opposed the mystical view of mathematics have typically embraced the skeptical view. The mathematical laws of nature are not God's arbitrary creations, the skeptics insist—instead, they are our own arbitrary creations. We choose to describe the "appearances" in mathematical terms because we find it convenient to do so; this description, however, implies nothing about the nature of reality, only about what human beings find convenient. As the English physicist James Jeans put it,

> We can never understand what events are, but must limit ourselves to describing the pattern of events in mathematical terms; no other aim is possible. . . . Our studies [of physics] can never put us into contact with reality, and its meaning and nature must be forever hidden from us.[1]

Again, mathematics is detached from the world, and its source is placed entirely within consciousness (this time human rather than divine).

Such views about the nature of mathematical concepts led Einstein to pose the unanswerable question: "How is it possible that mathematics, a product of human thought that is independent of experience, fits so excellently the objects of physical reality?"[2] An answer to this question is possible only when we reject the premise that mathematics is independent of experience. Like every other science, mathematics applies to reality because it is derived from our observations of reality. It is a conceptualization of facts, which are ultimately reducible to observed similarities and differences.

In order to indicate the objectivity of mathematics, let us briefly consider the counting numbers. Take, for example, the concept "three," which refers to what is the same among the three birds in a tree, the three coins in my pocket, and the three pens in the drawer of my desk. Each group has the same multiplicity, i.e., the same number of units. For a few small integers, the similarity is grasped perceptually.

Concepts of higher numbers can then be formed by the method of pairing; for instance, a shepherd may compare the number of sheep on a hillside to the number of fingers on his hands. This enables him to grasp the difference between a group of nine sheep and a group of ten sheep, which cannot be grasped by direct perception. By focusing on relations of numbers such as "one-fewer" or "one-more," we can arrive at the concept "one" and then recognize the tremendous advantages of including it as the first number of a *sequence*. We can then count, extend the sequence without limit, and develop the methods of arithmetic.[3]

Thus, like all other concepts, number concepts are integrations of similar concretes. Contrary to Plato and his many followers, they are abstractions that do not exist in reality apart from us. But this does not imply that they are subjective inventions. They refer to facts, as processed by our conceptual faculty; i.e., they are objective.[4]

Reduction to perceptual data is more complex for higher-level mathematical concepts. Given the difficulty of the task and the widespread confusion in epistemology, even the better mathematicians have given up the premise that their concepts are based on experience. For instance, Morris Kline wrote:

> [S]uch an explanation is far too simplistic. It may suffice to explain why fifty cows and fifty cows make one hundred cows. . . . But human beings have created mathematical concepts and techniques in algebra, the calculus, differential equations, and other fields that are not suggested by experience.[5]

If the concepts of higher mathematics are not derived from experience, however, then they are the equivalent of "phlogiston" or "absolute space"—i.e., they are invalid. Then it would be impossible to understand the successful application of these ideas. The astronauts who landed on the moon would be very surprised to hear that they arrived at their destination by relying on invalid ideas.

In fact, mathematical concepts—from counting numbers to "imaginary numbers" to "infinity" and beyond—are developed in essentially the same way as concepts in the physical sciences; it is a step-by-step process of abstraction that begins with observation. I will not attempt to identify those steps here, which would take me well beyond the scope of this book. Instead, I refer the interested reader to Pat Corvini's work in this field.[6]

Taking for granted the objectivity of mathematics, our question is: Why is it only by means of mathematics that we can gain scientific knowledge of the physical world? In this connection, recall Kepler's profound statement that just as the eye perceives light and the ear sound, *the human intellect is a faculty for grasping quantities.* We have seen abundant evidence that he was right; we now seek to understand why this is true by the very nature of a conceptual consciousness.

Rand identified that the similar concretes united by a concept differ from one another only quantitatively. We form a concept by noticing that two or more existents have the same characteristic(s), but that these characteristics vary along a quantitative continuum of more or less. By omitting the implicit, approximate measurements of the characteristics, we can integrate the existents and treat them as interchangeable instances of a single concept.

Concepts are the means by which we identify the nature of existents, and they are based on our grasp of quantitative relations among their referents. In performing such an integration, our minds grasp that the various instances we perceive are commensurable, i.e., reducible to the same unit—and therefore that the instances are the same except for their varying measurements. For example, we take any particular instance of length and relate all other instances as either more or less. When we omit the measurements, the result is a conceptual category to which all belong: "length"—which is a mental integration of all the commensurable referents we can measure by reference to a perceivable instance that we adopt as the unit. The same principle applies to forming other types of concepts.[7] Thus when we say "I know what something is," we mean "I know what it is through a quantitative operation my mind performs," i.e., through grasping the quantitative connection of instances to some concrete taken as the unit—and then dropping the measurements.

In concept-formation, we create file folders, which contain all the referents of a concept, those known and those unknown. We are then ready to gather further data about some instances and generalize, applying our conclusions to all of the instances in the folder. We fill the file folders by using the methods of difference and agreement to discover causal connections, which are the basis of our inductive generalizations. But how do we, in the deepest sense, grasp such connections among physical existents?

In seeking cause and effect, we are relating objects/attributes that are subsumed under different concepts. We are attempting to discover the effects of one type of existent on another, for example, to identify the effect of temperature on the pressure of a gas, or the effect of length on the period of a pendulum, or the effect of distance on the gravitational force between two bodies. Our conceptual vocabulary enables us to pursue such knowledge—for example, we can seek out the relation between temperature and pressure, discarding the irrelevant, such as color or shape, even if it floods our perceptual field. Thus we can ask specific causal questions: How does A affect B, ignoring everything else?

Furthermore, our conceptual faculty provides us with the number system and hence the ability to measure not just implicitly and approximately, as in the concept-formation stage, but explicitly and numerically. As conceptually developed adults, we continue with the process of establishing quantitative relationships as our means of knowledge—but at this later stage we can relate objects from different file folders to one another by the conceptual method of grasping quantity: numerical measurement.

As an illustration of this process, let us revisit Galileo's law relating the length of a pendulum to its period.

First, we must form the concept "length" by grasping implicit measurements, which we then omit. We use the concept, in this case, to describe a narrower category: the length of a pendulum (still a conceptual description that subsumes an endless number of concrete lengths of pendulums). Similarly, we reach the concept "time" by observing the actions of bodies (e.g., "day" and "year" are based on the relative motion of the sun and Earth, and lesser time intervals are estimated relative to regular motions of shorter duration); we then omit the implicit measurements. We subdivide the broad concept "time" to form the narrower concept "period," which refers to the time interval between recurring instances of a repeated motion (still a concept that subsumes an endless number of specific periods).

With this conceptual apparatus and the number system, we saw that Galileo devised a way to vary and numerically measure the length and corresponding period of different pendulums. On the basis of his measurements, he generalized to an algebraic law: The length is proportional to the square of the period. After grasping this causal relationship, knowing the measurements of either variable enables one to calculate the numerical value of the other (given a particular system of units).

Thus preconceptual measurement leads to concepts, which in turn make possible conceptual measurement, which is the basic activity of experimentalists in physical science. Scientists begin by identifying numerical relationships and then generalize to mathematical laws, which is our form of grasping causal relationships.

Mathematics enables us to reduce to the scale of our perception countless instances beyond our perception. For instance, the law of gravitation covers not only an unlimited number of instances but also an unlimited scale of magnitude. We study the fall of the apple, which is easily perceivable—and we can now deal with the force of attraction one galaxy exerts on another. Or we study the behavior of electrically charged balls, which is easily perceivable—and we can now deal with the force exerted by subatomic particles on each other.

The same principle is at work in concept-formation and in the practice of physics. We start with the perceptual level of concretes and then, by a process of abstraction, ascend to the level of concepts—which Rand, in an eloquent analogy, compared to starting with arithmetic and then, by a process of abstraction, ascending to the level of algebra. In physics, the equivalent of the perceptual level is the numerical measurements taken by the experimenter or observer; this is the arithmetic of physics. The laws induced from these measurements are the return to the abstract, algebraic level—and this is what enables the physicist to comprehend the relationships between different variables, and thereby to relate his knowledge, gained from a handful of perceivable instances, to all the instances throughout the universe, no matter what their number or scale.

Thus we acquire knowledge of the physical world by means of two forms of measurement: approximate and preconceptual, and then numerical and conceptual. *Human consciousness is inherently a quantitative mechanism.* It grasps reality—i.e., the attributes of entities and their causal relationships to one another—only through grasping quantitative data. In this sense, quantity has epistemological primacy over quality.

It is crucial to recognize that this point is epistemological, not metaphysical. Pythagoras was wrong to claim that quantity is the substance of *reality*; it is not true that "all things are numbers." Quantity is always quantity of something, i.e., of some entity or attribute. But quantity is the key to the nature of human *knowledge*. We can grasp and identify the qualities of things only through grasping quantity—and we can grasp causal relations between entities and actions only through grasping quantitative relations between them.

If we could know qualities simply by perception, without any quantitative processing, then we could know causal relationships by direct perception, without numerical measurements. On the lowest levels of cognition, we can approximate this purely qualitative state, because we can hold first-level concepts, and first-level generalizations, ostensively and perceptually. To know that fire burns, we simply touch it and yell "Ouch!"—no numerical measurements are required. But on the higher levels of cognition, a conceptual consciousness can grasp the relations of qualities only through measurement.

Physics, in effect, completes the job of concept-formation.

Once we have developed the requisite conceptual vocabulary, the physicist says: Let us now reinstate the measurements we deliberately left out at the concept-formation stage and see what quantitative relationships we can find. In other words: we omit measurements to form concepts; the physicist then takes these same omitted measurements, but in numerical terms, and discovers the relation between one set of numerical measurements and another, which we call the laws of nature. From narrow laws to fundamental theories, this is the method by which scientists identify the causal relations operative in the universe, and thereby explain our observations.

After the initial qualitative, prescientific stage, there is nothing a scientist studying a conceptualized physical world can do to grasp the relationships among bodies except to reinstate in numerical terms the very measurements that had to be dropped to conceptualize that world. And this is so by nature of our conceptual faculty.

This is the reason why mathematics is the language of physics. Mathematical physics is necessitated by the fact that the entity that is learning is a conceptual consciousness that knows objects only through quantity.

The Science of Philosophy

From Plato to Descartes to Kant to Hegel, rationalist philosophers have attempted to deduce the nature of the world from "a priori" ideas, and their spectacular failure has done much to discredit philosophy in the eyes of physicists. Philosophy does not tell us the specific nature of the world—but it does tell us that there *is* a world, that it has a nature and must act accordingly, and that we discover that nature by following certain principles of method.

Philosophy is the science that defines the relationship between a volitional consciousness and reality. Thus it is the fundamental science of human life, on which all more specialized disciplines rest. It is the voice telling us how to pursue those disciplines while staying in cognitive contact with reality at each point—which is a prerequisite of our successfully achieving rational goals in any field. All other sciences presuppose the essentials of a rational view of the universe, of knowledge, and of values.

Philosophy is and has to be an *inductive* subject in every branch except metaphysics. (See the first chapter of Dr. Peikoff's book *Objectivism: The Philosophy of Ayn Rand* for a discussion of how we know metaphysical axioms, which are the base of all thought.) The normative ideas of philosophy are not innate; they must be learned by starting with perceptual observation and then proceeding up the necessary hierarchy, just as in physical science. All knowledge of reality must be gained on the basis of observation, including the knowledge of how to gain knowledge. Induction is inescapable in every subject.

The data integrated by philosophic generalizations come primarily from two sources. The first is *personal experience*, including the introspective awareness of one's conscious processes and the study of others. Introspection is clearly an indispensable source of data, since philosophy studies consciousness and an individual has direct access only to his own. The second major data source is *history*, which Rand once called "the laboratory of philosophy." There are obviously many generalizations about knowledge and values that one can discover by a study of ancient Egypt versus ancient Greece, Athens versus Sparta, the Middle Ages versus the Renaissance, the American Revolution versus the French Revolution, East Germany versus West Germany before the Berlin Wall came down, and so on.

In order to give a brief indication of the inductive process in philosophy, let us revisit the question raised at the start of this book: What is the proper method of reaching generalizations about the physical world? We now ask: What inductive generalizations had to be grasped before it was possible to think of this question?

Clearly, we must grasp the need of a method. One of the first steps here is to recognize that we are fallible. An idea is not true merely because it occurs to us or because we wish it to be true; sometimes we are wrong. Children grasp this very early in their development, and people certainly knew it while they were still living in caves. A caveman who mistook a poisonous plant for an edible one soon learned that he had made an error.

Of course, fallibility by itself does not take us very far toward the discovery of a rational method. The primitive solution to the problem of error was to trust some allegedly infallible authority, for example, the tribal chieftain, the witch doctor, or the Pharaoh's revelations from the gods. It took mankind a long time to discover that there is a fact-based method by which an individual can arrive at and prove his ideas.

This discovery was made possible when the philosophers of ancient Greece grasped the crucial distinction between concepts and percepts. Plato was the first to clearly identify differences between these two forms of awareness. Concepts are universal, i.e., they refer to all existents of a given type, whereas percepts are the direct awareness of particulars; concepts are products of thought, whereas percepts are the automatic result of the interaction of our senses with the physical world; concepts are stable, whereas percepts change with the circumstances and with changes in the perceived bodies.

Unfortunately, Plato used these differences to argue that concepts cannot originate from our perception of the physical world, but must instead have their source in a supernatural world of ideas. By assigning concepts and percepts to two different worlds and thereby driving a wedge between them, he reduced his philosophy to mysticism and gave up the pursuit of a reality-based method.

It was Aristotle who rejected Plato's error and reunited ideas with the evidence of our senses. He grasped that we form concepts by a process of abstraction from our sensory awareness of particulars. Abstraction is a selective mental focus on similarities among existents; it is the process of mentally separating the similarities from the array of differences in which they are embedded. Thus Aristotle recognized that all conceptual knowledge is derived from our perception of the world of entities around us.

Furthermore, he identified a crucial difference between concepts and percepts that had eluded Plato. In contrast to the realm of conceptual thought, percepts are *in*fallible. They are simply the product of an automatic physiological response of our senses to reality; they cannot be wrong, just as an apple cannot be wrong in its response to a gravitational field. It is only the judgments that we make on the basis of our percepts that can be in error. Such judgments, however, are not automatic; they are in our control; we can subject them to critical evaluation and revise them as the evidence warrants.

At this stage, Aristotle could grasp the possibility of validating our knowledge by a rational method. The fallible, conceptual realm of human cognition can be checked against the infallible perceptual data. We can demand that the conclusions reached by any volitional thought process integrate the sensory data without contradiction, and we can reject any conclusion that does not meet this demand. Because this method has been used so extensively and so successfully for centuries, it is now easily taken for granted and regarded as obvious. But many abstract, inductive generalizations concerning human cognition had to be grasped before anyone could arrive at the idea of such a method.

Once Aristotle had grasped the need for and the possibility of a rational method, he asked: What are the specific rules of this method, the rules we must follow in order to ensure that our conclusions correspond to the facts? He began with a study of deduction, which is simpler in form than induction. Greek thinkers had been arguing for centuries, constructing chains of premises leading to conclusions. Aristotle undertook the task of identifying the rules that distinguish valid from invalid arguments, and abstracting the basic principle of validity.

His monumental discovery here, which makes him the father of logic, was that deductive validity is determined solely by the form of the argument, not by its content. Some forms are logically valid, i.e., the conclusion follows from the premises, no matter what the content; other forms are invalid—again, independent of content. For example, consider the argument: "Socrates is a man; men are mortal; therefore, Socrates is mortal." We can symbolize it as follows: "S is M; M is P; therefore S is P." Any argument with this structure is deductively valid. In contrast, consider the argument: "Socrates is mortal; pigs are mortal; therefore Socrates is a pig." Any argument with this structure is invalid.

Note that our first grasp of the distinction between valid and invalid arguments is based on direct observation. For instance, we know that the second argument is invalid simply because it is perceptually self-evident that Socrates is not a pig. Later, we can symbolize the argument, draw diagrams, and grasp what is wrong with its form. But the initial separation of valid and invalid arguments is prior to the abstract analysis, and it is possible because invalid forms can lead to conclusions that are observably false.

Thus Aristotle *induced* his theory of deduction; he examined an enormous range of particular arguments and arrived at generalizations that identified the various types of valid and invalid structures. Then, ascending to an even greater level of abstraction, he asked: What is the common error at the root of all invalid arguments? He found that all such arguments imply a contradiction, i.e., they imply that something is A and non-A at the same time and in the same respect. Thus he grasped (inductively) that the law of noncontradiction is the fundamental principle of valid thought.

The theory of deduction was an unprecedented achievement in epistemology, but it was obvious that deductive validity alone is no guarantee of truth. False premises combined in a valid structure can lead to false conclusions. Knowledge requires that one validate the entire chain of reasoning that leads from observation to the final conclusion. Every conclusion of a deductive argument depends on generalizations that can be reached only by induction. Hence the question with which we began this book: How can we know the truth of such generalizations?

In answering this question as it pertains to physics, we have relied heavily on the history of science. The theory of induction presented here has itself been induced by observing the scientific discovery process in action. We have treated the history of science as our laboratory, identifying the principles of method that have led to truth and the departures from that method that have led to error. We have used the methods of agreement and difference to abstract the methodological principles common to cases of successful discovery, and to contrast them to cases of failure.

For instance, consider the principle that a proven scientific theory must be based throughout on causal relationships, as opposed to descriptive regularities. The law of causality, of course, is grasped implicitly at a very early stage of cognitive development; we do not arrive at it by studying scientific theories, which presuppose knowledge of countless causal relationships. Yet the history of science does give new insight into the role of causality in developing abstract theories of the physical world, and this insight could not be obtained in any other way. When we identify the noncausal approach of Ptolemy and see the resulting stagnation in astronomy, and then contrast it to the explicitly causal approach of Kepler and see his landmark discovery of the true structure of the solar system, then we have the data to grasp a crucial principle of scientific method.

Next, consider the principle that the methods of difference and agreement provide the means of discovering causal relationships (experiment is the primary form of these methods, but—as Kepler showed—it is not the only form). It is one thing to acknowledge that difference and agreement play some important role in science (even rationalists usually concede this much); it is quite another thing, however, to grasp the fundamental and indispensable nature of that role. Here again, the history of science provides abundant evidence. For example, the contrast between the physics of Descartes and that of Newton illustrates this point. Despite the fact that Descartes performed experiments occasionally, experiment did not play an essential role in his physics—which, as a result, was a hash of assertions that had no basis in reality. On the other hand, experiment was fundamental to Newton's method—and, as a result, he discovered truth on an unprecedented scale and became the father of modern physics.

The role of mathematics is also induced from the history of science. Prior to Galileo, even the best thinkers did not fully grasp the unique power of mathematics as a tool for understanding the physical world. Even after Galileo, Descartes made relatively little use of mathematics in his physics (despite the fact that he was an excellent mathematician). It was only after the work of Newton that mathematics was fully recognized as the language of physical science.

From history we also learn that man *can* discover the fundamental nature of matter, and that such theoretical knowledge has practical benefits. Here again, Newton paved the way. He was the first to conceive the possibility of explaining the enormous variety of observed phenomena by means of a few fundamental laws. Such knowledge then made possible the Industrial Revolution, resulting in dramatic increases in the longevity and prosperity of human life. And, if we are slow to learn the lesson, history is kind enough to repeat it for us. For example, we can look at the discovery of the atomic theory of matter, at the disastrous opposition to the theory by positivists who denied the possibility of such knowledge, and finally at the extraordinary life-promoting technology that has emerged from the theory.

Finally, consider the principle that the inductive method is self-corrective. Could we have grasped this principle without inducing it from the history of science? We might have argued as follows: (1) Reality is a causally interconnected whole that has no contradictions; (2) the inductive method keeps one in cognitive contact with reality; (3) such contact therefore guarantees that one will eventually become aware of facts that contradict and thereby disprove any false idea. By itself, however, this is nothing more than a series of unconvincing, floating abstractions. The argument becomes convincing only when we give content to the abstractions by examining a wide range of actual errors from the history of science, and seeing in every case that the continued application of the inductive method led to the correction of the error.

The theory of induction must be evaluated by the same criteria that it proposes for evaluating theories in physical science. Let us now examine whether these criteria have been satisfied.

First, consider the range of historical data that has been offered in support of the theory. We have looked closely at the discovery of three relatively narrow theories (Galileo's kinematics, Kepler's theory of the solar system, and Newton's theory of colors) and at the discovery of two fundamental theories (Newtonian mechanics and the atomic theory of matter). These theories differ in level of abstraction, they involve different sciences (astronomy, physics, and chemistry), and they deal with phenomena that range from the very large (the solar system) to the very small (atoms). In each case it was demonstrated that the same principles of method led to proof, and that the missteps committed along the road to discovery were caused by some departure from that method. Any reader who desires further evidence is referred to the history of electromagnetism, which showcases the same method.[8]

I have deliberately chosen uncontroversial, proven theories. A philosopher of science who is attempting to identify principles of method must do this for the same reason that the physicist must eliminate confounding factors in his experiments. Just as the physicist cannot identify a cause when an experiment involves several relevant but uncontrolled variables, the philosopher cannot identify the principles of proper method by examining the development of a theory that has an unknown relationship to reality.

In addition to being induced from the history of science, a theory of induction in physics must also be an integrated part of a broad philosophic system that has been validated. Induction is an advanced topic in epistemology, and thus it presupposes answers to many prior questions regarding the foundations and nature of knowledge. Our theory is part of a total philosophic framework that identifies the basic axioms on which all knowledge rests and the nature of concepts. Thus we have accepted the responsibility of satisfying our own criteria of proof: We have presented a theory of induction that is based throughout on observation, that integrates with a valid conceptual framework, and that has been induced from a sufficient range of data.

I began this section by emphasizing that philosophy is the foundation of the specialized sciences, and yet now I have emphasized that some crucial philosophic knowledge is induced from the history of those sciences. Both points are true and consistent with one another. One must have the essentials of a this-worldly, rational approach in order to discover specialized knowledge; then, once a significant amount of such knowledge has been discovered, one can reflect on the process and come to a more explicit understanding of method. The philosophic knowledge needed at the beginning is hierarchically lower than the principles of method that are induced from the successful discovery of scientific theories. For example, we must first grasp that observation is the base of knowledge before we can grasp the role of experiment in physical science; we must first grasp the law of noncontradiction and the interdependence of our ideas before we can grasp the principle that all knowledge must form an integrated whole; and we must first grasp the practical benefits of lower-level knowledge before we can grasp the extraordinary value of abstract theories.

In Chapter 4, we discussed the relationship between early knowledge of physics and later discoveries. We saw that Galileo's kinematics was an essential prerequisite that enabled Newton to expand the concept "acceleration" and to grasp the concept "gravity." In his more advanced context of knowledge, Newton could then look back and see implications of Galileo's experiments that Galileo himself could not grasp. The use of later discoveries to deepen and expand one's understanding of earlier points is characteristic of knowledge in any field, and this is particularly true in philosophy. The science of philosophy begins by telling us that we must use reason to grasp reality if we wish to stay in reality—and then, as it advances, philosophy repeats the same message, but with an ever-deeper understanding of reason and the requirements of human life.

The sciences of philosophy and physics use a similar method. Both start from low-level generalizations based on observation and arrive at principles by means of a step-by-step process of integration. Concepts play the same role in both fields: Valid concepts direct one on the path to true generalizations, and invalid concepts bring progress to a halt. And the theories of both sciences must satisfy the same criteria of proof.

But there are two obvious differences of method that have blinded intellectuals to the fact that philosophy is an inductive science.

First, philosophy does not use experiment. The subject of philosophy is man, and it is clearly wrong to control and manipulate men. Furthermore, even the diabolical attempt to treat men like inanimate objects would fail; since men have free will, there is always a causal factor that is inherently beyond the control of any would-be experimenter. But, as we have seen, philosophy has its own parallel to experiment that is completely adequate for its purposes: It uses the methods of difference and agreement to exploit the rich data sources provided by personal experience and history.

Second, philosophy does not use mathematics. Philosophy studies the relationship between man's consciousness and reality, and consciousness is not numerable. It is measurable in an approximate way because thoughts and emotions do vary along quantitative continua. For example, we can say that Newton's idea of universal gravitation is greater in scope than his idea regarding the clothes he will wear on a particular occasion; or we can say that a woman's love for her husband is more intense than her love for chocolate. But we will never be able to say that the idea of gravitation is 8,719 times as big, or that the woman's love is 163 times as intense.

States of consciousness are measurable (approximately and nonnumerically) only because of their relationship to matter. In one way or another, it is always the matter that is being measured, not the state of awareness qua awareness. A thought that has a large scope is one that subsumes more physical objects or attributes. An emotion that has great intensity is one that leads to more actions, and/or more time in action, and/or the choice of certain actions over others. When researchers speak (loosely) of applying numerical measurement to consciousness, they are in fact measuring physical entities, attributes, or actions that are related to conscious states.

Consciousness does have a nature, i.e., awareness is achieved by specific means; but everything measurable pertaining to the nature of consciousness relates to its physical instrumentalities: a particular type of senses and a particular type of brain. The phenomenon of consciousness itself is unanalyzable, because it is nothing but the faculty of perceiving existence. By itself—i.e., considered apart from any relation to the physical world—it is contentless and characterless, so there is no mystery about why it cannot be quantified. Numbers are applicable only to entities and their attributes, but conscious states are not entities—they are the awareness of entities.

A neurologist may measure electrical impulses in a brain and correlate them with states of consciousness, but the numbers always refer to the brain states. A psychologist may give multiple-choice tests designed to measure intelligence or self-esteem, but such tests give (at best) only rough estimates. The numerical scores are determined by the location of physical marks on sheets of paper. It may be clear that a particular man is more intelligent or more confident than another man, but there is no literal meaning to the claim that he is 28 percent more intelligent or that his self-esteem is 17 percent higher. There is nothing to serve as a numerical unit of intelligence or self-esteem.

Ideas within a mind are an inseparable part of a total cognitive state in a way that is not true of physical bodies. The constituents of a table or an alloy or even an atom can be separated and exist without connection to their former whole, and they retain an independent identity of their own even when they are parts of a larger whole. But since an idea is meaningless apart from the cognitive context in which it is embedded, it cannot be separated in this way, much less defined as a unit and related numerically to other ideas. When an idea is combined with another idea to arrive at yet another idea, the assignment of numbers might lead to the conclusion that one plus one equals one. Consciousness is an integrating faculty, and as such it must elude any form of counting.

The fact that philosophy cannot use mathematics has no negative consequences; it does not cast doubt on the status of philosophic knowledge. Physics must use mathematics to discover causes and acquire integrated knowledge of a vast array of physical bodies and their bewildering variety of properties. Philosophy, in contrast, is a more abstract and much more *delimited* subject: It studies *one aspect of one species*— and it thereby provides the foundation of all our knowledge and our values. Unlike physics, it does not need mathematics to provide a specialized method of integration.

Those who regard philosophy as a "soft" and unscientific discipline, in contrast to the "hard" and scientific fields of mathematics and physics, have accepted a Big Lie. The ideas of mathematicians and physicists can be no more objective or certain than the philosophic ideas on which they depend. Philosophy is the discipline that tells us how to be objective and how to achieve certainty. Without a theory of knowledge, how would mathematicians or physicists know the relationship of their concepts and generalizations to reality?

It is the inductive science of philosophy that teaches the "hard" scientist how to be scientific.

An End—and a New Beginning

Four centuries ago, Kepler and Galileo broke the chains that had kept men in Plato's cave and began the scientific revolution. It was a revolution that gathered momentum quickly and scored one victory after another. But while scientists were expanding their knowledge and conquering new territory, they failed to notice that their base of operations was being sabotaged. Philosophers had launched a counterrevolution that began to gather its own momentum.

The leader of the counterrevolution was Immanuel Kant.

Despite their errors, most philosophers prior to Kant had attempted to validate the capacity of the mind to know reality. Some acknowledged their failure and gave up in despair. But the skeptics were always followed by others who renewed the effort to show that consciousness could somehow grasp existence. Kant was the first philosopher to renounce, on principle, all such efforts—and to present his renunciation not as a failure but as a profound triumph.

The Sophists of ancient Greece argued that because we perceive things in a way that depends on the nature of our senses, we do not actually perceive the external things, but only their effects on us. Their argument assumed that, in order to be aware of an object, the conscious subject must have no nature of its own. Our organs of perception, and the specific means by which they operate, allegedly prevent us from perceiving an object as *it really is*.

The Sophists concluded that we perceive only subjective appearances, which bear an unknowable relationship to the external objects. Kant's attack on the efficacy of the mind was a radical extension of this old error. If our faculty of *per*ception is invalid because our senses operate by specific means, what about our faculty of *con*ception? All awareness results from processing the data of cognition, and that processing is done in specific ways that depend on the nature of the conscious entity. If the nature of our sensory apparatus is an insurmountable barrier to *perceiving* reality, then by the same reasoning, the nature of our conceptual apparatus must be regarded as an insurmountable barrier to *thinking* about reality. Kant concluded that consciousness, by the very fact of having a nature, is cut off from existence.

The influence of previous skeptics had been mitigated because they bewailed their inability to validate human knowledge. But Kant was different: He rejected the criterion by which his philosophy would be condemned as a failure. The standard of truth, he claimed, is not correspondence between our ideas and reality. He banished reality from the realm of human reason and replaced it with the "phenomenal world," a world of appearances created by our minds. He referred to reality as the "noumenal world" of "things-in-themselves," and he insisted that it is unknowable and *cognitively irrelevant*. "What the things-in-themselves may be I do not know, nor do I need to know, since a thing can never come before me except in appearance," he wrote in the *Critique of Pure Reason* (1787).[9] According to Kant, we never perceive reality, and reason is powerless to know anything about it. Reason deals only with the subjective world of its own creation.

The philosophers of the past, Kant claimed, had it backward when they assumed that ideas should correspond to the facts of an independently existing world. "Hitherto it has been assumed that all our knowledge must conform to objects," he wrote. "We [now] make trial whether we may not have more success in the tasks of metaphysics if we suppose that objects must conform to our knowledge."[10] The objects we perceive, says Kant, will always conform to our basic ideas—because they are merely appearances constructed by means of those very ideas, which are inherent in the structure of the human mind.

In a bizarre contortion of language, Kant referred to this fundamental shift of perspective as his "Copernican Revolution." It was a brazen attempt to usurp that prestigious name and attach it to ideas of the opposite nature. The actual Copernican Revolution was led by men who confidently asserted that reason can grasp reality, and who rebelled against the skeptical tradition of merely describing "appearances." Because these scientists acknowledged that the physical world is fully real and independent of us, they were able to discover that the universe is not centered on and designed around us. Kant, on the other hand, claimed that the world we observe is *created by us*. His view of the universe was incomparably worse than the geocentric astronomy—what he offered was an *anthropocentric delusion*.

Like Plato and Descartes, Kant based his epistemology on innate ideas. Unlike Plato and Descartes, he denied that such ideas correspond to reality; he insisted that they are merely subjective constructs, inapplicable to "things-in-themselves." Hence his theory synthesized the worst errors of his predecessors: He combined the arbitrary method of the rationalists with the skeptical content of the empiricists.

Kant recognized that his philosophy required the science of physics to be reconceived. We grasp things by means of our subjective human concepts, he claimed—therefore we do not grasp the real things, only the inner objects created by our minds. This premise demanded the rejection of Newton's inductive method. Since we create the phenomenal world, we are the *authors* of its basic laws, not the *discoverers*. He wrote that "the universal laws of nature . . . are not derived from experience, but experience is derived from them."[11] We allegedly start with the laws and create the experience that obeys them.

Subjectivism—the view that the subject creates the objects of knowledge by his own inner processes—comes in different varieties. According to Kant, the innate concepts and forms of intuition that create the phenomenal world are inherent in the human mind, and therefore we all create the same world. But many of Kant's followers have rejected this aspect of his system; they prefer a more freewheeling approach, in which one group of people can adopt ideas and thereby create their own reality, different from the realities created by other groups.

Since the 1960s, this *pluralistic subjectivism* has been the dominant view in philosophy of science. Two of its most influential advocates have been Thomas Kuhn and Paul Feyerabend.

In his most popular book, *The Structure of Scientific Revolutions*, Kuhn divided scientists into two types. There are the creators of new "paradigms" (i.e., scientific theories viewed as subjective constructs), and then there are the "normal" scientists who adopt these paradigms on the basis of authority. In other words, Kuhn describes science in the way that one might accurately characterize a religious cult. Faith, he claims, plays a central role: "[The scientist] must . . . have faith that the new paradigm will succeed with the many large problems that confront it, knowing only that the older paradigm has failed with a few. A decision of that kind can only be made on faith."[12]

According to Kuhn, a scientist cannot make a rational choice between theories on the basis of observational evidence. Observation itself is allegedly "theory-laden," and therefore the theories accepted by a scientist create the world he observes. As a result, Kuhn claims that "the proponents of competing paradigms practice their trades in different worlds."[13] Two scientists who accept different theories cannot even hope to communicate with each other, unless one or the other experiences the inexplicable conversion that Kuhn refers to as a "paradigm shift."

Consider, for example, the nineteenth-century discovery of the atomic composition of matter. In the Kuhnian view, scientists did not painstakingly gather observational evidence, objectively evaluate that evidence, design crucial experiments to answer key questions, and eventually achieve a definitive proof of the theory. Scientists have no cognitive access to a real world made of atoms; there is only the world they construct from their ideas. In the eighteenth century, most chemists studied a world where there were no atoms; after Dalton's work, they "came to live in a world where reactions behaved quite differently from the way they had before."[14]

Feyerabend took this radical subjectivism a step further and arrived at a position that can only be described as *epistemological nihilism*. In his view, objective knowledge is not only a myth—it is an enemy that must be fought and destroyed. "A truth that reigns without checks and balances," Feyerabend wrote, "is a tyrant who must be overthrown, and any falsehood that can aid us in the overthrow of this tyrant is to be welcomed."[15] Because scientists are known as exemplars of objectivity and discovers of truth, Feyerabend made them the targets of his hostility. "Scientists," he wrote, "will not play any dominant role in the society which I imagine. They will be more than balanced by magicians, priests, and astrologers."[16] We can look back at history to see Feyerabend's ideal society: It was called the Dark Ages.

More than two millennia ago, in a culture that exalted reason and laid the foundation for science, the name "philosophy" was derived from the Greek words meaning "love of wisdom." But today the state of philosophy is very different. Intellectuals have finally reached the end of the Kantian road—only to find Paul Feyerabend waiting for them, laughing at them, and littering the barren ground with books titled *Against Method* and *Farewell to Reason*.

What happens to physics when it is abandoned by rational philosophy, as it has been during the past century? The answer can be found by examining three fundamental theories of contemporary physics: quantum mechanics, big bang cosmology, and string theory.

Quantum mechanics has its origins in a series of discoveries made during the late nineteenth and early twentieth centuries, and its basic mathematical formulation was completed in the 1920s. Some of the first crucial discoveries concerned the nature of light. The electromagnetic wave theory of light had explained an enormous range of data—yet, surprisingly, phenomena such as black-body radiation and the photoelectric effect seemed to demand that physicists regard light as a particle. Later, the same "wave/particle duality" was discovered in connection with matter that has mass; for example, electrons were found to exhibit wave properties in addition to their well-known particle properties.

The expressions for the energy and momentum of such "matter waves" were identified in 1924 by Louis de Broglie. Using these relationships, Erwin Schrödinger was able to derive the fundamental wave equation describing the dynamics of the subatomic world. A close look at this early history reveals that the mathematics of quantum theory was developed in an admirably logical way; it was guided by experiment, by the conservation-of-energy principle, and by the requirement that the theory reduce to Newtonian mechanics in the macroscopic limit.

As a mathematical formalism, quantum theory has been enormously successful. It makes quantitative predictions of impressive accuracy for a vast range of phenomena, providing the basis for modern chemistry, condensed matter physics, nuclear physics, and optics. It also made possible some of the greatest technological innovations of the twentieth century, including computers and lasers.

Yet, as a fundamental theory of physics, it is strangely empty—"a skeleton scheme of symbols," to use the eloquent phrase of Sir Arthur Eddington.[17] It gives a mathematical recipe for predicting the statistical behavior of particles but fails to provide causal models of subatomic processes. The founders of quantum theory rejected the very goal of developing such models; Niels Bohr, the leading interpreter of the theory, insisted that there was nothing to model. "There is no quantum world," he wrote. "There is only an abstract quantum description."[18]

What, then, does the theory describe? Most physicists regard the question as futile; the reality underlying the mathematical formalism is widely held to be unintelligible. The standard version of quantum theory (the "Copenhagen" interpretation) rejects Aristotle's law of identity; the basic entities composing matter, it says, exist in an unreal state without specific properties. "Atomic physics deprives of all meaning the well-defined attributes that classical physics would ascribe to the object," Bohr wrote.[19] The elementary particles have no identity—they are not something, and not nothing—until we measure or observe them, at which time the observed property suddenly pops into existence as something definite. In the words of physicist John Archibald Wheeler, "No elementary phenomenon is a real phenomenon until it is an observed phenomenon."[20]

Thus the theory claims that a measurement does not tell us about a preexisting state of a particle; rather, it creates that state. Prior to measurement, a particle exists in several incompatible states simultaneously, with each assigned a probability. Physicists insist that it is not merely our ignorance of the actual state of the entity that necessitates the use of probabilities. The probabilities are regarded as a *complete* description of the physical system. It is *reality* that is regarded as incomplete, or, in the words of mathematical physicist Hermann Weyl, "afflicted with a sort of vagueness."[21]

Causality is supposedly inapplicable to this "vague," unreal quantum world. "Through quantum mechanics," wrote Werner Heisenberg, "the invalidity of the law of causation is definitely established."[22] The law of causality states a relation between an entity and its actions; it says that the nature of the entity determines how it will act in any circumstances. If one denies that the fundamental constituents of matter have specific natures, it follows that there is nothing to determine their actions. According to Bohr and Heisenberg, individual particles act randomly, with no cause.

The theory makes no attempt to explain how a measurement transforms a "nothing in particular" into a something with definite properties. Some physicists have opted for a "mind over matter" interpretation of quantum theory. In this view, the physical world has no existence independent of our consciousness; as Kant said, it is a creation of consciousness. "Only with the entry of the result of measurement into somebody's consciousness will the entire pyramid of quantum 'limbo' states collapse into concrete reality," writes physicist Paul Davies.[23] Others have claimed that quantum theory actually describes an *ensemble of universes*, each of which is in a definite state. The observation then determines which of the many universes we inhabit. Faced with such alternative interpretations, most physicists today prefer to take a "practical" approach: They stick to doing calculations and try not to think about the meaning of the theory.

The proponents of the Copenhagen interpretation were not troubled by the wave/particle duality. Bohr argued that "we must accept the fact that a complete elucidation of one and the same object may require diverse points of view which defy a unique description," i.e., we must accept the use of *contradictory* models.[24] Quantum theory, said Bohr, ensures that we can never observe simultaneously the contradictory properties ascribed to micro-objects, because an observation "collapses" the entity into a definite, unique state. He concluded that it was proper for the theory to contain such contradictions, so long as the "measurement miracle" saves us from perceiving them. And if this makes anyone feel uncomfortable, the problem can be avoided by not using the harsh word "contradiction." Instead Bohr calls the wave and particle models "complementary," which has a soothing and reassuring sound.

The failure to properly integrate the wave and particle models (i.e., the acceptance of "wavicles") has led to the paradoxes of quantum theory. Tragically, most physicists have reacted with a shrug. James Gleick, in his biography of Richard Feynman, described the widespread resignation: "[Physicists] recognized that their profession's relationship to reality had changed. Gone was the luxury of supposing that a single reality existed, that the human mind had reasonably clear access to it, and that the scientist could explain it."[25]

But these premises are not luxuries—they are *necessities*, and they have been surrendered without much of a fight. The surrender was not caused by experimental facts; the knowledge gained by experimental discovery of facts can never lead to the denial of knowledge and fact. The surrender was caused by the influence of post-Kantian philosophy, an enemy that operated behind the front lines and provided the corrupt framework used to misinterpret the facts. By rejecting causality and accepting the unintelligibility of the atomic world, physicists have reduced themselves to mere calculating machines (at best)—and thus they are unable to ask further questions or to integrate their knowledge.

Copenhagen quantum mechanics is not a theory—it is a mathematical formalism coupled with skepticism. It amounts to the claim that no physical theory of the quantum world is possible. It is worth noting that this claim has been refuted by David Bohm, a physicist who developed a quantum theory in which waves are waves, particles are particles, and contradictions are rejected as contradictions (rather than accepted as "complementary," diverse viewpoints). Bohm's theory may or may not be correct, but it does qualify as a theory, and as such it deserves more attention.

Let us now turn from the subatomic world to the universe as a whole. If one considers the questions that have gone unanswered during the past century, including fundamental questions about quantum mechanics and its problematic relationship to relativity theory, one might be surprised that physicists dare to put forth a theory of the universe. Yet, with the big bang theory, they have done so with the false bravado of a megalomaniac.

Perhaps we should not be surprised. The big bang is the latest in a long history of creation myths, and rational standards of evidence are never applied to such myths. Since reason cannot approve the idea of creation—in this case, the claim that fourteen billion years ago the entire universe inexplicably popped out of a point with infinite mass density—it is unrealistic to expect that high epistemological standards will be applied to the rest of the theory.

The big bang model of the universe was proposed in 1931 by George Lemaître, an astrophysicist who was also a Catholic priest. Initially, its leading advocates were explicit about favoring a creation theory on philosophic grounds. But they did make attempts at scientific arguments. Lemaître argued that the big bang was the only possible source of cosmic rays; Eddington argued that the law of entropy implies a universe that has been degenerating from an initial state of simplicity at the moment of creation; George Gamow argued that the high energies required for nucleosynthesis of heavy elements could exist only in the immediate aftermath of big bang. All three arguments have been decisively refuted.

The big bang theory itself, however, managed to survive. It is now justified on the basis of three types of observational evidence. First, the observed redshift of light from distant stars and galaxies is allegedly caused by the "expansion of space" that began with the big bang. Second, it is claimed that the relative abundances of light elements (deuterium, helium, and lithium) are explained by the theory. Third, the microwave background radiation that was first detected in the 1960s is supposed to be a relic from the big bang.

In order to account for these phenomena, however, proponents of the big bang have been compelled to modify the theory with a growing list of unsubstantiated hypotheses. Contrary to expectations, the redshift data seem to imply an accelerating expansion rate, which is supposedly caused by a repulsive force associated with "dark energy" (a mysterious form of energy that is unrelated to matter and allegedly makes up more than 70 percent of the energy in the universe). The observed mass density of the universe is far too low to account for the relative abundances of light elements, so the missing mass is assumed to exist in the form of "dark matter" (an unknown form of matter that makes up more than 80 percent of the mass in the universe). The distribution of the microwave background radiation is too uniform, which is explained by a superexpansion called "inflation" that allegedly occurred during the first instant of the big bang. The distribution of galaxies is too nonuniform, which is explained by quantum fluctuations during this first instant. In short, big bang theorists rely on energy, matter, and unique events that are inaccessible to observational astronomers. To use their terminology, it is a "dark" theory.

Historically, theories that have been reached by a proper application of the inductive method—for example, Newtonian mechanics, atomic theory, electromagnetism—have quickly led to accurate quantitative predictions for an impressive range of new phenomena. But the history of the big bang theory is different: It is a history of observational astronomers providing unwelcome surprises, while cosmologists scramble to adjust the theory. As one astrophysicist, Eric Lerner, points out,

> [T]he big bang theory can boast of no quantitative predictions that have subsequently been validated by observation. The successes claimed by the theory's supporters consist of its ability to retrospectively fit observations with a steadily increasing array of adjustable parameters, just as the old Earth-centered cosmology of Ptolemy needed layer upon layer of epicycles.[26]

Yet the vast majority of physicists regard the theory as proven, in the same way that astronomers five centuries ago regarded Ptolemy's theory as proven. The central question asked by these physicists is not: What is the nature of the universe? but rather: What must the universe be like in order to conform to big bang theory? The small minority of researchers who express doubt—those who are concerned with anomalous redshifts, or consider alternative explanations of the microwave background radiation, or question whether dark matter exists in the quantity required by the theory—are dismissed as heretics. As befits a creation myth, the big bang is treated as religious doctrine and cosmologists play the role of theologians protecting the faith.

Premature attempts to develop a complete theory of the universe have often stifled progress in the physical sciences. In ancient Greece, Eudoxus offered a theory of the universe in terms of interconnected, rotating celestial spheres—and his theory had the effect of reinforcing false ideas about the nature of motion, forces, and matter. Today, physicists know much more than Eudoxus, but it is still too early for a theory of the universe. The data consist primarily of light from very distant sources, but physicists do not yet have an adequate understanding of light "wavicles" or of the fields through which they travel. Cosmological theory is based on general relativity and quantum field theory—which, at this stage, are mathematical formalisms that contradict each other. Before a theory of the universe is possible, physicists need answers to the questions that have accumulated over the past century.

Some of the answers are allegedly offered by string theory, which has dominated theoretical physics for the past generation.

Early in the twentieth century, physicists looked forward to the prospect of explaining all matter in terms of a few elementary particles. As they explored the subatomic world, however, they became progressively more discouraged by its complexity. The standard theory accepted today contains a dozen elementary particles, plus their antiparticles, plus the "exchange" particles that mediate the four basic forces. Furthermore, physicists have been frustrated by the fact that gravitation has resisted all attempts to describe it in terms of quantum field theory (which is used to describe the other three forces).

String theory claims to reduce this complexity and explain it by means of one type of entity moving in accordance with one law. Everything is made of strings, which have simple properties: They are described by a tension constant (the energy per unit length) and a coupling constant (the probability of a string breaking into two strings). The strings all move such that the area traced out in spacetime is minimized. All the particles and forces are associated with the vibration or breaking or joining of strings. Gravitation is included in this scheme as the vibration of closed loops.

If you think this theory sounds too good to be true, you are right. String theory is a magic trick. It does not make problems actually disappear; it merely hides them in a different place. It is a hiding place where very few people would look: *the geometry of eleven-dimensional spacetime*. According to string theorists, the complexity of the world does not arise from the nature of matter, but from the complexity of space considered as a thing in itself. The three-dimensional world we perceive is supplemented by seven additional spatial dimensions that are curled up into structures too small to perceive. Thus the unification supposedly achieved by the theory is an illusion. One physicist, Lee Smolin, puts the point this way:

> The constants that denote the masses of the particles and the strengths of the forces are being traded for constants that denote the geometry of the extra six [now seven] dimensions. . . . Nothing was constrained or reduced. And because there were a huge number of choices for the geometry of the extra dimensions, the number of free constants went up, not down.[27]

String theorists are lost in the world of geometrical ideas that they have invented, and they cannot find their way back to the real world. The arbitrary nature of their creation has led to the problem of "nonuniqueness": There is not *one* string theory, but a *countless number*, with no way to choose among them. None of these theories makes any predictions that have been confirmed by observation. And, despite the extraordinary freedom with which these theories are created, they all contradict the observational data; for example, they predict nonexistent pairs of particles with equal mass and nonexistent long-range forces. As a result, string theory evokes a mixed reaction—one does not know whether to laugh at the absurdity or cry at the tragedy of it.

By the rational standards that many scientists accepted in the past, string theory is a catastrophic failure. It is the leading theory in physics today only because those standards have been rejected. Smolin has described the new attitude of string theorists: "No more reliance on experiment to check our theories. That was the stuff of Galileo. Mathematics now sufficed to explore the laws of nature. We had entered the period of postmodern physics."[28]

"Postmodern" physicists adopt the aesthetic criteria of rationalism and judge their theories solely by the elegance, symmetry, and beauty of the mathematics. Steven Weinberg, a Nobel laureate and leading theorist, expressed the idea that now dominates physics: "The reality we observe in our laboratories is only an imperfect reflection of a deeper and more beautiful reality, the reality of the equations that display all the symmetries of the theory."[29] Of course, this idea is unoriginal—it is, in essence, what Plato said in the fourth century B.C.

Plato was the first to replace the physical world with geometric forms imposed on space itself. As I mentioned in Chapter 3, Greek mathematicians knew that there are five solid geometric figures that can be constructed from identical plane surfaces, and these figures were admired for their perfect symmetry. It was also commonly believed that there are five material elements: earth, air, water, fire, and the ether that makes up celestial bodies. The coincidence of numbers led Plato to equate each material element with one of the regular solids. When he was done, there was nothing left in the physical universe except space and the spatial relationships constituting geometrical figures. Spatial relationships of what? Shapes of what? He had no answer, just as his contemporary followers have no answer.

At the root of Plato's philosophy is a fundamental antagonism toward sense perception and the physical world. This antagonism is expressed in his dialogue *Phaedo*, where he identifies the premises that led him to reify space and reduce physics to geometry:

When [the soul] tries to investigate anything with the help of the body, it is obviously led astray. . . . [T]he person who is likely to succeed in this attempt most perfectly is the one who approaches each object, as far as possible, with the unaided intellect, without taking account of any sense of sight in his thinking, or dragging any other sense into his reckoning—the man who pursues the truth by applying his pure and unadulterated thought to the pure and unadulterated object, cutting himself off as much as possible from his eyes and ears and virtually all the rest of his body, as an impediment which by its presence prevents the soul from attaining to truth and clear thinking. . . . [I]f we are ever to have pure knowledge of anything, we must *get rid of the body* and contemplate things by themselves with the soul by itself.[30] (Italics added.)

Like gangsters in the night, string theorists are also trying to "get rid of the body." By accepting Platonism, however, they are getting rid of the science of physics. They have turned the clocks back—not merely to the era of prephysics, but to the era of prelogic.

The "end of physics" has become a fashionable topic in the recent literature. The Platonists claim that theoretical physics will end with omniscience, which will be achieved as soon as they receive their final revelation about the eleven-dimensional structure of spacetime. The skeptics agree that physics is coming to an end, but for a different reason: They claim that man has exhausted his capacity to say anything intelligible about the world.

In one sense, the skeptics are right; "exhausted" is an accurate way to characterize the state of physics today. Even Weinberg, despite his Platonism, makes the following concession: "There's never been a time when there's been so little excitement in the sense of experiments suggesting really new ideas or theories being able to make new and qualitatively different kinds of predictions that are then borne out by experiments."[31] In effect, theoretical physics has come to an end—not because everything has been discovered, or because we have no capacity for discovery, but because physicists have not yet identified *the method of discovery*.

Physics, however, is only four hundred years *young*, and there are many basic questions that are still unanswered. There is reason for a new excitement. The extraordinary rate of progress that characterized the era of classical physics can be achieved again and even surpassed— if physicists explicitly grasp the method that made such progress possible.

Physics is dead—long live physics!

REFERENCES

Preface

1. E. Bright Wilson, *An Introduction to Scientific Research* (New York: Dover, 1990), p. 298.

Chapter 1

1. Paul K. Feyerabend, *Against Method,* revised edition (New York: Verso, 1988), p. 73.
2. E. Bright Wilson, *An Introduction to Scientific Research* (New York: Dover, 1990), p. 293.
3. Ayn Rand, *Introduction to Objectivist Epistemology* (New York: Penguin, 1990), p. 13.
4. Ibid., p. 18.
5. Leonard Peikoff, *Objectivism: The Philosophy of Ayn Rand* (New York: Penguin, 1990), p. 90.
6. As our knowledge expands, definitions serve a crucial function for first-level concepts as well; for example, the definition of man as "the rational animal" represents an enormous condensation of knowledge.
7. Rand, *Introduction to Objectivist Epistemology,* p. 48.
8. Ibid., pp. 66–67.
9. Peikoff, *Objectivism,* p. 133.
10. Ibid.
11. Ibid., pp. 172–73.
12. Duane Roller, *The Development of the Concept of Electric Charge* (Cambridge, Mass.: Harvard University Press, 1967), p. 63.

Chapter 2

1. A. Mark Smith, "Ptolemy's Search for a Law of Refraction," *Archive for History of Exact Sciences* 26 (1982), pp. 221–40.
2. Galileo's initial derivation of the chord theorem is invalid. Later, after his experimental discovery of the constant acceleration down inclined planes, he gave a correct proof of the theorem. Stillman Drake discusses this point in *Galileo: Pioneer Scientist* (Toronto: University of Toronto Press, 1990), p. 91.
3. Michael R. Matthews, *Time for Science Education* (New York: Kluwer Academic/ Plenum Publishers, 2000), p. 104.
4. Quoted in ibid., pp. 84–85.
5. Ibid., p. 82.
6. Stillman Drake, *Galileo: Pioneer Scientist* (Toronto: University of Toronto Press, 1990), p. 96.
7. Stillman Drake, *Galileo at Work* (Chicago: University of Chicago Press, 1978), p. 128.
8. Matthews, *Time for Science Education,* p. 98.
9. *Galileo: Dialogue Concerning the Two Chief World Systems,* translated by Stillman Drake, 2nd edition (Berkeley: University of California Press, 1967), pp. 17–21.
10. Drake, *Galileo at Work,* pp. 387–88.
11. *The Philosophic Writings of Descartes,* vol. 1, translated by John Cottingham, Robert Stoothoff, and Donald Murdoch (New York: Cambridge University Press, 1985), p. 249.
12. I. Bernard Cohen and Richard S. Westfall, eds., *Newton* (New York: Norton, 1995), p. 148.
13. J. E. McGuire and Martin Tamny, *Certain Philosophic Questions: Newton's Trinity Notebook* (Cambridge, England: Cambridge University Press, 1983), p. 263.
14. Ibid., p. 389.
15. Richard S. Westfall, *Never at Rest* (Cambridge, England: Cambridge University Press, 1980), p. 164.
16. *Newton's Philosophy of Nature: Selections from His Writings,* edited by H. S. Thayer (New York: Hafner, 1953), p. 6.
17. Ibid.
18. Ibid., pp. 7–8.
19. Newton restricted his inductive method and his rejection of arbitrary claims to the realm of science. He was devoutly religious, and hence he did not hold that all knowledge must be based on observation. However, in contrast to Descartes, who explicitly invoked God in his attempt to validate the laws of motion, Newton rarely allowed his religious views to affect his science (the crucial exception is his view of the nature of space and time).
20. Cohen and Westfall, eds., *Newton,* pp. 148–49.
21. Morris Cohen and Ernest Nagel, *An Introduction to Logic and Scientific Method* (New York: Harcourt, Brace & World, 1934), p. 205.

22. Ibid., p. 266.
23. Ibid., p. 257.

Chapter 3

1. Pierre Duhem, *To Save the Phenomena,* translated by Edmund Doland and Chaninah Maschler (Chicago: University of Chicago Press, 1969), p. 31.
2. Nicolaus Copernicus, *On the Revolutions of Heavenly Spheres,* translated by Charles Glenn Wallis (New York: Prometheus, 1995), p. 26.
3. Ibid., p. 27.
4. I. Bernard Cohen, *The Birth of a New Physics* (New York: Norton, 1985), p. 23.
5. Copernicus, *On the Revolutions of Heavenly Spheres,* pp. 12–13.
6. Ibid., p. 17.
7. Max Caspar, *Kepler,* translated and edited by C. Doris Hellman (New York: Dover, 1993), p. 102.
8. Gerald Holton, *Thematic Origins of Scientific Thought: Kepler to Einstein* (Cambridge, Mass.: Harvard University Press, 1973), p. 72.
9. Caspar, *Kepler,* p. 62.
10. Holton, *Thematic Origins of Scientific Thought,* p. 78.
11. Caspar, *Kepler,* p. 134.
12. Arthur Koestler, *The Sleepwalkers* (London: Penguin, 1989), pp. 327–28.
13. Holton, *Thematic Origins of Scientific Thought,* p. 74.
14. Koestler, *The Sleepwalkers,* p. 334.
15. *Selections from Kepler's Astronomia Nova,* translated by William H. Donahue (Santa Fe, N.M.: Green Lion, 2004), p. 94.
16. Koestler, *The Sleepwalkers,* p. 337.
17. Caspar, *Kepler,* p. 19.
18. Holton, *Thematic Origins of Scientific Thought,* p. 68.
19. Caspar, *Kepler,* p. 67.
20. Koestler, *The Sleepwalkers,* p. 398.
21. Holton, *Thematic Origins of Scientific Thought,* p. 85.
22. Caspar, *Kepler,* pp. 280–81.
23. Ibid., p. 135.
24. For more on Galileo's astronomy and his battle with the Church, see my three-part article "Galileo: Inaugurating the Age of Reason," *The Intellectual Activist* 14, nos. 3–5 (March–May 2000).

Chapter 4

1. Isaac Newton, *Principia,* vol. 2, *The System of the World* (Berkeley: University of California Press, 1934), p. 398.
2. James Gleick, *Isaac Newton* (New York: Pantheon, 2003), p. 58.
3. Galileo Galilei, *Two New Sciences,* translated by Henry Crew and Alfonso de Salvio (New York: Dover, 1954), pp. 182–83.
4. Gleick, *Isaac Newton,* p. 59.

5. Ernst Mach, *The Science of Mechanics* (Chicago: Open Court, 1960).

6. Isaac Newton, *Principia,* vol. 1, *The Motion of Bodies,* preface to the first edition (Berkeley: University of California Press, 1934), p. xvii.

7. Newton, *Principia,* vol. 2, *The System of the World,* p. 519.

8. A. Rupert Hall, *From Galileo to Newton* (New York: Dover, 1981), pp. 310–14.

9. Newton, *Principia,* vol. 2, *The System of the World,* p. 547.

10. Hall, *From Galileo to Newton,* pp. 315–16.

11. David Harriman, "Cracks in the Foundation," *The Intellectual Activist* 16, no. 12 (December 2002), pp. 19–27.

12. See the fifth letter of Leibniz in *The Leibniz-Clarke Correspondence,* edited by H. G. Alexander (Manchester, England: Manchester University Press, 1965).

13. Nicolaus Copernicus, *On the Revolutions of Heavenly Spheres,* translated by Charles Glenn Wallis (New York: Prometheus, 1995), p. 5.

Chapter 5

1. Thomas L. Hankins, *Science and the Enlightenment* (New York: Cambridge University Press, 1985), p. 112.

2. Ibid., p. 109.

3. *The World of the Atom,* vol. 1, edited by Henry Boorse and Lloyd Motz (New York: Basic Books, 1966), p. 169.

4. J. R. Partington, *A Short History of Chemistry* (New York: Dover, 1989), p. 204.

5. *The World of the Atom,* vol. 1, p. 321.

6. Ibid., p. 327.

7. *The Beginnings of Modern Science,* edited by Holmes Boynton (Roslyn, N.Y.: Walter J. Black, 1948), p. 198.

8. Humphry Davy, "An Essay on Heat, Light, and the Combinations of Light," in *Contributions to Physical and Medical Knowledge,* edited by T. Beddoes (Bristol, England, 1799), reprinted in *Davy's Collected Works* (London, 1839), vol. 2, p. 9.

9. Later researchers such as Clausius and Maxwell realized that Waterston's model was oversimplified. Heat absorbed by a polyatomic gas does not merely increase the speed of the molecules; it can also increase their rate of rotation and vibration. Fortunately, the basic law of gases depends only on the proportionality between temperature and average translational kinetic energy, and therefore Waterston's model was adequate for his purpose. In order to understand the heat capacities of gases, the other motions must be taken into account.

10. Stephen G. Brush, *The Kind of Motion We Call Heat* (Amsterdam: Elsevier Science B.V., 1986), p. 146.

11. *The Scientific Papers of James Clerk Maxwell,* edited by W. A. Niven (New York: Dover, 1965), vol. 2, pp. 344–45.

12. Brush, *The Kind of Motion We Call Heat,* p. 190.

13. This result is true to first-order approximation, which applies to bodies moving slowly through gases within a certain range of pressure. It does not apply when

the pressure is extremely low or high—and, as baseball pitchers can testify, it does not apply to curveballs thrown at Coors Field in Denver.

14. Brush, *The Kind of Motion We Call Heat*, p. 191.
15. Ibid., p. 76.
16. *The World of the Atom*, vol. 1, p. 278.
17. Frankland originated the concept, but used the term "atomicity" instead of "valence." The word "valence" came into use in the late 1860s.
18. W. G. Palmer, *A History of the Concept of Valency to 1930* (London: Cambridge University Press, 1965), p. 34.
19. Ibid., p. 14.
20. Ibid., p. 27.
21. Ibid., p. 76.
22. Cecil J. Schneer, *Mind and Matter* (New York: Grove, 1969), p. 178.
23. Alexander Butlerov, "On the Chemical Structure of Substances," reprinted in *Journal of Chemical Education* 48 (1971), pp. 289–91.
24. Palmer, *A History of the Concept of Valency to 1930*, p. 62.
25. John Hudson, *The History of Chemistry* (New York: Chapman & Hall, 1992), p. 148.
26. John Buckingham, *Chasing the Molecule* (Stroud, England: Sutton, 2004), p. 206.

Chapter 6

1. Karl R. Popper, *Objective Knowledge*, revised edition (Oxford: Clarendon Press, 1979), pp. 9, 16, 198–201.
2. W. G. Palmer, *A History of the Concept of Valency to 1930* (London: Cambridge University Press, 1965), p. 66.
3. *The Beginnings of Modern Science*, edited by Holmes Boynton (New York: Walter J. Black, 1948), pp. 393–94.
4. Ibid., pp. 443–61.
5. J. R. Partington, *A Short History of Chemistry* (New York: Dover, 1989), p. 48.
6. Walter Pagel, *The Religious and Philosophical Aspects of van Helmont's Science and Medicine* (Baltimore: Johns Hopkins Press, 1944), pp. 16–22.
7. Edmund Whittaker, *A History of the Theories of Aether and Electricity* (New York: Thomas Nelson, 1951), p. 75.
8. A. E. E. McKenzie, *The Major Achievements of Science* (Cambridge, England: Cambridge University Press, 1960), p. 111.
9. Ruth Moore, *The Earth We Live On* (New York: Knopf, 1956), p. 268.
10. Joe D. Burchfield, *Lord Kelvin and the Age of the Earth* (New York: Science History Publications, 1975), p. 81.
11. Ibid., p. 42.
12. Ibid., pp. 143–44.
13. Ibid., p. 168.
14. Moore, *The Earth We Live On*, p. 385.
15. Burchfield, *Lord Kelvin and the Age of the Earth*, p. 176.

16. Steven Weinberg, *Dreams of a Final Theory* (New York: Vintage, 1992), p. 13.

17. Gary Taubes, *Bad Science: The Short Life and Weird Times of Cold Fusion* (New York: Random House, 1993), p. 127.

18. Ayn Rand, *For the New Intellectual* (New York: New American Library, 1961), p. 30.

19. Rene Descartes, *Principles of Philosophy* (Dordrecht, Netherlands: Kluwer Academic Publishers, 1991), p. 20.

20. *The Philosophical Writings of Descartes,* translated by John Cottingham, Robert Stoothoff, and Dugald Murdoch (Cambridge, England: Cambridge University Press, 1985), p. 288.

21. Descartes, *Principles of Philosophy,* p. 69.

22. *The Philosophical Writings of Descartes,* p. 245.

23. Ibid., p. 266.

24. Descartes, *Principles of Philosophy,* p. 283.

25. A. Rupert Hall, *From Galileo to Newton* (New York: Dover, 1981), p. 120.

26. For an analysis of Kant's philosophy and his approach to science, see my paper "Enlightenment Science and Its Fall," *Objective Standard* 1, no. 1 (2006), pp. 83–117.

27. Immanuel Kant, *Kant's Philosophy of Material Nature,* translated by James W. Ellington (Indianapolis: Hackett, 1985), p. 93.

28. W. H. Brock, *The Atomic Debates* (Leicester, England: Leicester University Press, 1967), p. 10.

29. Stephen G. Brush, *The Kind of Motion We Call Heat,* book 1 (Amsterdam: Elsevier Science B.V., 1976), p. 140.

30. Brock, *The Atomic Debates,* p. 77.

31. Ibid., p. 51.

32. Ibid., pp. 14, 48.

33. Alan J. Rocke, *Chemical Atomism in the Nineteenth Century* (Columbus: Ohio State University Press, 1984), p. 314.

34. Ibid.

35. Ibid., p. 315.

36. Ibid.

37. *The Question of the Atom*, edited by Mary Jo Nye (Los Angeles: Tomash, 1984), p. 143.

38. Rocke, *Chemical Atomism in the Nineteenth Century,* p. 316.

39. Ibid., p. 315.

40. Ibid., p. 323.

41. *The Question of the Atom,* p. 246.

42. Rocke, *Chemical Atomism in the Nineteenth Century,* p. 324.

43. Ernst Mach, *History and Root of the Principle of Conservation of Energy* (Chicago: University of Chicago Press, 1910), p. 49.

44. Ibid., p. 48.

45. Paul Forman, "Weimar Culture, Causality, and Quantum Theory, 1918–1927: Adaptation by German Physicists and Mathematicians to a Hostile Intellectual Environment," *Historical Studies in the Physical Sciences* 3 (1971), pp. 1–115.

Chapter 7

1. James Jeans, *Physics and Philosophy* (Cambridge, England: Cambridge University Press, 1943), pp. 15–16.

2. Quoted in Morris Kline, *Mathematics: The Loss of Certainty* (New York: Oxford University Press, 1980), p. 340.

3. Pat Corvini explains the step-by-step development of the number system in her lecture course, "Two, Three, Four and All That," which is available from the Ayn Rand Bookstore.

4. Leonard Peikoff, *Objectivism: The Philosophy of Ayn Rand* (New York: Penguin, 1990), pp. 111–21.

5. Kline, *Mathematics,* p. 339.

6. See, for example, Dr. Corvini's lecture course titled "Achilles, the Tortoise, and the Objectivity of Mathematics" (which is available through the Ayn Rand Bookstore). Dr. Corvini is currently working on a book titled "Conceiving Infinity."

7. Ayn Rand, *Introduction to Objectivist Epistemology,* 2nd edition, edited by Harry Binswanger and Leonard Peikoff (New York: Penguin, 1990).

8. See, for example, Duane Roller, *The Development of the Concept of Electric Charge* (Cambridge, Mass.: Harvard University Press, 1954) and Sir Edmund Whittaker, *A History of the Theories of Aether and Electricity,* vol. 1 (New York: Thomas Nelson, 1951).

9. Immanuel Kant, *Critique of Pure Reason,* translated by Norman Kemp Smith (New York: St. Martin's, 1965), p. 286.

10. Ibid., p. 22.

11. Immanuel Kant, *Kant's Philosophy of Material Nature,* translated by James W. Ellington (Indianapolis: Hackett, 1985), pp. 55–56.

12. Thomas Kuhn, *The Structure of Scientific Revolutions,* 2nd edition (Chicago: University of Chicago Press, 1970), p. 158.

13. Ibid., p. 150.

14. Ibid., p. 134.

15. Paul K. Feyerabend, "Philosophy of Science 2001," in *Methodology, Metaphysics and the History of Science,* edited by Robert S. Cohen and Marx W. Wartofsky (Boston: D. Reidel, 1984), p. 138.

16. Ibid., p. 147.

17. *Quantum Questions: Mystical Writings of the World's Great Physicists,* edited by Ken Wilber (Boston: New Science Library, 1984), p. 180.

18. Nick Herbert, *Quantum Reality: Beyond the New Physics* (New York: Anchor, 1987), p. 17.

19. Donald Murdoch, *Niels Bohr's Philosophy of Physics* (Cambridge, England: Cambridge University Press, 1987), p. 139.

20. Herbert, *Quantum Reality,* p. 18.

21. Quoted in Paul Forman, "Weimar Culture, Causality, and Quantum Theory, 1918–1927: Adaptation by German Physicists and Mathematicians to a Hostile Intellectual Environment," *Historical Studies in the Physical Sciences* 3 (1971), p. 78.

22. George Greenstein and Arthur G. Zajonc, *The Quantum Challenge* (Sudbury, Mass.: Jones & Bartlett, 1997), p. 53.

23. *The Ghost in the Atom,* edited by P. C. W. Davies and J. R. Brown (Cambridge, England: Cambridge University Press, 1986), p. 31.

24. Niels Bohr, *Atomic Theory and the Description of Nature* (Cambridge, England: Cambridge University Press, 1934), p. 96.

25. James Gleick, *Genius: The Life and Science of Richard Feynman* (New York: Vintage, 1993), p. 243.

26. Eric Lerner, "Bucking the Big Bang," *New Scientist,* May 22, 2004, p. 20.

27. Lee Smolin, *The Trouble with Physics* (New York: Houghton Mifflin, 2006), p. 121.

28. Ibid., pp. 116–17.

29. Steven Weinberg, *Dreams of a Final Theory* (New York: Vintage, 1994), p. 195.

30. *Phaedo* (65–66), in *The Collected Dialogues of Plato,* edited by Edith Hamilton and Huntington Cairns (Princeton, N.J.: Princeton University Press, 1961), pp. 48–49.

31. John Horgan, *The End of Science* (New York: Broadway, 1997), p. 73.

ABOUT THE AUTHOR

David Harriman earned his master's degree in physics from the University of Maryland, and his master's in philosophy from Claremont Graduate University. He has worked as an applied physicist, analyzing errors in gravitational models used by inertial navigation systems, and he is the editor of *Journals of Ayn Rand*. He has lectured and published articles on the scientific revolution, the concept "space," and the influence of Kantian philosophy on modern physics. Recently, he cofounded Falling Apple Science Institute (with Tom VanDamme), a nonprofit that is developing a unique science curriculum based on the inductive method.

ABOUT THE AUTHOR

INDEX

abstraction, 234
  (*see also* concepts, Rand's theory of)
acceleration, concept of, 47–48,
  118–20, 143
acidity, 194–96
Against Method, 247
agreement, method of, 70
air pressure, 123–24
allotropes, definition of, 160
Anaxagoras, 81
Apollonius, 102, 132
arbitrary claims, 64–66, 72–73,
  145, 215
Archimedes, 102, 124, 149
Aristarchus, 81
Aristotle, 6, 25, 30, 35, 149, 189,
  234–36, 248
atom,
  definition of, 157
  structure of, 204
atomic theory, 151–88, 238
  in ancient Greece, 151–52, 157
  positivist rejection of, 216–22
atomic weight, 159, 161–63, 171–72
Averroes, 84
Avogadro, Amedeo, 158, 162–63, 167

Bacon, Francis, 212
benzene, 174–75, 185, 191
Berthelot, Marcellin, 220
Bertholett, Claude Louis, 155
Berzelius, Jons Jacob, 156–57, 160,
  163, 171
big bang theory, 251–53
Bohm, David, 250
Bohr, Niels, 248–50
Boyle, Robert, 59, 124
Brahe, Tycho, 89–90, 93–97, 101, 110
Brodie, Benjamin, 217–19
Broglie, Louis de, 247
Brownian motion, 222
buoyancy, principle of, 124, 149
Buridan, Jean, 45–46, 78–79
Butlerov, Alexander, 174

caloric, concept of, 164–65
Cannizzaro, Stanislao, 171–74
Carlisle, Anthony, 199
Caspar, Max, 103, 109
Cassini, Gian, 135
causality,
  and experimental method,
    67–74

causality (*cont.*)
  as essential to generalization,
    21–22, 236
  as grasped through quantitative
    relations, 229–32
  as perceived, 22–24
  law of, 9, 21–22, 236–37
  rejection of, x, 103, 216–23, 249
Certain Philosophic Questions, 59
Chamberlin, Thomas, 204–5
Charles, Jacques, 167, 179
chemical bonding, 162–63, 170–71
Clausius, Rudolf, 167
Cohen, Morris, 72–73
cold fusion, 207–9
comets, orbits of, 140–41, 144
Comte, Auguste, 215
concepts,
  as file folders, 14, 76, 152, 229
  as green lights to induction, xi, 2,
    76–77, 177–79
  hierarchical nature of, 11
  in relation to scientific theory, 186
  Rand's theory of, 9–14, 228–32
  versus percepts, 234
conceptual framework, 32–34, 72, 74,
    79, 179, 194
conic sections, 132
Copernicus, Nicolaus, 24, 85–89, 91,
    102, 113–14, 150
Corvini, Pat, 228
Cosmic Mystery, 107
Critique of Pure Reason, 244
culture, influence of physics on, ix
Curie, Pierre and Marie, 205
cycloid pendulum, 55, 122

Dalton, John, 156, 162–63, 166,
    216, 246
Da Vinci, Leonardo, 44–45, 57
Davy, Humphry, 159, 163–64, 181,
    196, 199–201
Davies, Paul, 249
deduction, 29, 34, 189, 235–36

definitions, 12–13
Descartes, Rene, 58, 63, 180, 212–15,
    225, 232, 237, 245
difference, method of, 68–69
Duhem, Pierre, 180, 222
Dulong, Pierre, 159, 161, 163

Earth,
  age of, 201–6
  as a magnet, 90, 99
  orbit of, 94–96
  precession of spin axis, 140
  shape of, 139–40
  size of, 82–83
Eddington, Sir Arthur,
    248, 251
education, 146
Einstein, Albert, 20, 104, 147–49,
    222, 226
electric battery, 199
electric current, 197–201
electricity,
  Greek observations of, 13
  static theory of, 196–97
electrolysis, 161–62, 207, 221
element, concept of, 153–54
Elements of Chemistry, 155
empiricism, 21, 30, 130, 142, 151, 211,
    215–23, 245
energy, concept of, 165–66, 179
enumeration, 8–9
epicycles, 86
equant points, 91–92
Eratosthenes, 82–83
Euclid, 102
Eudoxus, 253
Euler, Leonhard, 56
experiment,
  definition of, 36
  crucial, 179–80
    (*see also* agreement and difference,
      methods of)
*Experiments and Considerations
    Touching Colors,* 59

fallacy,
  of "cognitive fixation," 206
  of "cognitive promiscuity," 206-9
  of dropping context, 8
  of inadequate experimental
    controls, 200
  of substituting a regularity for a
    cause, 196
  of "theory-stealing," 220
Faraday, Michael, 161-62, 174, 185
Farewell to Reason, 247
Fermi, Enrico, 44
Feyerabend, Paul, 5, 246-47
Feynman, Richard, 250
Fleischmann, Martin, 207-9
force, concept of, 90, 143
Frankland, Edward, 172-73, 219
Franklin, Benjamin, 31-34, 153
free fall, 43-44, 46-47, 125
friction, 16, 44

Galileo, 9, 24, 102, 118-20, 133, 149,
    211-12, 237-38, 240, 243
  chord theorem, 40
  discoveries with telescope, 114, 180
  errors in physics, 54-57, 209-10
  free fall, 43-44, 46-47, 125, 132
  free horizontal motion, 15-16,
    49-50
  inclined planes, 48-50, 122
  parabolic trajectories, 50-51, 190
  pendulums, 38-42, 127, 229-30
  relativity of motion, 53-54, 89,
    114, 116
Galvani, Luigi, 197-200, 209
Gamow, George, 251
gas, concept of, 192-93
Gay-Lussac, Joseph Louis, 157-58
generalization,
  as a form of conceptualization, 28, 72
  as based on causal connections, 21
  as contextual, 19-20
  as hierarchical, 14-20
  first-level, 16, 18-28

geocentric theory, 37, 83-88, 91, 150,
    180, 237, 252-53
geology, 201-6
Gilbert, William, 90, 99, 212
Gleick, James, 250
gravitation,
  concept of, 42, 56, 77, 120-21, 144
  law of, 131-145
Greek theory of elements, 153-54
Greek theory of motion, 45, 78

Halley, Edmund, 124, 141
Harmony of the World, 108
Harvey, William, 212
heat, as a form of internal motion,
    164-66
heaviness, concept of, 67, 123-24
Hegel, Georg Wilhelm Friedrich, 232
Heisenberg, Werner, 249
heliocentric theory, ix, 17, 84-89
Helm, Georg, 222
Hipparchus, 140
Holton, Gerald, 108
Hooke, Robert, 63, 180
horizontal, concept of, 74-75
Hume, David, xi, 21, 215
Hutton, James, 201
Huygens, Christian, 54-55, 135
hypotheses, Newton's rejection of,
    64-66, 142
hypothetico-deductive method, 145-46

identity, law of, 10, 22, 248
impetus, concept of, 45-46, 78-79
inclined planes, 48-50, 122
  rolling versus sliding, 55-56, 209-10
induction,
  as inherent in conceptualization,
    74-77
  as self-corrective, 210, 238
  contrasted with deduction, 34-35
  problem of, 6-9, 143
  structure of, 29-35
  theory of, 239

Ingenhousz, Jan, 192
integration,
    as criterion of proof,
        184–85
    as the essence of thought, 53
    *Introduction to Objectivist
        Epistemology*, xi, 9
ion, concept of, 161, 179
isomers, 160, 175–77

Jeans, James, 226
Joule, James, 165–66
Jupiter,
    moons of, 114, 116, 135
    shape of, 140

Kant, Immanuel, x, 215–16, 221, 232,
    243–45, 249
Kekule, August, 175
Kelvin, Lord (aka William Thomson),
    169–70, 201–6, 209
Kepler, Johannes, 9, 24, 89, 116, 212,
    228, 237–38, 243
    as influenced by Plato, 106–9, 225
    idea of solar force, 90, 99–100,
        113–14
    laws of planetary motion, 57,
        95–104, 110–13, 120, 131–33,
        185, 190
    proof of theory, 113–15
kinetic energy, definition of,
    165–66
kinetic theory of gases, 166–69
Kirch, Gottfried, 141
Kline, Morris, 227
Koestler, Arthur, 97
Kroenig, August, 171
Kuhn, Thomas, 246

Ladenberg, Albert, 191
Lavoisier, Antoine, 9, 157
    as father of chemistry, 153–55,
        178–79
    theory of acidity, 194–96, 209

Law,
    of Avogadro, 158, 162–63, 167,
        170–71, 179, 182–85, 216
    of buoyancy, 124, 149
    of circular motion, 117–19
    of constant composition, 155, 179
    of combining gas volumes, 157–58,
        179, 182
    of electrolysis, 161–62, 179, 182
    of free fall, 43–44, 46–47, 125
    of gaseous diffusion, 168, 183
    of gaseous heat conduction, 168, 183
    of gravitation, 120–21, 131–45
    of heat capacities, 159, 161, 163, 170,
        172, 179, 182–83
    of ideal gases, 166–67, 171, 179, 217
    of inclined plane motion, 48–50, 122
    of Mendeleyev, 173, 179, 185
    of motion (first), 118, 121
    of motion (second), 121–26
    of motion (third), 127–29
    of multiple proportions, 156–57,
        179, 182
    of pendulums, 38–42, 127, 229–30
    of planetary motion, 95–104, 110–13,
        131–33
    of refraction, 37, 58
    of viscosity, 168–69, 183
Lemaitre, George, 251
Lerner, Eric, 252
Liebig, Justus von, 160
light, speed of, 17
lightness, Greek concept of, 123–24
lightning, nature of, 31–34
limit, concept of, 48, 79, 119
logic,
    definition of, 29
    purpose of, 189
Loschmidt, Joseph, 169, 175

Mach, Ernst, 130, 221–22, 225
magnets,
    Gilbert's study of, 90, 99
    Newton's experiment with, 127–28

Marignac, Jean de, 170
Mars, orbit of, 91–102
mass, concept of, 123–25, 144
  as proportional to weight, 126
mathematics,
  as inapplicable to consciousness,
    241–42
  as the model of cognition, 11
  explanation for role of, 228–32
  objectivity of, 226–28
  power of, 80, 109–13, 133–34,
    181, 237
Matthews, Michael, 52
Maxwell, James Clerk, 9, 167–69, 183,
  187, 217–18
McGuire, J. E., 59
mean free path, concept of, 167–69, 179
measurement omission, 10, 28, 228–29
  (*see also* concepts, Rand's theory of)
measurement, numerical, 10, 110,
  180–81
Mendeleyev, Dmitry, 173–74, 185, 187
Mercury, precession of orbit, 147
Meyer, Lothar, 172
Michelson, Albert, 206
Mill, John Stuart, 68
molecular structure theory, 174–77, 183
momentum, concept of, 79, 128–29
Moon,
  gravitational force on, 120, 136–37
  mountains of, 116
  orbit of, 137–38
  size and distance from Earth, 82, 136

Nagel, Ernest, 72–73
natural motion, 45, 78, 116
New Astronomy Based on Causation,
  102
New System of Chemical Philosophy, 156
Newton, Isaac, ix, 5, 9, 20, 58, 104–5,
  115, 186, 206, 211, 224, 237–38,
  240, 245
  analysis of circular motion, 117–19
  first law of motion, 118, 121

law of gravitation, 120–121, 131–45
  second law of motion, 121–26, 149
  third law of motion, 127–29
  theory of colors, 58–67, 180
  theory of tides, 138–39
  view of space and time, 148–49
Nicholson, William, 199
noncontradiction, law of, 236, 240
nuclear fusion, 205, 207–9

*Objectivism: The Philosophy of Ayn
  Rand*, 9, 19, 233
Odling, William, 219
optical activity, 176
Optics, 150
Ostwald, Wilhelm, 222
ozone, 170–71

Pascal, Blaise, 124
Pasteur, Louis, 175–76
Pearson, Karl, 222
Peikoff, Leonard, 9, 18, 233
  contributions to this book, 1–2
pendulum,
  Galileo's law of, 38–42, 67–68,
    229–30
  cycloid, 54–55
  Newton's experiments with, 126–27
periodic table, 173–74
Petit, Alexis, 159, 161, 163
Phaedo, 255–56
philosophy,
  as the foundation of the specialized
    sciences, 224–25, 242–43
  as an inductive science, 225,
    232–43
  as compared to physics, 240–43
phlogiston, 178–79, 227
planets,
  area law, 95–96, 101, 104, 112, 131
  elliptical orbit law, 98–101, 104,
    110–11
  inclinations of orbits, 90
  inner versus outer, 87

planets, (cont.)
  period/radius law, 102, 104, 113
  relative size of orbits, 85
  relative speed of, 85
  retrograde motion of, 86–87
plant growth, 192–194
Plato, 37, 58, 83, 105–8, 225, 232,
  234, 243, 245, 255–56
Poincare, Henri, 222
Pons, Stanley, 207–9
Popper, Karl, 189
positivism, 215–23
Priestley, Joseph, 192
Principles of Philosophy, 212–15
Principia, ix, 58, 130–131, 140–41,
  143–44, 146, 150
proof,
  criteria of, 184–87, 238–39
  of atomic theory, 177–88
  of Kepler's theory, 113–15
  of Newton's laws, 143–50
Proust, Joseph Louis, 155
Ptolemy, Claudius
  study of refraction, 37–38
  geocentric theory of, 37, 83–88, 91,
    150, 180, 237, 252
Pythagoras, 231

quantity, role in human cognition,
  228–32
quantum mechanics, 222, 247–50
Quine, Willard, 180

radioactivity, 205
rainbows, theory of, 58, 63
Rand, Ayn, 233
  theory of concepts, xi, 9–14, 35, 152,
    228–32
rationalism, 30, 105, 142, 151–52,
  211–15, 245
reduction (of knowledge to sense
  perception), 15–18
reflection of colors, 62–63
refraction, 37, 58–62, 75

religion, 25, 66, 148
Richer, Jean, 124
Roemer, Olaus, 17
Rumford, Count (aka Benjamin
  Thompson), 164, 181
Rutherford, Ernest, 205

Saturn, orbit of, 135
Schrodinger, Erwin, 247
Smolin, Lee, 254–55
Snell, Willebrord, 37, 58
Socrates, 235–36
Sophists, 243
specific heat, definition of, 159
spectrum, concept of, 61, 77
speed, concept of, 47–48
stereochemistry, 175–77
string theory, x, 253–56
Structure of Scientific Revolutions, 246
Strutt, Robert, 205
subjectivism, x, 74, 245–47
substance, concept of, 153
Sun,
  age and source of energy, 203–5
  as cause of planetary orbits, 90,
    99–100, 113–14, 120
  size and distance from Earth, 81–82
sunspots, 114

Tamny, Martin, 59
telescope,
  chromatic aberration, 58, 63
  reflecting, 63
  discoveries with, 114, 135, 180
temperature, 13, 165–66, 183
Thales, 194
tides, explanation of, 138–39
Torricelli, Evangelista, 123–24, 149

valence, concept of, 172–73, 179
Van Helmont, J. B., 192–94, 209
Van 't Hoff, Jacobus, 176–77, 191
variations, method of, 68
Venus, phases of, 114, 180

vertical, concept of, 74–75
Vieta, Francois, 102
violent motion, 45, 78, 116
viscosity, 168–69, 179, 183
Volta, Alessandro, 161, 198–200, 209

Waterston, J. J., 166–67, 171, 217

wave/particle duality, 247, 249–50
Weinberg, Steven, 255–56
Weyl, Hermann, 249
Wheeler, John Archibald, 248
Wilson, E. Bright, 1–2, 6
Wohler, Friedrich, 160
Wurtz, Adolphe, 220